MEMOIRS OF THE GEOLOGICAL SURVEY
ENGLAND
EXPLANATION OF SPECIAL OXFORD SHEET

The

Geology of the Country around Oxford

By T. I. Pocock, M.A.

With contributions by

H. B. Woodward, F.R.S., and G. W. Lamplugh, F.R.S.

Second Edition

By J. Pringle

With contributions by

K. S. Sandford, M.A., D.Ph. & C. J. Bayzand, M.A.

London
Printed under the Authority of H.M. Stationery Office.
To be purchased from
E. STANFORD, Ltd., 12, 13, and 14, Long Acre, London, W.C.2;
W. & A. K. JOHNSTON, Ltd., 4, George Street, Edinburgh;
H.M. STATIONERY OFFICE, Adastral House, Kingsway, W.C.2.
and 28, Abingdon Street, S.W.1
(and Edinburgh, Manchester, Cardiff and Belfast);
or from any Agent for the sale of Ordnance Survey Maps;
through any Bookseller; or from the DIRECTOR-GENERAL,
Ordnance Survey, Southampton.

1926
Price 4s. 0d. Net

PREFACE TO FIRST EDITION

The original geological survey of the area included in the new Oxford Sheet was carried out during the years 1857 to 1863 by Messrs. E. Hull, H. Bauerman, W. Whitaker, T. R. Polwhele, and A. H. Green. Their work was published on the Old Series Sheets 13, 45 S.W. and 45 S.E., and in accompanying Explanatory Memoirs. Some revisions at Islip (45 S.E.) were made in 1867 by H. W. Bristow.

The re-survey on the six-inch scale was commenced in 1896 by the late Mr. John Hopwood Blake and continued until the time of his death early in 1901. It was afterwards decided to complete the field-work over an area sufficient for the publication of a map with Oxford as a centre, and Mr. T. I. Pocock was deputed to do this work under the superintendence of Mr. H. B. Woodward, who personally surveyed portions of the country near Wheatley. Aid was also given in the examination and revision of the Lower Cretaceous areas by Mr. G. W. Lamplugh, whose observations have led to a separation of the freshwater Shotover Sands, now regarded as of Wealden age, from the marine Lower Greensand with which they were formerly grouped by the Geological Survey.

The preparation of the Memoir was entrusted to Mr. Pocock, who has dealt very fully with the Pleistocene and Recent deposits, to which he has given especial attention. The chapters dealing with the Jurassic Rocks have been partly written by Mr. Woodward, those on the Lower Cretaceous rocks have been contributed by Mr. Lamplugh, and that on the Upper Cretaceous rocks is based on the published observations of Mr. Jukes-Browne.

Owing to the resignation of Mr. Pocock in 1906, a larger share of the work than was expected has fallen to Mr. Woodward, who has written the Introductory Chapter and prepared the Appendix.

We are indebted to Mr. T. Codrington for a section of the railway-cutting near Horsepath, and to Mr. W. W. Fisher, Mr. R. H. Tiddeman, of Oxford, and Mr. George Winship, of Abingdon, for records of well-borings.

The fossils collected during the progress of the geological survey have been named in the Palaeontological Department.

A list of the six-inch geological maps with the authors and dates of survey is appended. MS. copies of these maps are deposited in the Office for public reference.

J. J. H. Teall,
Director.

Geological Survey Office,
    28, Jermyn Street, London,
    5th November, 1907.

(18772.) Wt. 21886—S 131/1597. 1000. 6/26. Wy. & S., Ltd. Gp. 50 (3).

PREFACE TO SECOND EDITION

The preparation of the second edition of this memoir has been entrusted to Mr. John Pringle, who has visited the district frequently and has revised and in large part re-written the chapters on the Secondary rocks. In naming the Jurassic and Cretaceous ammonites he has had the advice of Mr. S. S. Buckman and Dr. L. F. Spath. Dr. E. Neaverson kindly lent proofs of his memoir on the ammonites of the Kimmeridge Clay, and these have been of great service.

Mr. C. J. Bayzand, of the University Museum, Oxford, has given valuable help in many ways: he supplied details of many field exposures, lists of fossils from this Sheet now in the University Museum, and photographs and drawings of important sections. Thanks are also due to Mr. W. J. Arkell and Mr. C. C. Gaddum for their help during the progress of the field-work.

The chapters on the Pleistocene deposits have been contributed by Dr. K. S. Sandford, who has incorporated Mr. T. I. Pocock's contributions to the first edition wherever suitable.

The work has been done under the general superintendence of Mr. J. A. Howe.

Thanks are due to the Council of the Geological Society of London for permission to reproduce figs. 10 and 12, to Mr. Bayzand for the photograph from which the frontispiece is taken, and to Mr. J. Pringle, junr., for the photograph which served as the original for Plate III B. The other photographs were taken by Mr. John Rhodes, junr.

JOHN S. FLETT,
Director.

Geological Survey Office,
  28, Jermyn Street,
    London, S.W.1.
  10*th March*, 1926.

CONTENTS

vi

ILLUSTRATIONS

List of Six-inch Geological Maps

Copies can be supplied at the cost of drawing and colouring

BERKSHIRE

6 S.W.   (Oxford 39 S.W.). Bessels Leigh. By J. H. Blake, 1899, and T. I. Pocock, 1904.

9 N.W.   Hinton Waldrist, Kingston Bagpuize. By J. H. Blake, 1899.

N.E.   Fyfield, Marcham. By J. H. Blake, 1899, and T. I. Pocock, 1905.

BUCKINGHAMSHIRE

26 S.E.   (Oxford 28 S.E.). Muswell Hill. By H. B. Woodward, G. W. Lamplugh and T. I. Pocock, 1904–05.

S.W.   (Oxford 28 S.W.). Ot Moor. By T. I. Pocock, 1905.

27 S.W.   (Oxford 29 S.W.). Brill. By H. B. Woodward and G. W. Lamplugh, 1904–05.

31 N.E.   (Oxford 34 N.E.). Oakley. By H. B. Woodward and T. I. Pocock, 1904–05.

S.E.   (Oxford 34 S.E.). Worminghall, Waterperry. By H. B. Woodward, 1904–05.

32 N.W.   (Oxford 35 N.W.). Ixhill. By H. B. Woodward, 1905.

S.W.   (Oxford 35 S.W.). Little Ickford. By H. B. Woodward, 1905.

OXFORDSHIRE

26 S.W.   Wilcote, North Leigh. By T. I. Pocock, 1904.

S.E.   Bladon, Church Hanborough. By T. I. Pocock, 1904.

27 S.W.   Begbroke, Kidlington. By T. I. Pocock, 1904.

S.E.   Islip, Oddington. By T. I. Pocock, 1905.

32 N.W.   Eynsham Hall. By T. I. Pocock, 1904.

N.E.   (Berks 1 N.E.). Eynsham, Cassington. By T. I. Pocock, 1904.

S.W.   South Leigh, Hardwick. By T. I. Pocock, 1904.

S.E.   (Berks 1 S.E.). Swinford. By J. H. Blake, 1897, and T. I. Pocock, 1904.

33 N.W.   (Berks 2 N.W.). Yarnton. By J. H. Blake, 1899, and T. I. Pocock, 1904.

N.E.   Woodeaton, Elsfield. By J. H. Blake, 1898, and T. I. Pocock, 1904.

S.W.   (Berks 2 S.W.). Wytham and Binsey. By J. H. Blake, 1898, and T. I. Pocock, 1904.

S.E.   N. Oxford and Headington. By J. H. Blake, 1898, and T. I. Pocock, 1905.

34 N.W.   Stanton St. John, Beckley, and Studley. By T. I. Pocock, 1904–05.

S.W.   Forest Hill and Holton. By J. H. Blake, 1897 ; H. B. Woodward, G. W. Lamplugh, and T. I. Pocock, 1904–05.

38 N.W.   Brighthampton and Standlake. By J. H. Blake, 1897, and T. I. Pocock, 1904.

Geology of Oxford (Mem. Geol. Surv.).

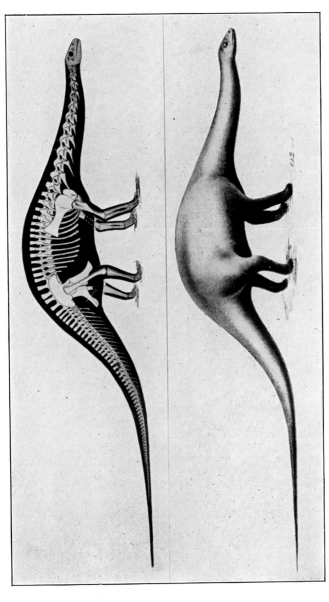

PLATE I.—*Ceteosaurus oxoniensis Phill. from the Forest Marble of Enslow Bridge. Outlined and photographed by Mr. C. J. Bayzand. Scale : one inch = 10 ft.*

THE GEOLOGY OF THE COUNTRY AROUND OXFORD

CHAPTER I

INTRODUCTION

THE map to be described in the present memoir embraces an area of 216 square miles, in which are included parts of Oxfordshire with the city of Oxford, of Berkshire with the town of Abingdon, and of Buckinghamshire with the large village of Brill. The district lies entirely within the drainage area of the Thames and its tributaries. The main river, locally known as the Upper Thames, or Isis, enters the country at the hamlet of Duxford, near Hinton Waldrist, and receives on its left bank :—

(1) The Windrush, which rises in the Eastern Cotteswolds, traverses the Lower Oolites between Burford and Witney, and joins the main river south of Standlake.

(2) The Evenlode, which likewise has sources in the Eastern Cotteswolds, and in the hills that form the eastern borders of the Vale of Moreton. After crossing a considerable tract of Lias, this river traverses the Lower Oolites between Charlbury and Hanborough, where it is joined by the Glyme, and then enters the Thames near Eynsham.

(3) The Cherwell, which rises among the Lias hills near Banbury, and flows across the Lower Oolites between Lower Heyford and Shipton Cherwell. It is joined at Islip by the Ray, and thence continues its course along the eastern side of Oxford, passing beneath Magdalen Bridge to join the main river a little farther south.

(4) The Thame, which has its source in the Vale of Aylesbury, drains the eastern portion of the district between Ickford and Newington, and joins the Upper Thames, or Isis, at Dorchester (to the south of the area embraced by the map). The main river thence flows on as the Thames.

On its right bank the Upper Thames receives at Abingdon :—

The Ock and certain tributary streamlets that drain the south-western part of the area.

GEOLOGICAL FORMATIONS

The geological formations represented at the surface are as
follows :—

		Thickness Ft.
Recent and Pleistocene	Alluvium	15
	Brickearth	10
	Valley Gravel	30
	Plateau Gravel	20
Upper Cretaceous	Upper Greensand	90
	Gault	200
Lower Cretaceous	Lower Greensand	50
	Wealden—Shotover Sands	45
Upper Oolites	Purbeck Beds	6
	Portland Beds	40
	Kimmeridge Clay	120
Middle Oolites	Corallian Beds { Coral Rag and Oolite, Calcareous Grit and sands } Ampthill Clay	50 to 100
	Oxford Clay and Kellaways Beds; about	400
Lower Oolites	Cornbrash	9 to 17
	Forest Marble	12 to 35
	Great Oolite Series	140
	Inferior Oolite	

(The bracket at the left for Upper Oolites through Lower Oolites is labelled **Jurassic**.)

STRATA PROVED BY BORING

No borings have reached the Palaeozoic rocks underlying the area
to be described ; and the information, gained from similar under-
takings in which these strata have been proved outside the district,
adds little to our knowledge of the formations that enter into the
structure of the Palaeozoic floor.

Dealing generally in 1871 with the possibility of finding coal,
Phillips concluded 'that coal-measures, if they exist, would not be
situated at an inaccessible depth in the country north of Oxford ;
but there is no good reason for selecting that or any other situation
in the upper drainage of the Thames, excepting that there the Upper
Oolites and Chalk are not to be encountered in the sinking.'[1]

Soon afterwards these views were substantially supported by
the boring made (1875–1877) at Burford Signet, 7 miles west of
Witney, and about 16 miles west of Oxford. Coal Measures were
there reached at a depth of 1,184 ft. beneath Oolites, Lias, and New
Red Marl. Coal Measures have also been proved near Batsford in
Gloucestershire, at a distance of 25 miles north-west of Oxford, and
at a depth of 1,021 ft. below the surface. Silurian rocks were
found beneath them. On the other hand, Cambrian shales were
penetrated at the relatively small depth of 153½ ft. below Ordnance

---

[1] 'Geology of Oxford and the Valley of the Thames,' pp. 296, 297 ; see also Hull,
Quart. Journ. Geol. Soc., vol. xvi, 1860, p. 80.

Datum in the boring at Calvert, about 15 miles north-north-east of Oxford.[1]

It is believed that Rhaetic rocks were penetrated in the boring at Kidlington,[2] and although evidence is wanting, it is probable that Triassic rocks are present beneath the Lias in the northern half of the sheet.

Liassic rocks, which should come to the surface in the neighbourhood of Ashford Mill, have been proved in borings at Witney, at Ramsden (just beyond the western margin of the sheet), and at Kidlington and Oxford. The boring at Wytham, completed in 1829, is thought to have been made in search of coal. It was carried down to a depth of 633 ft., and probably reached the Lower Lias.

The remarkable attenuation of the Lias that is noticeable when the beds are traced south-eastwards in the direction of dip is also proved in the borings. Thus, while the entire thickness of that formation at Chipping Campden in the Northern Cotteswolds was proved to be 1,361 ft., it does not exceed 627 ft. in the boring at Burford. At Fawler, in the Evenlode Valley, the Upper Lias is but 16 ft. thick, and the Middle Lias is about 40 ft. In the record of the Witney bore-hole there was no indication of any mass of Upper Lias, while in the boring at the City Brewery, Oxford, rocks referred to the Inferior Oolite were found to rest on the Capricornus Beds of the Lower Lias, the whole of the Middle and Upper subdivisions having disappeared. It is of interest to note that in the Calvert boring the Chipping Norton Limestone was proved to overlie the lowest zone of the Middle Lias.[3]

In like fashion, though perhaps not so strikingly, the Oolites also undergo continued thinning and planing-down by erosion as they approach the rising slope of the Palaeozoic floor. The full sequences seen in the north-west become interrupted by gaps and unconformities south-eastwards. In our district the upper members of the Inferior Oolite, having overlapped the lower zones, rest unconformably on the Upper Lias near Fawler (see p. 11), and, as is shown above, are believed to continue underground as far as Oxford, where they repose on Lower Lias. Lithological variability and the existence of non-sequences characterize the lower part of the Great Oolite Series, but at the top of the Great Oolite Limestones there is a marked stratigraphical break, the Forest Marble resting on an eroded surface of the Oolites. Again, there is an unconformity at the base of the Cornbrash, and there are numerous eroded surfaces of beds within

[1] Those who desire further to consider this subject should consult the Final Report of the Royal Commission on Coal Supplies, part ix—Resources of the Concealed and Unproved Coalfields of the United Kingdom, 1905. See also W. B. Dawkins, Rep. Brit. Assoc. for 1894, p. 647 ; E. A. N. Arber, ' The Concealed Oxfordshire Coalfield,' Trans. Inst. Min. Engineers, vol. L, part 2, 1916, p. 373 ; A. M. Davies and J. Pringle, Quart. Journ. Geol. Soc., vol. lxix, 1913, p. 308.
[2] ' The Water Supply of Oxfordshire ' (Mem. Geol. Surv.), 1910, p. 55.
[3] Davies, A. M. and J. Pringle, op. cit., p. 311.

the formation indicating interrupted sedimentation and contemporaneous erosion. The thinness of the Middle and Upper Oolites when contrasted with the greater thickness of these deposits in the buried syncline of the Weald[1] is in all probability due to the absence of beds through non-deposition or intraformational erosion.   Thus there is a marked stratigraphical break at the top of the Corallian ; and the Gravesia Beds of the Kimmeridge Clay, though well-developed in Dorset and in some localities in Kent, are feebly represented at Swindon, and appear to be absent in the Oxford district. At the base of the Upper Portland there is a striking break in the stratal sequence ; nearly 246 ft. of sands and clays, well seen in the cliffs at Chapman's Pool, near St. Alban's Head, are unrepresented in this area.   Finally, the Purbeck Beds are present only in a few sections as remnants that have escaped destruction before the deposition of the Shotover Sands.

The Upper Oolites and Lower Cretaceous rocks appear to have been corrugated by small folds striking north-west to south-east in the troughs of which the Portland, Purbeck, Shotover Sands, and probably also Lower Greensand and Lower Gault are now preserved. These troughs were further bent into a series of shallow basins, and the Upper Cretaceous strata which cut across these folds are not affected by them.[2]

The Oolitic rocks do not range far under the Upper Cretaceous strata. Recently, at Marsh Hill Farm, near Aylesbury, a boring, starting in Gault, proved the absence of the Portland and Purbeck Beds within a mile of their outcrop.[3]   Borings at Little Missenden and Great Marlow show that the Lower Greensand overlies the Renggeri Zone of the Oxford Clay.   The concealed outcrop of the Kimmeridge Clay, the Corallian Series, and the upper part of the Oxford Clay therefore lies in the intervening area ; and it has been suggested that Lower Cretaceous sediments rest on a sand of Great Oolite age in the boring at the Slough Motor Transport Depot.[4] In the borings at Richmond, Streatham and Meux's Brewery, London, Great Oolite strata rest on the Palaeozoic floor.   Indeed, all the evidence from these borings tends to prove that the South Midland and Wealden areas had a similar tectonic history during Jurassic times, as suggested by Mr. Lamplugh.[5]

[1] See Lamplugh, G. W., F. L. Kitchin and J. Pringle, ' The Concealed Mesozoic Rocks in Kent ' (Mem. Geol. Surv.), 1923, p. 121.
[2] ' Excursion to Swindon,' Proc. Geol. Assoc., vol. xxxiv, 1923, p. 237.
[3] In ' Summary of Progress for 1924 ' (Mem. Geol. Surv.), 1925, p. 121.
[4] ' The Geology of the Country around Beaconsfield ' (Mem. Geol. Surv.), 1922, pp. 8, 9.
[5] ' The structure of the Weald and analogous tracts.'   Quart. Journ. Geol. Soc., vol. lxxv, pt. I, 1919, pp. lxxxiii–lxxxvii.

The following is a summary of the deeper borings in and adjacent to the area[1] :—

Formations	Burford	Witney	Ramsden	Wytham	Oxford, City Brewery	Oxford, St. Clement's Brewery	Kidlington
	Ft. In.	Ft. In.	Ft. In.	Ft. In.	Ft. In.	Ft. In.	Ft. In.
Alluvium			6 0	15 0	30 0		11 0
Gravel						265 0	2 0
Oxford Clay and Kellaways Beds			21 0	258 0	210 0		13 0
Cornbrash		43 0	11 0	17 0	17 0		20 6
Forest Marble	62 6	141 6	25 0	26 6	32 8	155 0[2]	180 6
Great Oolite Series	27 8	30 0	142 0	96 0	116 6		
Inferior Oolite	81 6		27 0	35 6	16 4		7 0
Upper Lias	98 1	55 6+	128 0+	14 6	17 0+		233 0+
Middle Lias	447 4			170 6+			
Lower Lias	466 11						
Rhaetic and New Red Marl	226 0						
Coal Measures							
	1410 0	270 0	360 0	633 0	439 6	420 0	467 0

[1] The details of the Burford boring were given in 'The Jurassic Rocks of Britain,' vol. iv, (*Mem. Geol. Surv.*), 1894, pp. 303, 304; those of the Witney, Wytham, and St. Clement's in vols. iv, pp. 372, 513, v, pp. 42, 43; and an abstract of the City Brewery boring, Oxford, in the 'Summary of Progress for 1898' (*Mem. Geol. Surv.*), 1899, p. 139. The record of the Ramsden boring is here published for the first time.

[2] The thickness of rock-beds passed through has usually been given as 135 ft, but Prestwich ascertained at the St. Clement's Brewery that it was 155 ft. *Geol. Mag.*, 1876, pp. 238, 239.

Physical Features and Soils

The strike of the Lower Oolites is from north-east to south-west, with a gentle south-easterly inclination of the strata. This is modified locally by the faulted anticline that brings in the Cornbrash and other rocks at Islip. With this exception the general strike and dip are maintained not only in the succeeding Oolitic strata, but in the Lower and Upper Cretaceous rocks which have transgressed unconformably on to some of the older formations. The N.W. and S.E. faults that accompany the anticlinal disturbance at Islip are continued by Forest Hill to Wheatley, and are probably connected with the inlying tract of Kimmeridge Clay at Great Milton, and with the faulted tract of Shotover Sands at Great Haseley.

The Lower Oolites rise to nearly 450 ft. in the north-western part of the area, and they lie a little over 30 ft. below Ordnance Datum at Oxford, about eleven miles distant.

The features which characterize the outcrops of the successive strata are well marked, and at the same time, owing to the irregular distribution of the overlapping Cretaceous rocks, and the varied influences of the agents of denudation, considerable diversity of scenery has resulted.

The nature of the soil, as might be expected, is changeable. The area comes within that described by Arthur Young[1] under two broad divisions, namely (1) *The District of the Stonebrash* and (2) that of *Miscellaneous loams*; and the greater part of it was included by him in this mixed group. The first division would embrace only the small areas of the Lower Oolites; the second would include the great clay-tracts and the impersistent band of Corallian limestones, belonging to the Middle and Upper Oolites, with the isolated masses of Portland Beds, the Cretaceous tracts, and the larger areas of Valley drift. There is thus a remarkable diversity of soil and of land in arable cultivation and pasture, including much good dairy-land and tracts of woodland.

The Stonebrash region commences with the Great Oolite Series of the country bordering the Evenlode above Hanborough. It there forms the margin of a tract of fairly level upland that descends steeply to the river. Stone fences divide the fields, and the soil is a brashy or rubbly loam or clay.

The area occupied by the Oxford Clay is for the most part gently undulating ground, with here and there a low escarpment, above the Cornbrash, where the sandy strata of the Kellaways Beds are developed. Much of the ground is low-lying and almost alluvial in aspect; the soil is stiff and heavy, except where the clay is lightened by thin coverings of gravel or downwashes from the scarps of Lower Calcareous Grit; and the slopes are damp and rushy in places. The hedgerows, as a rule, are well timbered, with oak and elm, ash, willow, and poplar.

---

[1] 'View of the Agriculture of Oxfordshire,' 1809, p. 3. *See also* article 'On the Farming of Oxfordshire,' by Clare Sewell Read, *Journ. Roy. Agric. Soc.*, vol. xv, 1854, p. 189.

The Corallian Beds yield a variable soil, for the most part light and brashy. Much of it is a rich, friable, sandy loam, generally brown, but sometimes of red colour. The ground is mostly under cultivation for corn and roots, and to some extent as meadow land.

An analysis of a soil-sample taken from Little Hill field, Wick Farm, Headington, has been made at Reading College. The soil, which lies on the Calcareous Grit, is described as a light sandy loam, 6 to 9 inches deep, and free from stones. ' The nitrogen and organic matter of this soil are very low, but there is a good supply of phosphoric acid and potash.' The subsoil is ' free sand, with the rock of the Calcareous Grit in many cases coming near the surface. Although the underlying rock contains lime, the soil is, as a rule, poor in lime, except where the rock comes near the surface.'[1]

Near Littlemore the Upper Corallian Beds are argillaceous, and the soil is comparatively stiff. The grass-lands on the Corallian clays in the area north-east of Wheatley are generally good ; indeed, the higher tracts of meadow-land near Ickford, Waterperry, and Holton are regarded as among the best grazing and dairy-lands in the western part of the Vale of Aylesbury.

The Upper Oolites, consisting of the Kimmeridge, Portland and Purbeck divisions, occupy a smaller superficial area than the Corallian, as they are partially concealed by the overlap of the Cretaceous strata. The Kimmeridge Clay forms a stiff clay soil that is locally improved by downwashes from bordering hills of Portland Beds and Shotover Sands. Noticeable landslips of recent date may be seen along the slopes of Kimmeridge Clay, south-west of Wheatley railway station ; and there are evidences of older slips on Shotover Hill and Red Hill.

Along the eastern tract alone are remnants of the Portland and Purbeck strata preserved. Resting on a foundation of clay, and supporting sands and clays of the Cretaceous system, these strata form groups of isolated hills and winding ridges trenched by many combes, and thus they stand out in bold relief from the vales of Jurassic clay and Gault around them. They form the outliers of Shotover (516 feet) and Brill (over 600 feet) and the hills about Great Milton.

The Portland Beds yield a calcareous and sandy soil, much of it under arable cultivation. Between Great and Little Milton a considerable area of fairly open country is occupied by these strata. Milton field was described by A. Young as ' one of the finest soils I have met with in the county ; a dry, sound, friable loam on gravel [rubble]—convertible land, as they call it in Oxfordshire.'[2]

The Purbeck division has only been detected in a few places, and is but a few feet thick.

The freshwater Shotover Beds and the marine Lower Greensand yield a variety of soils, differing alike in texture, composition, and

[1] ' First Ann. Rep. on the Soils of Dorset, etc.' by D. A. Gilchrist and C. M. Luxmore, 1899, pp. 26, 27, 40.
[2] ' Agriculture of Oxfordshire,' 1809, p. 8.

colour.   The higher beds of ironsand form a red ferruginous earthy soil, as on Red Hill and parts of Shotover Hill.   Loamy or clayey beds form the surfaces in places, near the windmill at Great Milton, and between Great Haseley and Little Haseley.

The Gault which forms the slopes near Latchford gives rise to a stiff clay-soil.   The land is mostly under grass.

On the Alluvial areas of the Vale of Isis, between Eynsham and Standlake, where the low-lying gravels are composed largely of rolled fragments of limestone, there is a reddish-brown brashy soil not unlike that of the Cornbrash.   This is fairly dry considering the situation, and furnishes good corn-land.

An analysis of a sample of soil from Stanton Harcourt made in 1870 by Dr. A. Voelcker, showed 32 per cent. of carbonate of lime. He described the soil as a clay-marl with a gravelly subsoil, and considered that it should ' be used as arable rather than as meadow land.'   Some of the gravelly tracts in this neighbourhood, at Standlake, Northmoor, and Eynsham, were liable to serious floods, especially from the Windrush, but considerable protection has been afforded by embankments made during 1866-67.[1]   Elsewhere the Alluvial meadows form excellent grazing grounds.

The industries are chiefly agricultural, but they include stone-quarrying, lime-burning, and brickmaking for local purposes.

The city of Oxford stands at the southern extremity of a long insulated tract mostly of Oxford Clay, capped by gravel, and sur-rounded by Alluvium.   This tract extends from Kidlington on the north to the confluence of the Thames and Cherwell, above which is the bank of gravel on which the city is built.

Of the history of the occupation of the site James Parker states that there is no evidence of any settlement of importance in British times, and the site was not traversed by any of the old Roman ways ;   that the founding of a nunnery by St. Frideswide about the year 727 'upon the spot now occupied by Christ Church,' is legendary, although not improbable ; but that nothing about Oxford is known with certainty prior to ' A.D. 912, when King Edward the Elder took possession of the place.'

The name then recorded of *Oxnaforda* is the earliest form of spelling, and " distinctly represents ' the ford of the Oxen ' " ; but it has been held ' that the name is a corruption of Ouse-ford or Ousen-ford,' that is, ' the ford over the *river*.'   On this subject authorities are not agreed.

" The earliest foundation provided for scholastic purposes in Oxford " dates from 1249, and is represented by University College ;[2] but Merton College claims to have been the first to establish the college system in 1274.[3]   From that date, at any rate, the city became a seat of learning ;   and in due course geology found a place in the curriculum.

---

[1]   Druce, S. B. L., *Journ. Roy. Agric. Soc.*, ser. 2, vol. vi, 1870, p. 373.
[2]   Parker, James, ' The Early History of Oxford,' 1885, pp. 2, 53, 63, 348, 351.
[3]   ' Memorials of Merton College,' by the Hon. G. C. Brodrick, 1885, p. 6.

John Phillips[1] has recorded that ' the Museums of the University of Oxford contain the oldest public collection ever formed in the British Isles for the illustration of natural history, antiquities, and archaeology.' The Ashmolean Museum, when completed in 1683, was placed in charge of Robert Plot, and afterwards of Edward Lhuyd, to both of whom we are indebted for early knowledge of the fossil organic remains of the neighbourhood of Oxford.

About a century later systematic investigation of the strata was commenced by William Smith, who published geological maps of the three counties, portions of which are included in our district.

The study of geology was first taught by Dr. John Kidd, the Professor of Chemistry, who may be said to have inspired W. D. Conybeare, William Buckland, and others. To them, to Fitton, John Phillips, J. F. Whiteaves, J. F. Blake, W. H. Hudleston, James Parker, and to the more recent observations of Prof. W. J. Sollas, Dr. A. Morley Davies and Mr. S. S. Buckman, our knowledge of the local geology, apart from the work of the earlier Geological Survey, is largely due.[2]

[1] *See* Phillips, ' Geology of Oxford,' etc., 1871, p. 1 ; and W. J. Sollas, ' The Influence of Oxford on the History of Geology,' *Science Progress*, vol. vii., 1898, p. 23, reprinted in ' The Age of the Earth and other Geological Studies,' 1905, p. 219.
[2] *See* Preface and Appendix I.

CHAPTER II

LOWER OOLITIC ROCKS

THE Lower Oolites are the oldest rocks exposed in the area. They come to the surface along the banks of the Evenlode above the point where it enters the Oxford plain, and rise from beneath the Kellaways Beds in nearly the same direction as the valley, but at a slightly greater angle, so that successively lower strata are exposed when traced up-stream. The main divisions represented are as follows :— Inferior Oolite (upper part only), Great Oolite Series, Forest Marble and Cornbrash ; and it is likely that they are all represented in the neighbourhood of Ashford Mill, where the river probably flows over the Lias. The strike of the formations is from north-east to south-west, with a gentle south-westerly dip of the strata, modified locally by the faulted anticline that brings in a series of inliers of the Lower Oolites, which protrude in isolated ridges along the west and north-west margin of Ot Moor.

Underground, Lower Oolitic rocks probably extend beneath the whole of the area. They have been proved in borings at Kidlington, Wytham, and Oxford (*see* p. 5).

INFERIOR OOLITE

This division is represented by the Clypeus Grit and the Upper Trigonia Grit, formerly grouped under the somewhat comprehensive zone of *Parkinsonia parkinsoni*, but now regarded as falling within the Schloenbachi and Truelli Zones of the modern scheme of zonal classification. The formation rests with a pebbly basement-bed on the clays of the Upper Lias, the lower zones of the Inferior Oolite having been overlapped in succession eastward from the Cotteswold escarpment.[1] In the first edition of the memoir, the Chipping Norton Limestone was regarded as forming the highest part of the Inferior Oolite, but for reasons given on p. 12 it is here included in the Great Oolite Series.

Unfortunately, no good sections are exposed within the area of the map. The outcrop on the right bank of the river by Ashford Mill is brought up by a fault running southward to Holly Court Farm, and that on the left by a sharp up-fold or a fault. The presence of ironshot oolite was proved by digging a small pit in the field adjoining the railway. The Clypeus Grit was exposed during the year 1924, in the road leading to Ashford Cottages, and yielded a few of its characteristic fossils, including fragments of *Clypeus sinuatus* Leske.

---

[1] Hull, E., ' On the South-easterly Attenuation of the Lower Secondary Formations of England,' etc. *Quart. Journ. Geol. Soc.*, vol. xvi, 1860, p. 72 ; and H. B. Woodward, ' The Jurassic Rocks of Britain ' (*Mem. Geol. Surv.*), vol. iv, 1894, p. 150.

At Fawler, just outside the area, excellent sections are to be found in the excavations, now disused, made in working the Marlstone iron-ore. The succession is as follows :—

		Ft.
Clypeus Grit Zone of *Parkinsonia schloenbachi*	Rubbly oolitic marls and coarse marly oolites with *Clypeus sinuatus, Parkinsonia schloenbachi*, etc.	10 to 12
	Marly limestone..	6
Upper Trigonia Grit	Coarse oolitic limestone with numerous fossils , including *Lima gibbosa, Modiola lonsdalei, Parkinsonia parkinsoni*, etc.	4
Zone of *Strigoceras truelli*	Hard ironshot limestone, bored with *Lithodomi*, containing *Rhynchonella sub-decorata*, and *Acanthothyris spinosa* .. about	1
Upper Lias	Blue Clay	

From the basement-bed, the late E. A. Walford obtained small blocks of limestone covered with *Plicatulae* and pierced by *Lithodomi* ; he also recorded the occurrence of *Trigonia producta* Lyc. and *T. angulata* J. de C. Sow. The presence of *Rhynchonella sub-decorata* Dav., a shell characteristic of the Scissum Beds, suggests, unless derived, that this horizon may also be represented, but the zonal ammonite, *Tmetoceras scissum* (Benecke), has not been found.

Strata of Inferior Oolite age have been recorded in the borings at Kidlington, Wytham, and Oxford. The Clypeus Grit was stated to have been passed through in the deep boring at the City Brewery, Oxford, but an examination of the specimens from this borehole, preserved in the Survey collections, does not confirm the statement. The rock-specimens assigned to this horizon resemble more strongly certain beds of the Chipping Norton Limestone. Indeed, it is highly probable that the Inferior Oolite has been completely overlapped before reaching Oxford.

GREAT OOLITE SERIES

The term Great Oolite Series is here used to include all deposits between the Clypeus Grit and the Forest Marble, and, in this restricted sense, it is practically uniform with the same title employed to denote these beds on the geological map. It differs in one respect, however, in including the Chipping Norton Limestone, which was regarded in the former edition of the memoir as the uppermost member of the Inferior Oolite.

The succession is as follows, in descending order :—

Great Oolite Limestones
Stonesfield Slate
Neaeran Beds
Chipping Norton Limestone.

While it is probable that the whole of the Series is represented in the neighbourhood of Ashford Mill, there are no sections in which the complete succession is displayed. The highest beds of limestone may be seen in numerous quarries, but the lower subdivisions are poorly exposed, and good sections are to be seen only in the area beyond the confines of the map. Thus, the sequence of beds from the base of the Great Oolite Limestones down to the Clypeus Grit may be studied in the lane leading from Stonesfield to the river Evenlode.

The Great Oolite Limestones are mainly white or cream-coloured oolites with beds of marl. The uppermost bed, which is usually a compact 'cream-cheese' limestone, shows a well-marked eroded surface, indicating a pause in sedimentation accompanied by erosion of the sea-floor. A marl-bed situated a short distance below the top is, as a rule, crowded with the characteristic brown shells of *Epithyris bathonica* S. Buckman, showing various growth-stages in examples ranging from small uniplicate forms to robust strongly biplicate specimens. This brachiopod has been appropriately chosen as the zonal index for the highest beds of the Series. The underlying oolites with '*Rhynchonella*' *hopkinsi* are not exposed in the district.

As already remarked, the Stonesfield Slate does not crop out in the area, but full particulars of the strata, the method of working formerly employed, and lists of fossils have been given elsewhere.[1] The 'Neaeran' Beds, however, were proved in the deep boring at the City Brewery, Oxford. They consisted of beds of grey and black clays, 28 ft. thick, and they were grouped by J. H. Blake and H. B. Woodward with the Upper Estuarine Series. Particulars of these strata and of the fossils met with are given in the record of the boring (p. 174). The clays overlie the Chipping Norton Limestone, and have been proved to occur beneath the Stonesfield Slate at Stonesfield. From the occurrence of '*Neaera*' (=*Cuspidaria*) the late E. A. Walford designated them as the Neaeran Beds.

A portion of the Chipping Norton Limestone is exposed at Ashford Mill Cottages. This rock weathers into slabby layers, and on this account is easily distinguishable from the Clypeus Grit, which breaks into a rubble of rounded fragments containing oolite grains of large size.

In the past some confusion has arisen respecting the stratigraphical position of the Chipping Norton Limestone. This oolite was described under this name by W. H. Hudleston,[2] who regarded it as forming the highest part of the Inferior Oolite in this district. H. B. Woodward, although of the opinion that this lithological unit could not be separated on stratigraphical grounds from the Inferior Oolite, recognized the inconsistency of thus including a bed which overlies the Clypeus Grit, the uppermost part of the Inferior Oolite in the Cotteswolds.[3] He admitted, however, that the fossils recorded from it, as pointed out by E. A. Walford and others, appear to be more closely related to the Bathonian ; and the occurrence of such diagnostic species as *Zigzagiceras zigzag* and *Oppelia fusca* proves the

[1] Woodward, H. B., ' The Jurassic Rocks of Britain ' (*Mem. Geol. Surv.*), vol. iv, 1894, pp. 310–317, 484, 485.
[2] *Proc. Geol. Assoc.*, vol. v, 1878, p. 384.
[3] Woodward, H. B., ' The Jurassic Rocks of Britain ' (*Mem. Geol. Surv.*), vol. iv, 1894, p. 247.

limestone to be equivalent to the lower part of the Lower Fuller's Earth clay (*see* below).

Some difficulty has also been experienced in correlating the Great Oolite Series with the equivalent argillaceous facies in Somerset, Wiltshire and Dorset, but the evidence now available indicates that the Series, regarded as a unit, corresponds in all probability with the Fuller's Earth of these areas.

In these counties the Fuller's Earth is represented by a mass of clay, divisible into a lower and upper clay, separated by a calcareous rock-band, the Fuller's Earth Rock. The lower clay, which rests on the Clypeus Grit, falls within the zones of *Zigzagiceras zigzag*, *Oppelia fusca* and *Ostrea acuminata* (*sensu stricto*), and thus clearly represents the variable series of clays and limestones which occur between the Clypeus Grit and the Great Oolite Limestones in Oxfordshire. The Fuller's Earth Rock yields *Tulites subcontractus* (Morr. & Lyc.) and *Morrisites morrisi* S. Buckman, and the former ammonite characterizes the lower portion of the Great Oolite Limestones in Oxfordshire. In the absence of diagnostic species, the deposits above this level in the two areas are not at present directly comparable ; but it is highly probable that the remaining beds of Great Oolite are the calcareous equivalents of the Upper Fuller's Earth clay, as indicated in the following table.[1]

ZONES AND SUBDIVISIONS OF THE GREAT OOLITE SERIES.

Wiltshire and Somerset	Zones.	Oxfordshire and Gloucestershire
Forest Marble	Epithyris marmorea	Forest Marble
Upper Fuller's Earth Clay	Epithyris bathonica ' Rhynchonella ' hopkinsi Oxycerites waterhousei	Great Oolite Limestones
Fuller's Earth Rock	Morrisites morrisi Tulites subcontractus	
Lower Fuller's Earth Clay	Ostrea acuminata[2] Gracilisphinctes gracilis Zigzagiceras wagneri Oppelia fusca Zigzagiceras zigzag	Stonesfield Slate Neaeran Beds { Chipping Norton { Limestone
Clypeus Grit	(Inferior Oolite)	Clypeus Grit

[1] *See* Richardson, L. ' The Inferior Oolite and Contiguous Deposits of the Chipping Norton District, Oxfordshire.' *Proc. Cotteswold Nat. Hist. Field Club*, vol. xvii, part 2, 1911, pp. 201–206 ; also A. M. Davies, ' Handbuch der Regionalen Geologie,' III, Band I. Abteilung. ' The British Isles,' 1916, pp. 222, 223, 238.

[2] *Sensu stricto.*

FOREST MARBLE

The Forest Marble consists mainly of false-bedded, shelly, oolitic limestones with beds of bluish-grey laminated clay, and has an average thickness of 12 ft. at the outcrop. Underground, and towards the south-west, it appears to expand considerably, and in the City Brewery boring at Oxford the formation is nearly 33 ft. thick.

The division is exceedingly variable in lithological character, the beds of clay frequently passing laterally into thin-bedded flaggy limestones. Thus, at the north-west end of the railway-cutting at Long Handborough station, where the Forest Marble is mainly represented by clay, the argillaceous beds are replaced by false-bedded limestones bearing so close a resemblance to the upper members of the Great Oolite that they are difficult to separate unless fossils are found.

The fact that the lowest beds of the Forest Marble in the district are in a calcareous facies, similar to that of the Great Oolite Limestones, has in a large measure concealed the real relationship between these formations, although an eroded surface, indicating a pause in sedimentation, is always present at the top of the Great Oolite. It can be shown, indeed, that there is a marked unconformity between the formations, and as a result of this break in the stratal sequence, the greenish-black clays and marls characterized by *Epithyris marmorea* (Oppel) are absent over the greater part of the area included within the Special Oxford Sheet. These greenish-black lignitiferous clays, which themselves indicate an abrupt change in the conditions of deposition, are of widespread occurrence in the district to the north-north-east, where the Forest Marble is represented by fluvio-marine sediments termed the Blisworth Clay. Similar greenish-coloured deposits in the lower part of the formation have also been found in deep borings in Norfolk[1] and in Kent[2], and in outcrop-exposures in the Boulonnais[3], often in association with *E. marmorea*.

Although the Forest Marble is rich in shelly limestones, the fauna is relatively poor in species. The commonest forms met with are *Acrosalenia hemicidaroides* Wright, ' *Rhynchonella* ' *concinna* Auctt., *Ostrea sowerbyi* Morr. & Lyc., *Pecten* (*Chlamys*) *fibrosus* J. Sow., *Gervillia waltoni* Lyc., *Modiola imbricata* J. Sow., and the remains of the gigantic saurian *Ceteosaurus oxoniensis* Phill. (see *Frontispiece*). The absence of *Gervillia crassicosta* Morr. & Lyc. is noticeable. This shell is remarkably abundant in the under-

---

[1] Pringle, J., 'On the Concealed Mesozoic Rocks in south-west Norfolk,' in ' Summary of Progress for 1922 ' (*Mem. Geol. Surv.*), 1923, pp. 126–129.

[2] Lamplugh, G. W., and F. L. Kitchin, ' On the Mesozoic Rocks in some of the Coal Explorations in Kent ' (*Mem. Geol. Surv.*), 1911. *See also* G. W. Lamplugh, F. L. Kitchin, and J. Pringle, ' The Concealed Mesozoic Rocks in Kent ' (*Mem. Geol. Surv.*), 1923.

[3] Pruvost, P., and J. Pringle, 'A Synopsis of the Geology of the Boulonnais, including a Correlation of the Mesozoic Rocks with those of England,' *Proc. Geol. Assoc.*, vol. xxxv, 1924, p. 42.

ground extension of this formation in Kent. In the quarry at Islip certain brachiopods, such as *Dictyothyris coarctata* (Park.), *Ornithella digona* (J. Sow.) and *Eudesia cardium* (Lam.), are found in a bed above the false-bedded limestones. These shells are usually regarded as characteristic of the Bradford Clay. The same species have also been noted in the Greenhill Quarries, but in both localities the fossils are found in beds well above the clays with *Epithyris marmorea* (Oppel) and thus cannot be correlated with the Bradford Clay of Wiltshire.

The surfaces of many of the thin bands of limestone that are found in the formation are often traversed by curious markings, believed to be the tracks of Crustaceans. Worm throws and burrows, together with ripple-marks, are also abundant. There are many curious ochreous clayey inclusions in the limestones, and these appear to have originated from clay-pebbles formed contemporaneously by the breaking-up of some argillaceous stratum. The Forest Marble generally bears evidence of its deposition in shallow waters under marine conditions, but the presence of green and greenish-black clays at the base suggests that these deposits were laid down in an estuary.

Epithyris marmorea has usually been selected in this country as the zonal fossil of the Forest Marble, but it is evident from a study of the Oxfordshire sections that this brachiopod has a narrow vertical range and characterizes only the lowest beds. It also appears to be confined to the lower part of the formation in Kent. In the Boulonnais it occurs near the base of the zone of *Rhynchonella elegantula* of the French classification. At Pickwick, near Corsham, where the type[1] was obtained, the shell is restricted to a 3-ft. band of flaggy limestone, above the Bradford Clay and about 6–8 ft. below the base of the Cornbrash. These facts suggest that the Forest Marble in our area represents only the upper part of the formation as developed in Wiltshire. A similar observation was made when the cores of the Westbury boring were described.[2]

CORNBRASH

In its lithological characters the Cornbrash is the least variable of the divisions described in this chapter. It consists of layers of tough, rubbly, shelly limestones, about 9 ft. thick, which are not oolitic except at the base, where the included grains of oolite may have been derived. A thin marly band with peculiar cylindrical concretions of limestone is usually found about the middle of the formation, and this conveniently serves to separate the limestones into a lower bed characterized by *Clydoniceras discus* (J. Sow.) and an upper limestone with *Clydoniceras hochstetteri* (Oppel) ; these sub-divisions are constant over the whole area. The higher

[1] Oppel, A., 'Die Juraformation,' 1856–1858, p. 496 ; and T. Davidson, 'British Oolitic and Liassic Brachiopoda,' (*Mon. Pal. Soc.*), 1851, vol. i, pl. ix, figs. 4 and 5.
[2] Pringle, J., 'On a boring for coal at Westbury, Wiltshire,' in 'Summary of Progress for 1921 ' (*Mem. Geol. Surv.*), 1922, p. 150.

Clydoniceras-bed is succeeded by a brown marl crowded with the shells of *Microthyris lagenalis* (Schloth.) in a more or less crushed condition, and during the recent revision it yielded poorly-preserved ammonites, formerly referred to the genus *Macrocephalites*.   These specimens were submitted to Mr. S. S. Buckman for identification, and he states that they are probably fragments of *Dolikephalites dolius* S. S. Buckman[1], a shell that is found in a blue marly stone at the top of the Cornbrash of Peterborough.   This brachiopod-marl, which is seen only in the Hanborough Quarry, is probably comparable with a portion of the so-called clays of the Cornbrash of Yorkshire, said to contain *Macrocephalites* and *Pseudomonotis echinatus* (J. Sow.). The top of the Cornbrash is similarly formed by a bed of fossiliferous clay in a boring at Westbury in Wiltshire[2], in the Cirencester neighbourhood, and in numerous borings in Kent.[3]   *Macrocephalites macrocephalus* has been recorded from the cuttings on the Woodstock Branch railway and at Witney[4], but the exact position of the specimens within the formation is not stated.

In the district under review the Cornbrash rests with marked unconformity on the Forest Marble, and the abruptness of the junction is further emphasized by a striking change in the fauna. The frequent occurrence of eroded surfaces of beds within the formation clearly indicates interrupted sedimentation and intra-formational erosion.   The stratal breaks implied cannot be more than of minor importance since they do not appear to be followed by important faunal changes.   These eroded surfaces are to be seen in almost every section, but they are particularly well displayed in the Hanborough Quarry.

The fauna of the Cornbrash is of constant character, each section yielding an abundance of the same species of brachiopods and lamellibranchs.   Ammonites, however, appear to be rare, and it is usual to visit many localities before a specimen is found.

In addition to the two broad, easily recognizable zones that can be established, that of *Clydoniceras discus* below and of *Clydoniceras hochstetteri* above, the brown shelly marl that succeeds the upper limestone in the Hanborough Quarry may form a third, a zone of *Dolikephalites dolius*.   In the zone of *Clydoniceras discus* two horizons can be noted : the base of the zone is characterized by an abundance of *Terebratula intermedia* J. Sow., and in the upper part *Ornithella obovata* (J. Sow.) is particularly plentiful.   *Nautilus truncatus* J. Sow. appears to be confined to this horizon.   Certain shells, such as *Astarte robusta* Lycett, *Trigonia moretoni* Morris & Lycett, *T. flecta* Lycett and *Eopecten gradus* (Bean) are confined to the Hochstetteri Zone, but do not appear to be restricted to any

[1] Buckman, S. S., ' Type Ammonites,' vol. iv, 1924, p. 55, pl. ccclxxii.
[2] Pringle, J., ' On a boring for Coal at Westbury, Wiltshire,' in ' Summary of Progress for 1921 ' (*Mem. Geol. Surv.*), 1922, p. 146.
[3] Lamplugh, G. W., F. L. Kitchin, and J. Pringle, ' The Concealed Mesozoic Rocks in Kent ' (*Mem. Geol. Surv.*), 1923.
[4] Woodward, H. B., ' The Jurassic Rocks of Britain ' (*Mem. Geol. Surv.*), vol. iv, 1894, p. 446.

definite horizon within it. It is probable that the Cornbrash is capable of further subdivision in districts where ammonites are more abundant, but material on which to base a narrower zonal classification is not at present available in the sections in the area included in the Special Oxford Sheet. A list of the principal fossils is as follows :—

Nucleolites clunicularis (*Wright*)
Pygurus michelini *Cott.*
Ornithella obovata (*J. Sow.*)
Terebratula intermedia *J. Sow.*
    „   maxillata *J. de C. Sow.*
Astarte elegans *J. Sow.*
Gresslya peregrina (*Phill.*)
Homomya gibbosa (*J. Sow.*)
Isocardia tenera *J. Sow.*
Lima (Limatula) gibbosa *J. Sow.*
Modiola imbricata *J. Sow.*
Pecten (Camptonectes) lens *J. Sow.*
    „   (Chlamys) vagans *J. de C. Sow.*
Pholadomya deltoidea *J. Sow.*
    „   lyrata *J. Sow.*
    „   phillipsi *Lycett*

The Great Oolite, together with the Forest Marble and Cornbrash, forms the bluffs of the river Evenlode between Handborough railway station and Ashford Mill and passes westward by a cross valley near Wilcote to the Windrush. This will be referred to in the local details as the Wilcote Valley. A small area of the Cornbrash in a tributary valley of the Windrush near Witney is also included in the map. East of Long Hanborough the series extends by Bladon to Kidlington, where it passes northward outside our region. At Islip there is a large inlier within the Oxford Clay, showing all three divisions. A smaller inlier on the north bank of the River Ray by Oddington extends to Charlton, beyond the margin of the map. Separate descriptions of the Great Oolite Series, Forest Marble and Cornbrash are not given in the following local details, since it frequently happens that the three formations are exposed in many of the sections.

LOCAL DETAILS

Near Witney the Forest Marble is represented by false-bedded oolitic limestones with thick bands of clay. The upper beds are well displayed below the Cornbrash in a quarry north-west of the town, where a grey earthy limestone, crowded with corals and brachiopods, is found overlying a greenish-black clay full of lignite.

A few small exposures of the Cornbrash may be seen by following the brook north-eastwards from Newland. The rock here, as in many other places, covers a wide area, the overlying Kellaways Beds and Oxford Clay having been denuded without any considerable destruction of the beds below, so that the dip of the strata nearly coincides with the surface-slope.

At The Hayes, near Ramsden, a boring made for the improvement of a water-supply was carried down to the depth of 360 ft. and proved the following formations :—Gravel, 6 ft. ; Oxford Clay ? and Kellaways Beds, 21 ft. ; Cornbrash, 11 ft. ; Forest Marble, 25 ft. ; Great Oolite Series, 142 ft. ; Inferior Oolite, 27 ft. ; Upper, Middle and Lower Lias, 128 ft. The boring was stopped in the Capricornus Beds.

In the Wilcote Valley the dip of the rocks is slightly east of south, so that the outcrop of the Forest Marble is much broader on the northern slope than on the southern.   Here, this formation rests with marked unconformity on the Great Oolite limestones as is shown by a section in the old quarry by the road about a quarter of a mile west-south-west of Wilcote.   At the southern end of Holly Grove Plantation, Wilcote, an exposure shows the hard, shelly, false-bedded oolite with clay-partings that forms the lower beds of the Forest Marble in the district.

Near North Leigh and New Yatt there are few sections, the Cornbrash, for the most part, being concealed by the wash from the drift at the top of the hill.

East of Bridewell Farm white limestones in the upper portion of the Great Oolite were formerly quarried for lime-burning ; similar limestones are again well exposed in a quarry south-east of Fisher's Gate, a quarter of a mile north-east of North Leigh Church.   The section shows the following beds :—

		Ft.	In.
Superficial Deposits	Gravel ; pockets filled with pebbles of flint, quartzite, vein-quartz, etc., extend downwards into the beds below ..	1	0
Great Oolite Series	White oolitic limestone, becoming decalcified towards the east end of working-face	2 to 5	0
	Dark brownish-black marl	0	6
	Pale brownish sandy limestone crowded with *Nerinea eudesi*	1	0
	White oolitic limestones, yielding reptilian fragments, etc.	10	0

The limestone, which probably comes within the zone of *Epithyris bathonica,* has been quarried for building purposes, but is now used only for lime-burning. Whitish and grey sandy limestones are dug in a series of shallow openings about 200 yds. north-west of Fisher's Gate for use on the local roads.

In the Evenlode Valley, below Ashford Mill, practically the whole of the Great Oolite Series is included in a bluff on the right bank of the River Evenlode.   The thickness may be estimated at about 130 ft. ; but the only exposure of the lower half of the formation is to be seen in an old quarry on the west side of Ashford Mill cottages.   At this locality a portion of the Chipping Norton Limestone, consisting of thin-bedded, somewhat shelly oolite, has been worked for local use.

A quarry showing the highest beds of the Great Oolite and the lowest portion of the Forest Marble may be seen on the roadside by Whitehill Wood, a quarter of a mile south-east of the Mill.   The succession is as follows :—

		Ft.	In.
	Soil	0	6
Forest Marble	Bluish-grey flaggy oolitic limestone ..	3	0
	Greenish-grey marl	2	6
Great Oolite (Zone of *Epithyris bathonica*)	Soft rubbly whitish marl	1	6
	White compact earthy limestone	2	3
	Soft white marly limestone, shelly at top..	7	0
	Creamy-white oolitic limestone with soft marly partings	5	2
	Brownish-grey marl with plant-fragments..	0	5
	White finely sandy limestone	1	2
	Brownish marl	3 to 0	6
	Thick beds of white and pinkish oolite ..	8	0

The limestones of the Great Oolite in this stone-pit are traversed by wide vertical fissures often filled with marl.   The section includes higher beds than those exposed in the railway cuttings at Bridgefield Bridge (*see* p. 19) and the rocks evidently belong to the series of white limestones and marly beds above the freestone of Taynton ; such as may be seen at Milton, near

Shipton-under-Wychwood, some miles west of the area. The mass of the Great Oolite between Milton and Woodstock appears to be of variable character, and the lower division is much attenuated.[1]

There are several quarries that again exhibit the white limestones of the Great Oolite, the Forest Marble and the Cornbrash at East End, north-east of North Leigh. The three divisions are well displayed in a disused quarry about 250 yds. north-west of the New Inn, and show the following details :—

		Ft.	In.
	Soil	1	0
Cornbrash	⎧ Hard grey brashy limestone with *Pseudo-* ⎪ *monotis echinatus, Terebratula intermedia,* ⎩ and *Ornithella obovata*	1	0
	⎧ Pale green clay	0	10
	⎪ Light-brown marl and racy limestone ..	0	6
Forest Marble	⎪ Flaggy oolitic shelly limestone with clay ⎨ partings	4	0
	⎪ False-bedded, ripple-marked oolites ..	1	10
	⎪ Flaggy shelly limestone	1	3
	⎩ False-bedded shelly oolitic limestone ..	3	6
	resting on eroded surface of		
Great Oolite	⎰ Hard marly ' cream-cheese ' limestone, with ⎱ *Cyprina loweana* and *Pinna cuneata* seen to	6	0

The beds of the Forest Marble are, as usual, highly fossiliferous, and in addition to showing ripple-marked and rain-pitted surfaces yield the following characteristic fossils : *Lima cardiiformis* J. Sow., *L. semicircularis* Goldf., *Modiola imbricata* J. Sow., *Ostrea sowerbyi* Morr. & Lyc., and *Pteroperna costatula* (Deslong.). It may be noted that the Cornbrash, though so thin, here spreads out into a plateau half a mile long, similar to the broad outcrop of the same formation near Witney.

The Great Western Railway (Worcester Branch) is carried along the valley by means of deep cuttings through the projecting spurs between the bends of the River Evenlode. These excavations, though now much overgrown, still show good sections of the higher beds of the Great Oolite Limestones, and the one exposed below Bridgefield Bridge, north of Ashford Mill, just beyond the limits of the map, is of interest, since it includes lower beds of the upper part of the Great Oolite than are exposed in the area. Though now much concealed, the following section may still be seen in parts of the cutting:—

		Ft.
	Rubble of oolite, marl, etc.	
	⎧ Fissile and false-bedded oolites and marls.. ⎫ ⎪ Oolitic limestone, with corals .. .. ⎭	15
Great Oolite	⎨ Marly and carbonaceous oolite .. .. ⎫ ⎪ Clay and sandy shales, with *Ostrea sowerbyi* ⎭	5
	⎪ Pale grey limestone with *Nerinea eudesi,* ⎪ *Astarte angulata*	1
	⎩ Fissile and shelly oolite with *Nerinea* at top	6 to 8

The section has been described by John Phillips and others,[2] as well as by R. F. Tomes,[3] who obtained from the Coral-bed, *Astrocoenia phillipsi* Tomes, *Cryptocoenia pratti* Edw. & Haime, *Isastrea gibbosa* Duncan, *I. limitata* Lamx., *Montlivaltia sp.*, *Thamnastrea lyelli* Edw. & Haime, etc. He also collected *Cyathophora bourgueti* Defr. from the bed above the *Nerinea* limestone. A number of Gasteropods and other fossils were obtained by

---

[1] Woodward, H. B., ' The Jurassic Rocks of Britain ' (*Mem. Geol. Surv.*), vol. iv, 1894, p. 318.

[2] Phillips, J., *Quart. Journ. Geol. Soc.*, vol. xvi, 1860, p. 116 ; A. Gaudry, *Bull. Soc. géol. France*, sér. 2, tome x, 1853, p. 594 ; J. F. Whiteaves, *Rep. Brit. Assoc.* for 1860, p. 105.

[3] Tomes, R. F., *Quart. Journ. Geol. Soc.*, vol. xxxix, 1883, p. 171.

T. J. Slatter from the Great Oolite in this cutting : they include *Fibula variata* Lyc., *F. eulimoides* Whit., *Natica michelini* d'Arch., *Neridomus minutus* J. Sow., *Ataphrus discoideus* Morr. & Lyc., *Delphinula alta* Morr. & Lyc., and *Solarium varicosum* Morr. & Lyc. Many other fossils, together with *Cypricardia nuculiformis* F. A. Roem. and *C. rostrata* (J. Sow.), have been recorded by Dr. J. F. Whiteaves. The shelly oolite at the bottom of the section is above the Stonesfield Slate, which is here under the line of railway.

On the left bank of the Evenlode, north of the railway, there is a small quarry about 100 yds. north-west of Westfield Farm showing false-bedded shelly oolite with a thin band of marl. This marl bed is crowded with specimens of *Rhynchonella concinna* Auctt. and *Ostrea sowerbyi* Morr. & Lyc., and has also yielded the following fossils : *Acrosalenia* cf. *wiltoni* Wright, *Clypeus sp.*, *Nucleolites* cf. *woodwardi* Wright, *Terebratula sp.*, *Lima (Limatula) gibbosa* J. Sow., *Lucina rotundata* ? (F. A. Roemer), *Pholadomya heraulti* ? Ag., etc. It is possible that this marl is the same as that found overlying the Stonesfield Slate at Stonesfield, as is shown in the record of the section at Stocky Bank, just beyond the northern margin of the map.[1]

Farther east, at Combe Cliff, the lower beds of the Great Oolite are, for the most part, below the level of the river, but a considerable thickness of the upper limestones is present, but unexposed in the railway cutting. Higher beds, however, are to be seen in a small quarry east of Grintleyhill Bridge, 400 yards north-west of Mill Wood. At this locality some of the oolites show pinkish patches that recall certain beds of limestone displayed in the section by Whitehill Wood (*see* p. 18). Indeed, to judge by the relation of the limestones to the outcrop of the Forest Marble, they must occupy the same stratigraphical position, and come within the zone of *Epithyris bathonica.* A prominent marl-band, 1 ft. thick, in this quarry is highly fossiliferous, and has yielded the following fossils :—

> Clypeus mülleri *Wright*
> Nucleolites woodwardi *Wright*
> Epithyris bathonica *S. S. Buckman*
> Ceromya undulata *Morr. & Lyc.*
> Cyprina nuciformis *Lyc.*
> Isocardia tenera *J. Sow.*
> Modiola imbricata *J. Sow.*
> Pholadomya heraulti *Ag.*
> Pinna cuneata *Phill.*
> Pleuromya calceiformis (*Phill.*)
> Tancredia gibbosa *Lyc.*
> Trigonia costata *J. Sow.*, var.
> Chemnitzia vittata *Phill.*
> Nerinea voltzi *Desl.*
> Trochus sp.

The white limestone of the Great Oolite was at one time well exposed along Combe Cliff, but the section is now almost completely overgrown ; a quarry in the wood on the north side of the road above Combe Cliff shows the lower Clydoniceras Bed of the Cornbrash overlying typical beds of the Forest Marble. The variable character of this formation is well shown at the eastern end of the quarry, where a greenish-grey clay, forming the uppermost bed of the Forest Marble, passes within the length of the quarry into flaggy shelly limestone.

On the south side of the Evenlode the Forest Marble and the Cornbrash rocks are again displayed in the Hanborough quarries, north of the Swan Inn. The south quarry, now disused, shows the following section, but some of the

---

[1] Walford, E. A., ' On some new Oolitic strata in North Oxfordshire ', Buckingham, 1906, pp. 17–20.

beds are perhaps seen to better advantage in the north pit, which is being actively worked :—

		Ft.	In.
Pleistocene	Gravel, composed of pebbles of oolitic limestone, quartzite, flint, chert, with *Camarotoechia*, etc. *Elephas antiquus* and *E. trogontherii* have also been found in the gravel (*see* p. 120) ..	5 to 6	0
Kellaways Beds ?	Blue clay, unfossiliferous	0	9

		Ft.	In.
Cornbrash	Brown marly clay with *Rhynchonella varians*, *Microthyris lagenalis, Pholadomya sp.,* ? *Dolikephalites dolius*, etc.	1	0
	resting on an eroded surface of		
	Hard brownish-grey sandy limestone	0	8
	Hard light-grey shelly limestone with thin layers of brownish-grey marl ; crowded with fossils : *Terebratula maxillata, T. intermedia, Pseudomonotis echinatus, Clydoniceras hochstetteri* (Second Clydoniceras Bed)	4	6
	Dark brownish racy clay with numerous peculiar cylindrical-shaped concretions of grey shelly limestone : *Ornithella obovata*, etc. ..	6 to 0	8
	Pale brown shelly marl	3 to 0	4
	resting on a well-marked eroded surface of		
	Hard light-grey sandy limestone with brownish specks. *Clydoniceras discus* in upper part ; *Terebratula intermedia* abundant below (First Clydoniceras Bed)	about 2	0
	resting on an eroded surface of		
Forest Marble	Dark well-bedded brownish-green clay with lenticles of thin flaggy bluish-grey limestone..	3	0
	Coarse shelly oolite, with indistinct false-bedding seen to	2	0

This quarry presents the most instructive section of the Cornbrash exposed within the area. It shows a brownish marly clay, crowded with the shells of *Microthyris lagenalis* (Schloth.), all in a more or less crushed condition, resting on the eroded surface of the Second Clydoniceras Bed. It represents the highest bed of Cornbrash in the district, and as already stated is probably comparable with somewhat similar marls found at the top of the formation in Kent, Wiltshire, Lincolnshire and Yorkshire. The numerous eroded surfaces shown in the section point to frequent intra-formational erosion and arrested deposition, but apparently do not indicate stratal breaks of any considerable magnitude since they are not followed by striking faunal changes.

The peculiar cylindrical-shaped concretions of a bluish-grey shelly limestone that are found in the dark racy clay between the First and Second Clydoniceras Beds are difficult to explain. Generally they lie parallel to the bedding-planes near the top of the bed, but some are found to extend obliquely downward in the clay, and these frequently simulate a rude kind of branching. They may possibly have originated during one of the periods of erosion. Similar concretions are found on the same horizon over a wide area.

Two ammonites, identified by J. F. Blake as *Clydoniceras hochstetteri* (Oppel) and *Perisphinctes sub-bakeriae* (d'Orb.), were obtained from this pit in 1904. They probably came from the Second Clydoniceras Bed, but were not found *in situ*. During the revision of the area in 1924 Mr. S. W. Hester collected a fragment of a massive Perisphinctid from the Hochstetteri Zone, and Mr. Buckman, who has examined the specimen, states that it is near to *Homoeoplanulites stabilis*, a shell found in the massive limestone of Stalbridge Weston.

In the ground between this quarry and the railway cutting at Handborough Station, the Forest Marble appears to undergo a marked lithological change.

At the top of the cutting the Cornbrash, with its characteristic *Terebratula intermedia*-bed at the base, can be seen all the way until it reaches the level of the rails at the end nearest Oxford. At the opposite end the Forest Marble division consists mainly of clays with thin flaggy oolitic limestones in the upper part, and a few beds of false-bedded oolite marked by a detrital bed at the base, containing fragments of the underlying Great Oolite. But near the bridge the clays are replaced by thick beds of oolitic limestones that come in 7 ft. below the base of the Cornbrash ; and in appearance these strongly resemble some of the Great Oolite strata. Similar limestones are exposed in the quarry at the corner of the roads north-east of Handborough Station ; the section shows the following details :—

		Ft.	In.
Cornbrash	{ Hard grey compact limestone with *Terebratula intermedia, Clydoniceras discus*, etc.		
	up to 3	0
	eroded surface		
	Grey clay with ' race '	4	2
	Compact shelly oolitic limestone	1	4
	Brownish marl	0	3
Forest	Whitish false-bedded limestone	6	0
Marble	Brown marly clay with lignite	0	3
	Whitish false-bedded limestone	5	6
	Grey marly clay .. .. .. 6 in. to	1	0
	eroded surface		
Great	Compact limestone with *Cyprina, Epithyris bathonica*, etc.	1	3
Oolite	Thick bedded blue-hearted oolitic limestone	4	6
	Grey marly clay .. .. .. seen	0	6

The grouping here adopted differs from that given by H. B. Woodward, who thought that the lower beds of the Forest Marble appeared to correspond with those referred to the Great Oolite in the quarry north-east of Bladon.[1] The deepening of the quarry, however, has shown that the limestones are above the eroded top of the Great Oolite. Quarrying operations in this pit frequently expose curious patches of Cornbrash which have dropped down into swallow-holes in the grey clay forming the highest bed of the Forest Marble. The following fossils have been obtained from the Forest Marble at this locality :—

> Clypeus sp.
> Serpula intestinalis *Phill.*
> Acrosalenia hemicidaroides *Wright*
> Nucleolites sp.
> ' Rhynchonella ' concinna ? (*J. Sow.*)
> Astarte ?
> Modiola compressa *Goldf.*
>   ,,   imbricata *J. Sow.*
>   ,,   sowerbyana *d'Orb.*
> Ostrea sowerbyi *Morr. & Lyc.*
> Placunopsis socialis *Morr. & Lyc.*
> Fish remains

The white limestones of the Great Oolite extend up the valley of the Glyme as far as Hensington. They are exposed in the road cutting at the south-west end of the village of Bladon ; and in the old quarry about 100 yards west of the Post Office, the stone was formerly worked for lime-burning. The quarry-section still shows a white oolitic limestone, 5 ft. thick, resting on a brownish marly band crowded with the characteristic brown shells of *Epithyris bathonica* S. Buckman. About 100 yards farther north, a small

---

[1] Woodward, H. B., ' The Jurassic Rocks of Britain ' (*Mem. Geol. Surv.*), vol. iv, 1894, p. 319.

exposure in an orchard on the west side of the road exhibits lower beds of the Great Oolite limestones with *Nerinea eudesi* Morr. & Lyc., overlain unconformably by coarsely oolitic false-bedded Forest Marble.

Fuller details of the Forest Marble and the Cornbrash are to be obtained, however, from the disused quarry in the Spinney, about 500 yards north-east of Bladon, in which the following section is exposed :—

		Ft.	In.
Cornbrash	Brashy limestone and marl	2	0
	Hard brown and grey rubbly limestone with *Terebratula intermedia*, etc.	2	6
Forest Marble	Yellow sandy marl	0	9
	Oolitic limestone	0	8
	Laminated brownish-grey clay	1	3
	False-bedded oolitic limestone	1	0
	Dark grey clay	0	10
	False-bedded oolitic limestone	1	6
	Dark blue-grey clay	1	0
	False-bedded oolitic limestone with clay partings	3	0
	Blue-grey clay	3	3
	Argillaceous limestone with '*Rhynchonella*' spp.	1	0
	Buff and blue oolitic shelly limestone, indistinctly false-bedded	10	0
Great Oolite	Compact shelly limestone with plant fragments	4	6
	Marly clay .. .. seen to	2	6

The Cornbrash and Forest Marble yield characteristic assemblages of fossils ; and it is highly probable that the argillaceous limestone with several species of Rhynchonellids, including *Kallirhynchia concina* (J. Sow.), corresponds with a bed of similar lithology and fauna in the Islip Quarry (*see* p. 26).

In Blenheim Park the boundaries drawn between Forest Marble and Great Oolite, north of the Glyme, are conjectural owing to the lack of evidence. A section north of the bridge below the lake at one time showed flaggy Forest Marble limestone resting on white marly stone of the Great Oolite. On the drive between the High Lodge and Lince Lodge there are occasional openings in the Forest Marble. The sections, in exhibiting the flaggy and highly oolitic limestones characteristic of the formation, serve to demonstrate their general persistence in the region.

To the east of Bladon the Cornbrash spreads in a broad, slightly inclined plane to the Cherwell. The Forest Marble crops out along the brooks north of Begbroke; and again west of Kidlington. These strata dip under the Kellaways Beds between the two villages, and are not seen again towards the south.

In this area there are not many good sections until Campsfield Farm is reached. Here, below the Cornbrash, the Forest Marble is represented by flaggy false-bedded oolitic limestones, 17 ft. thick. *Clydoniceras discus* (J. Sow.) has been found in the lower half of the Cornbrash in this pit, in association with *Nautilus truncatus* J. Sow.; in the upper part a poorly preserved fragment of a Perisphinctid was obtained during the recent re-examination of the section, but it is not possible to identify the species.

In the adjacent railway cutting the same two divisions have been exposed, the Cornbrash extending from the top at the north end downwards towards the station, where it is concealed by river gravel.

Half a mile due east of the railway cutting, H. B. Woodward[1] recorded a similar section in an old quarry, but this is no longer accessible. A large

[1] Woodward, H. B., ' The Jurassic Rocks of Britain ' (*Mem. Geol. Surv.*), vol. iv, 1894, p. 448.

collection of Cornbrash fossils, including about 76 species, was made in this neighbourhood by Dr. J. F. Whiteaves.[1]

Within a short distance of the sections above mentioned the Lower Oolites disappear under the flood-plain of the River Cherwell.

Before a description of the sections in the Ray Valley is given, reference may be made to a series of interesting quarries around Enslow Bridge, near Bletchington Station, just beyond the confines of the map. These exposures show Lower Oolitic strata, ranging upwards from the *Bathonica*-beds of the Great Oolite to the top of the zone of *Clydoniceras hochstetteri* of the Cornbrash. The chief sections have been described by Hull[2] and Phillips;[3] and more recently by Mr. M. Odling,[4] but certain beds included in the Great Oolite by Hull and Odling are here grouped with the Forest Marble. The strata in question are indicated by an asterisk in the combined section of the Lower and Upper Greenhill quarries, given below :—

		Ft.	In.
Cornbrash	Rubbly limestone (Second Clydoniceras Bed)	3	0
	Calcareous clay and platy limestone with *Terebratula intermedia* and *Ornithella obovata*	3	0
	Clay-marl and limestone	1	6
	Compact limestone, slightly oolitic, with *Nautilus truncatus, Clydoniceras discus, T. intermedia*, etc.	1	9
Forest Marble	Laminated grey clay with thin bands of limestone	3	0
	Flaggy false-bedded shelly limestone with bands of clay .. .. .. about	16	0
	*Dark green and greenish-black clay with lignite. At top there is a hard white-weathering band with ' race '; bones of *Ceteosaurus oxoniensis*	3	6
	*Brown oolitic shelly marl crowded with *Epithyris marmorea* and corals .. .. 1 to 1		6
	eroded surface		
Great Oolite	Massive limestone with marly parting at base. *Epithyris bathonica* abundant ..	10	0

Phillips was obviously not in agreement with the classification adopted by Hull, for in the year following the publication of the ' Woodstock ' memoir, he grouped the clay with the Forest Marble ; and a re-examination of the sections proves that his views are correct, since the top of the Great Oolite, as taken here and by him, falls below a brown oolitic marl crowded with the shells of *Epithyris marmorea* (Oppel). This characteristic brachiopod thus underlies the dark green clays that contain the remains of the gigantic saurian *Ceteosaurus oxoniensis* Phillips. On account of the unconformity at the base of the Forest Marble, these clays are unrepresented in the area comprised within the Special Oxford Sheet, but similar green clays are characteristic of the lower part of the Forest Marble in the railway cuttings at Ardley and Blackthorne Hill, near Bicester, and rest on an eroded surface of the ' cream-cheese ' top of the Great Oolite. As already pointed out, black and green clays are found in the underground extensions of the formation in Norfolk and Kent, and at the surface in the Bas Boulonnais in France.

[1] *Rep. Brit. Assoc.* for 1860, p. 107. *See also* Hull, ' Geology of Woodstock,' p. 25 ; and Phillips, ' Geology of Oxford,' p. 238.

[2] Hull, E., ' The Geology of the Country around Woodstock ' (*Mem. Geol. Surv.*), 1859, pp. 20, 21.

[3] Phillips, J., ' On some sections of the strata near Oxford,' *Quart. Journ. Geol. Soc.*, vol. xvi, 1860, p. 118.

[4] Odling, M., ' The Bathonian Rocks of the Oxford District,' *Quart. Journ. Geol. Soc.*, vol. lxix, 1913, pp. 493–498.

A.—*Section of Forest Marble and Cornbrash in Islip Quarry.*

B.—*Solution-pipes in the gravels of the Handborough Terrace.*

The bones of *Cetcosaurus oxoniensis* Phill. were obtained from the quarries, now disused, adjacent to Bletchington Station.[1] Similar remains are occasionally exposed in the Greenhill Quarries, close by, and in the Kirtlington Cement Co.'s pit. A restoration of this saurian has been made by Baron von Huene, and this has been outlined and photographed by Mr. C. J. Bayzand (*see Frontispiece*). *Cetcosaurus oxoniensis* attained a length of 66 ft., a width of 6½ ft., and a height of 16 ft.

Along the northern margin of Ot Moor there is a remarkable series of inliers of the Lower Oolites that protrude in isolated ridges surrounded by low alluvial tracts, over which wander the almost stagnant waters of the Ray and its tributaries.

These inliers are situated along a line of upheaval, approximately parallel to the general strike of the formations of the region taken as a whole. But there are minor disturbances in a direction at right angles to this that cause undulations in the strata of smaller amplitude and wave-length. The structure is further complicated by faults, which in one case have displaced all the strata up to the Shotover Sands along a line extending from Islip across the Thame valley, to Great Haseley. The faulted beds of Great Oolite, disclosed in the Kirtlington Portland Cement Company's quarry on the east bank of the Cherwell, north-west of the area, probably mark the continuation of the Islip faults into that district. The line of upheaval extends north-eastward into Buckinghamshire far beyond the limits of the map. In the opposite

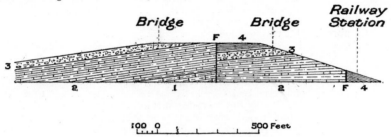

FIG. I.—*Section of Islip Railway-cutting.*

4. Oxford Clay.   2. Forest Marble.
3. Cornbrash.   1. Great Oolite.
                        F. Faults.

direction it may be clearly traced in the structure of Wytham Hill, though the disturbance is much less intense ; but farther on it appears to die out, for no Lower Oolites are brought up within the main outcrop of the Oxford Clay towards the south-west until we reach the neighbourhood of Trowbridge in Wiltshire.

The largest and most disturbed of the inliers is approximately bell-shaped, the length from north-west to south-east being a little over two miles, and breadth somewhat less. It supports the villages of Islip, Noke, and Woodeaton. The general structure is that of an anticlinal dome dislocated by faults, but the complication of detail is too great to be determined with exactitude by such field-evidence as is available at present. The railway cutting, of which a diagram is here given (*see* Fig. 1), though much overgrown, shows all the strata involved in the anticline.

On the west, south, and east sides of the inlier the Cornbrash is seen to dip normally towards the clay-tract beyond. North of Islip, however, the beds appear to strike towards the Oxford Clay, as if the inlier were bounded by a fault in that direction. At the summit of Noke Hill and at Islip the Forest Marble emerges in irregular outcrops, faulted for a considerable distance on the east side against Oxford Clay. The upper beds of the Great Oolite crop out on the west slope of Noke Hill, where they appear to dip normally under the Forest Marble towards the River Cherwell, but on the other side the junction is probably a fault, though there are no sections to prove this. The two divisions were observed in a quarry, now almost overgrown, at the cross-roads on the top of the hill between Noke and Woodeaton. The strata are nearly horizontal, and the following details can be made out :—

		Ft.
Forest Marble { Flaggy limestone	.. .. ..	6
{ Clay with Ostrea	.. .. ..	½
Great Oolite White limestone		

Between this quarry and Islip the Forest Marble was formerly worked for road-metal, but the quarries have been filled-in and ploughed over. A new excavation made in a field on the east side of the road, 600 yards south-east of the Islip Bridge, shows the white oolitic limestones that form the highest beds of Great Oolite.

At Islip Quarry (Pl. IIA), one-third of a mile south-west of the railway station, an interesting section is seen :—

		Ft.	In.
	Soil	1	0
Cornbrash	Brownish-grey shelly limestone with *Clydoniceras hochstetteri* (Second Clydoniceras Bed)	1	6
	Brownish marl with cylindrical concretions of limestone	0	9
	eroded surface		
	Brownish-grey limestone, marly at base ; *Terebratula intermedia, Ornithella obovata, Clydoniceras discus,* etc. (First Clydoniceras Bed)	1	6
	eroded surface		
Forest Marble	Laminated grey and brown clay, 1 ft., passing down into grey flaggy false-bedded limestone	2	6
	Brownish-grey laminated clay with thin beds of limestone	1	6
	Bluish-grey earthy limestone, highly fossiliferous ; *Kallirhynchia concinna* abundant .. .. 9 in. to 1	0
	Brownish-grey clay with oolite grains, 6 in. to 0	9
	eroded surface		
	False-bedded bluish-grey limestone ..	8	0
	Blue and greenish clay with lignite, proved in quarry-well		

This is probably the quarry from which Dean Buckland, who was at one time Rector of Islip, collected many of his Forest Marble fossils. It is by far the most fossiliferous locality in this formation within the area, and has yielded the following specimens, now preserved in the University Museum of Oxford. The list is given without revision of nomenclature :—

Anabacia orbulites (*Lam.*)
Acrosalenia hemicidaroides *Wright*
    ,,   loweana *Wright*
    ,,   pustulata *Forbes*
    ,,   spinosa *Agassiz*
Hemicidaris bradfordensis *Wright*
Holectypus depressus *Leske*
Pseudodiadema parkinsoni *Desor.*
Pentacrinus [ossicles of]
Serpula intestinalis *Phill.*

Terebellaria ramosissima (*Lam.*)
Cricopora straminea (*Phill.*)
Dictyothyris coarctata (*Park.*)
Eudesia cardium (*Lam.*)
Ornithella digona (*J. Sow.*)
' Rhynchonella ' concinna ? (*J. Sow.*)
Terebratula maxillata *J. de C. Sow.*
Terebratella (Disculina) hemispherica *J. Sow.*
Arca minuta *J. de C. Sow.*
Astarte angulata *Morr. & Lyc.*
 ,,   interlineata *Lyc.*
 ,,   minima *Phill.*
Cardium stricklandi *Morr. & Lyc.*
 ,,   subtrigonum *Morr. & Lyc.*
Corbula involuta *Goldf.*
 ,,   ´islipensis *Lyc.*
Cypricardia rostrata (*J. Sow.*)
Gervillia acuta *J. de C. Sow.*
 ,,   waltoni *Lyc.*
Leda lachryma (*J. de C. Sow.*)
Lima cardiiformis (*J. Sow.*)
 ,,   (Limea) duplicata (*J. de C. Sow.*)
 ,,   impressa *Morr. & Lyc.*
Modiola imbricata *J. Sow.*
Nucula variabilis *J. de C. Sow.*
Pecten (Camptonectes) annulatus *J. de C. Sow.*
 ,,   arcuatus *J. Sow.*
 ,,   divaricatus *Phill.*
 ,,   (Camptonetes) lens *J. Sow.*
 ,,   (Chlamys) personatus *Goldf.*
 ,,   (Camptonectes) rigidus *J. Sow*
Ostrea sowerbyi *Morr. & Lyc.*
Placunopsis socialis *Morr. & Lyc.*
Pteria costata (*J. Sow.*)
Pteroperna emarginata *Morr. & Lyc.*
Tancredia brevis *Morr. & Lyc.*
Trigonia costata *J. Sow.* var.
 ,,   moretoni *Morr. & Lyc.*
 ,,   pullus *J. de C. Sow.*
Actaeonina luidi *Morr.*
Amberleya nodosa *Morr. & Lyc.*
Ceritella acuta *Morr. & Lyc.*
 ,,   longiscata *Buv.*
Cerithium quadricinctum *Goldf.*
Eulima communis *Morr. & Lyc.*
Natica intermedia *Morr .& Lyc.*
Nerita minuta *J. de C. Sow.*
Patella cingulata *Goldf.*
Trochus spiratus *d'Arch.*
Nautilus baberi *Morr. & Lyc.*

In addition, the limestones show ripple-marks, rain-pittings, worm-tracks, and markings made by crustaceans.

The occurrence of such forms as *Cidaris bradfordensis, Terebellaria ramosissima, Dictyothyris coarctata, Ornithella digona, Eudesia cardium, Corbula islipensis,* and *Pteria costata,* appears to indicate a Bradford Clay horizon, as was thought by Lycett ;[1] but this correlation is unlikely in view of the fact that this fauna is found in beds which overlie blue and greenish lignitiferous clay, lithologically identical with the *Marmorea*-beds at the Greenhill

[1] Lycett, J., ' Supplement to the Great Oolite Mollusca ' (*Mon. Pal. Soc.*), 1863, p. 64.

Quarries (*see* p. 24). During the re-examination of the area numerous small Rhynchonellids were collected at Islip; these were examined by Miss H. Muir-Wood, who identifies them as *Cryptorhynchia bradfordensis* S. S. Buckman, and *Kallirhynchia concinna* (J. Sow.).

At the Home Farm, Woodeaton, a quarry exhibits a section of flaggy oolitic limestones, and the Cornbrash was formerly well displayed near a barn, a quarter of a mile to the south-west. The marked dip of the strata shows clearly the structure of the hill on this side. At the quarry west of Noke village, however, the Cornbrash is seen to dip to the north-east; between this locality and the Ray the formation is bent up into a subsidiary dome about half a mile in diameter, separated from Noke Hill by a depression, which probably marks the continuation of one of the faults in the Islip railway cutting.

On the other side of the river the villages of Oddington and Charlton stand on separate domes of Lower Oolite, each a mile long and a quarter of a mile broad, raised about 20 ft. above the alluvium of Ot Moor. The Cornbrash occupies the greater part of the surface, but the Forest Marble is found in the middle, at the crest of the domes. The white limestone of the Great Oolite does not crop out at Oddington, but it was seen by Prof. Green in a quarry, now disused, south-west of the church. The only exposures seen in 1924 showed a few feet of Cornbrash, containing characteristic fossils. The same author[1] has given the following section at Charlton (Fig. 2) :—

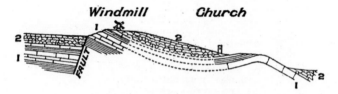

FIG. 2.—*Diagram section through Charlton.*

			Ft.	In.
2. Cornbrash	Rubbly limestone ..	.. .. ..	2	0
	Flaggy oolitic limestone ..	.. ..	0	6
1. Forest Marble	Yellowish marl	.. ..	0	3
	Soft whitish oolitic limestones	.. ..	3	0
	Pale blue clay	..		

The finest section of the Lower Oolites is that exhibited in the railway cuttings between Bicester and the Fritwell Tunnel, near Aynho, a few miles north of our area.

---

[1] ' Geology of the Country around Banbury,' etc. (*Mem. Geol. Surv.*), 1864, p. 36.

CHAPTER III

MIDDLE OOLITIC ROCKS

THE Middle Oolites comprise the Kellaways Beds, the Oxford Clay and the Corallian Rocks. The outcrop of these formations occupies more than half of the area included within the map. The Oxford Clay takes its name from the county of Oxford, where it enters so extensively into the structure of the ground. The Kellaways Beds appear to succeed the Cornbrash without any marked break, but as the junction is rarely exposed, definite proof of conformity has not been established. The general south-easterly inclination of the formations is maintained, but the dip is interrupted, as in the Lower Oolitic Rocks, by the anticlinal folds seen at Islip. The fault supposed to occur in the Botley Valley, west of Oxford, and the probable anticlinal structure of the Wytham and Seacourt Hills, are believed to be due to the feeble continuation of this disturbance. Similar folding or faulting in the Oxford Clay affords an explanation of the occurrence of the Wolvercot clays at Summertown.

In their range underground, the Middle Oolites have been penetrated in several borings, but the formations appear to extend only a short distance beneath the Cretaceous rocks (*see* p. 4).

KELLAWAYS BEDS

The hard sandstones underlying the Oxford Clay, to which the name Kellaways Rock was applied in Wiltshire, are represented in the neighbourhood of Oxford by sandy and loamy beds that have been exposed near Bicester and on the Woodstock branch-railway to the north of the area. Here, as in many other localities, there is from 10 to 12 ft. of clay at the base of this formation, and doggers of calcareous sandstone often occur in the higher beds.

The sands and clays of the Kellaways are now seldom to be seen, and it is probably for this reason that no attempt has been made to distinguish them by a special tint on the map. Their outcrop, however, is marked by a belt of marshy ground with springs, usually found shortly after passing from the Cornbrash towards the Oxford Clay area, and the harder bands appear to be accountable for the somewhat sharp features which are seen where the Kellaways Beds rise above the Lower Oolites, as in Burleigh Wood, south-west of Bladon, and to the east of Church Hanborough.

In the Hanborough quarry, north of the Swan Inn, the Cornbrash is succeeded by an unfossiliferous blue clay, a few inches thick. It is provisionally assigned to the Kellaways Beds, but in the absence of fossils this classification remains uncertain. It is possible, however, that the clay may represent some portion of the zone of *Proplanulites koenigi*. The higher Calloviensis Zone appears to have been exposed from time to time in the railway-cutting at Islip, and numerous doggers are said to have been found containing '*Kepplerites calloviensis*.'[1]

Oxford Clay

Rising in somewhat bold and rounded hills, the lowest part of the Oxford Clay spreads from the Windrush, near Witney, by Osney Hill and North Leigh to Long Hanborough, and thence by Bladon Heath to the Cherwell, beyond which it passes northward outside our area. The upper part forms the lower slopes of the Lower Corallian escarpment which runs with broad curves from Hinton Waldrist to Cumnor, and round Wytham Hill to the Hinkseys, and from Iffley by Elsfield, Beckley and Studley to the north of Muswell Hill. South-eastward of Ot Moor the outcrop is prolonged by the removal of the overlying Corallian rocks almost to the river Thame at Waterperry. Through the middle of the broad tract west of Oxford the river Thames flows as far as the gap in the Corallian formation below Iffley, and much of the surface of the clay is covered by sand and gravel deposited by the river at former stages of its history.

The greater part of the formation consists of bluish or greenish and lead coloured clay, but in the lower zones the predominating hue is brown to brownish green, a colour characteristic of these beds over widely separated areas, such as Norfolk, Wiltshire, Kent and the Boulonnais. On some levels, and more particularly in the upper part, the bedding in the clay is not distinct, and is marked only by bands of septaria and occasional layers of earthy limestone; but lower down the formation is more shaly, and this character is maintained even where the beds come near to the surface. Both clay and shale are often calcareous, and contain much iron-pyrites and selenite. At Oxford, the formation is estimated to be nearly 400 ft. thick. The fact that clays of the Duncani and Athleta Zones have been worked at a relatively shallow depth in the Summertown pit, strongly suggests that the beds have been folded as a result of the Islip disturbance.

Generally, the clays are highly fossiliferous, but frequently the shelly layers are separated by beds of stiff unfossiliferous clay, probably indicating intermittent deposition during the accumulation of the formation. Conspicuous members of the fauna are *Gryphaea bilobata* J. de C. Sow., *G. dilatata* Auctt., *Belemnites oweni* Pratt, and many genera of ammonites, including *Cosmoceras*,[2] *Creniceras*, *Lunuloceras*, *Perisphinctes*, *Peltoceras* and *Quenstedtoceras*. In the

---

[1] See 'The Geology of the Oxford District' (*Mem. Geol. Surv.*), 1st Ed., 1908, p. 24.

[2] Mr. S. S. Buckman has lately distinguished a number of new genera, in which certain species formerly grouped under *Cosmoceras* are placed. See 'Type Ammonites', vols. iii-v, 1919–1925.

highest clays *Cardioceras* makes its earliest appearance and is associated with the massive shells of *Gryphaea dilatata*. The ammonites are usually preserved in pyrites. Reptilian remains are also frequently uncovered in excavations, and from the Summertown pit, now disused, the remarkable dinosaur *Streptospondylus cuvieri* Meyer was obtained. This fine specimen now occupies a prominent position in the University Museum at Oxford and has been figured and described by Dr. Francis Baron Nopcsa.[1]

A list of the principal fossils of the Oxford Clay is given below, and the localities are indicated by numbers as follows :—

1. Pear Tree Hill and Wolvercot. Duncani Zone to about base of the Renggeri Zone.
2. Summertown. Athleta Zone to Quenstedtoceras Zones, perhaps higher
3. St. Clement's, brick-pit and well. From Scarburgense Zone downwards.
4. Cowley Fields. Renggeri Zone to Scarburgense Zone.

The specimens are preserved in the University Museum, Oxford, and the list is given here without a recent revision of nomenclature. A number of ammonites collected from the Summertown clay-pit is also given on p. 37.

Carpolithus sp., 3.
Acrosalenia sp., 3, 4.
Pentacrinus fisheri *Bailey*, 3, 4.
Serpula tricarinata *J. de C. Sow.*, 1, 2, 4.
    ,, vertebralis *J. de C. Sow.*, 1, 2.
Diastopora diluviana *Phill.*, 3.
Aulacothyris bernardina (*d'Orb.*), 1, 2.
Rhynchonella spathica (*Lam.*), 1, 2.
Cucullaea subtetragona (*Morr.*), 1.
Grammatodon concinnus (*Phill.*), 2, 4.
Gryphaea bilobata *J. de C. Sow.*, 1, 2.
    ,, dilatata *Auctt.*, 2, 4.
Modiola bipartita *J. Sow.*, 1, 2.
Nucula cottaldi *de Lor.*, 1, 4.
    ,, elliptica *Phill.*, 3, 4.
    ,, nuda *Phill.*, 3.
    ,, ornata *Quenst.*, 1, 2, 3, 4.
    ,, zieteni *de Lor.*, 2.
Ostrea (Alectryonia) gregaria *J. Sow.*, 2, 3.
Pecten (Chlamys) fibrosus *J. Sow.*, 1, 2, 4.
    ,, (Camptonectes) lens *J. Sow.*, 2, 4.
    ,, (Chlamys) vagans *J. de C. Sow.*, 1, 2, 3.
Perna mytiloides *Lam.*, 2, 3.
Pholadomya echinata *Ag.*, 1, 2, 4.
Pinna sp., 1, 3.
Pleuromya recurva (*Phill.*), 3.
Pteria (Oxytoma) inaequivalvis (*J. Sow.*), 1, 2, 3.
Thracia sp., 3.
Alaria bispinosa *J. Sow*, 1, 2, 3, 4.
    ,, gagnebini *Thur.*, 1, 4.
Cerithium muricatum (*J. de C. Sow.*), 3.
Pleurotomaria reticulata (*J. Sow.*), 2, 3.
Belemnites abbreviatus *Miller*, 1, 2, 3, 4.
    ,, hastatus *Blainv.*, 1, 2, 3, 4.
    ,, oweni *Pratt*, 1, 2, 3, 4.
    ,, ,, var. puzosianus *d'Orb.*, 1, 2, 3, 4.
    ,, porrectus *Phill.*, 3.
    ,, sulcatus *Miller*, 1, 2, 3.

[1] See *Geol. Mag.*, 1905, p. 291.

Belemnites tornatilis *Phill.*, 3.
Cardioceras cardia *S. Buckman*, 3, 4.
,,　scarburgense (*Young & Bird*), 3, 4.
Cosmoceras compressum (*Quenst.*), 2.
,,　duncani (*J. Sow.*), 1, 2, 3.
,,　gemmatum (*Phill.*), 1, 2, 3.
,,　jason (*Rein.*), 1.
,,　ornatum (*Schloth.*), 1, 2.
,,　proniae *Teisseyre*, 1, 2.
,,　spinosum (*J. de C. Sow.*), 1, 2, 3.
Creniceras crenatum (*Brug.*), 3, 4.
,,　renggeri (*Oppel*), 2, 4.
Hecticoceras hecticum (*Quenst.*), 2, 4.
,,　nodosum (*Quenst.*), 2, 3, 4.
Lunuloceras silinophorum *Bonarelli*, 2.
Oecotraustes bidentatus (*Quenst.*), 2, 4.
,,　scaphatoides *Coquand*, 2.
Peltoceras annulare (*Rein.*), 1, 2.
,,　　,,　*var.* annulosum *Quenst.*, 1, 2.
,,　athleta (*Phill.*), 1, 2, 3.
,,　athletoides *Lahusen*, 1, 2.
,,　eugenii (*d'Orb.*), 4.
,,　reversum *Leckenby*, 1, 2.
Perisphinctes bernensis *de Lor.*, 4.
,,　convolutus *Quenst.*, 1, 2.
,,　ledonicus *de Lor.*, 1, 2, 3, 4.
,,　matheyi *de Lor.*, 3, 4.
,,　perisphinctoides *Sinzov*, 2, 3, 4.
,,　planus *Siemir.*, 2, 4.
Quenstedtoceras lamberti (*J. Sow.*), 2, 3, 4.
,,　macrum (*Quenst.*), 2.
,,　mariae (*d'Orb.*), 2, 3.
,,　placenta (*Leckenby*), 4.
Nautilus calloviensis *Oppel*, 2, 3.
Glyphea stricklandi *Bean*, 1, 2, 3, 4.
Goniocheirus cristata *Carter*, 4.
Dakosaurus sp., 1, 2, 3.
Ichthyosaurus sp., 1, 2.
Megalosaurus bucklandi *Meyer*, 3.
Plesiosaurus oxoniensis *Phill.*, 1, 2, 3.
Pliosaurus grandis *Owen*, 4.
,,　gamma *Owen*, 3.
Rhamphorhynchus bucklandi (*Meyer*), 3.
Steneosaurus sp., 4.
Streptospondylus cuvieri *Meyer*, 2.
Eurycornus sp., 4.
Gyrodus sp., 3.
Hybodus grossiconus *Ag.*, 1, 3, 4.
,,　polyprion *Ag.*, 1, 3, 4.
Ischyodus egertoni *Ag.*, 1, 3, 4.
Lepidotus macrocheirus *Egerton*, 3, 4.
Notidanus daviesi *A. S. Woodw.*, 3.
Orthacodus sp., 4.
Leptacanthus sp., 4.

The Oxford Clay has been divided into the following ammonite zones, in downward succession :—

Cardioceras scarburgense
Quenstedtoceras spp. [=Mariae Beds of Kent]

Creniceras renggeri
Quenstedtoceras lamberti
Cosmoceras proniae
Peltoceras athleta
Cosmoceras duncani
Cosmoceras castor
Erymnoceras coronatum
Cosmoceras elizabethae
Gulielmites conlaxatum

It is unfortunate that the rarity of sections precludes an adequate test of the zonal classification of the formation in the type area. It may be safely assumed, however, that the zonal succession outlined above has full representation in the Oxford district; indeed, it is highly probable that, if the clays were well exposed, the number of recognizable zones could be greatly increased. The zones below that of *Cosmoceras duncani* may be said to include that part of the clay which comes to the surface north-west of the Thames alluvium as far as Yarnton, and in the neighbourhood of Islip. The beds are seldom exposed, but recently, a well sunk to the depth of 18 ft. at Gosford Hill Farm, south of Kidlington, passed through clays containing *Cosmoceras stutchburii* (Pratt), *Gulielmites sedgwicki* (Pratt) and *Anakosmokeras effulgens* S. Buckman. The deposits probably fall within the zone of *Cosmoceras elizabethae*. Again, in another well made on the west side of the road north of Freeland Church, similar beds yielded numerous finely ribbed Cosmoceratids identical with species that characterize the shales and clays below the Castor Zone in the Calvert brickyard. The zone of *Gulielmites conlaxatum*, distinguished by Dr. E. Neaverson in the Oxford Clay of the Peterborough district, has not as yet been recognized in the area[1]; nor is there a trace of a *Reineckia*-fauna at the base of the formation.

The upper part of the Duncani Zone is occasionally exposed in the brickpit at Wolvercot, which exhibits the only good section of the formation near Oxford. Here also may be seen the overlying zone of *Peltoceras athleta*, the base of which forms the floor of the present workings. At one time it was thought by some writers that the Athleta Bed marked the limit of the upward range of *Cosmoceras* and was followed by the zone of *Creniceras renggeri*; but during the re-examination of the Wolvercot section it was ascertained that species of *Cosmoceras* characterized the clays above the Athleta Zone throughout a thickness of 16 ft. *Cosmoceras proniae* Teisseyre, as determined by Mr. Buckman, is the commonest species, particularly in the lower part, where it is associated with *Cosmoceras gemmatum* (Phill.), *C. rowlstonense* (Y. & B.), *C.* cf. *subnodatum* Teiss. and *C. ornatum compressum* (Quenst.). The deposits form the zone of *Cosmoceras proniae* of our classification.

---

[1] Neaverson, E., 'The Zones of the Oxford Clay near Peterborough,' *Proc. Geol. Assoc.*, vol. xxxvi, 1925, pp. 27–37.

Mr. Buckman[1] has distinguished a zone of *Quenstedtoceras lamberti*, also below the Renggeri Beds, and its presence at Wolvercot may be indicated by the occurrence of *Quenstedtoceras* in the highest layer of clay. The zone, however, appears to have had full representation in the Summertown pit where the species was abundant.

The middle portion of the Oxford Clay, which comprises the zones of *Creniceras renggeri* and *Quenstedtoceras spp.*, is to a large extent covered by alluvial deposits, but the beds appear to have been well exposed in the now disused pits at Summertown and St. Clement's. The main feature of the fauna of the Renggeri Zone is the abundance of ammonites belonging to the genera *Creniceras*, *Hecticoceras*, *Quenstedtoceras* and *Taramelliceras*, while Cosmoceratids are absent. The higher zone of *Quenstedtoceras spp.* broadly corresponds with the clays included in the zone of *Quenstedtoceras mariae* in the Kentish borings[2]. The term Mariae Beds has not been used in this memoir on account of the doubt that exists in respect to the type of the index species. D'Orbigny[3] figured several distinct forms under the name of *Ammonites mariae*, and the late R. Douvillé added further confusion by applying the name to several more different species.[4] Further research will doubtless result in the recognition of several new ammonite-zones in the clays between the Renggeri and Scarburgense Beds. Indeed, it is highly probable that the zones of *Quenstedtoceras vertumnus* and *Q. gregarium*, established by Mr. Buckman in Yorkshire, may be equivalent to a portion of these deposits.[5]

The clays of the zone of *Cardioceras scarburgense* form the lower part of the sloping land leading up to the Corallian escarpment, and were at one time exposed in the brickfields at Cowley and St. Clement's. The term Scarburgense Zone takes the place of the Pre-*cordatum* Zone used by Mr. Buckman as a provisional name for the strata underlying the Vertebrale Zone of the Corallian.[6] Dr. A. Morley Davies[7] is of the opinion that two zones may be distinguished in these clays : a lower zone with fairly stout species of the *Cardioceras quadratoides*-type, and a higher containing thin forms with finer ribbing like that of *C. tenuicostatum*. Broadly, the zone is characterized by the occurrence of Cardiocerates, such as *Cardioceras cardia* S. Buckman, *C. nikitinanum* Lahusen, *C. rouilleri* Lahusen, *C. scarburgense* (Y. & B.), *C. tenuicostatum* (Nik.)

[1] Buckman, S. S., ' The Kelloway Rock of Scarborough,' *Quart. Journ. Geol. Soc.*, vol. lxix, 1913, p. 159.

[2] Lamplugh, G. W., and F. L. Kitchin, 'On the Mesozoic Rocks in some of the Coal Explorations in Kent' (*Mem. Geol. Surv.*), 1911, pp. 133, 165. *See also* ' The Concealed Mesozoic Rocks in Kent ' (*Mem. Geol. Surv.*), 1923, pp. 211, 212.

[3] d'Orbigny, A., ' Pal. Franc., Terr. Jur.,' Céph., pl. clxxix, 1848.

[4] Douvillé, R., ' Etude sur les Cardiocératidés,' *Mem. Soc. géol. France*, Paléontologie, vol. xix, Fasc. 2, 1912, Mém. No. 45, pl. v, figs. 1, 2, 5–7, 10–12.

[5] Buckman, S. S., in ' The Geology of the Country between Whitby and Scarborough ' (*Mem. Geol. Surv.*), 1915, p. 60.

[6] *See* ' On the Mesozoic Rocks in some of the Coal Explorations in Kent ' (*Mem. Geol. Surv.*), 1911, p. 132.

[7] Davies, A. M., ' The zones of the Oxford and Ampthill Clays in Buckinghamshire and Bedfordshire,' *Geol. Mag.*, 1916, p. 397.

and other species, while in the higher beds at Cowley *Peltoceras arduennense* (d'Orb.) and *P. eugenii* (d'Orb.) are conspicuous members of the fauna. Species of *Quenstedtoceras* appear to be absent in this zone. It is evident, therefore, that the upper part of the Oxford Clay of the Oxford district is equivalent to certain beds included in the Lower Corallian elsewhere. Thus,*Peltoceras arduennense* (d'Orb.)[1], *P. eugenii* (d'Orb.) and *Perisphinctes bernensis* de Lor. found at Cowley are also characteristic of certain marly beds in the Lower Corallian of Kent, and it is probable that the corresponding beds in Dorset are to be found in the upper part of the Oxford Clay and the lower beds of the Corallian near Weymouth. Although actual palaeontological evidence has not been obtained, it is considered possible that deposits equivalent to the upper portion of the Oxford Clay, are present in sands and clays near Appleton, about 5 miles south-west of Oxford, where, on account of their lithic character, the clay and sands were mapped as Lower Calcareous Grit. Mr. Buckman has pointed out that on palaeontological grounds the Scarburgense Zone is to be assigned to the Argovian stage, when that name is used to cover the strata, which are distinguished by the presence of *Cardioceras*.[2]

LOCAL DETAILS

Between Long Hanborough and North Leigh at 'The Demesnes,' where drift gravel has been obtained for road-metal, the lower beds of the Oxford Clay have been exposed. These appear to have been dark purplish shales but no ammonites have been recorded from them. On the west side of the road north of Freeland Church, however, a well was sunk to the depth of 45 ft., and from some of the shales thrown out, Mr. C. J. Bayzand has collected a large number of fossils, including *Gryphaea bilobata* J. de C. Sow., *Thracia sp.*, *Belemnites oweni* Pratt, *B. sulcatus* Miller, *Gulielmites sedgwicki* ? (Pratt) and numerous finely-ribbed species of *Cosmoceras*. The beds are undoubtedly equivalent to the shales exposed in the lower part of the section at the Calvert brickyard, outside our area.

Similarly-coloured shaly clays were observed in the foundations of the hall in Eynsham Park. North-west of Eynsham the formation is frequently penetrated in wells sunk through gravel. The brick pit on the top of Combe Hill shows a few feet of shaly brown clay, which to judge by its colour and stratigraphical position, appears to fall within the zone of *Cosmoceras elizabethae*. The shales are badly weathered and have yielded no fossils of zonal value.

In 1924, the lower part of the Oxford Clay was passed through in a boring made in search of water at Gosford Hill Farm, south of Kidlington, but the only material obtained for examination came from a well dug to the depth of 15 ft. from the surface. At 8 ft. a thin band of brown marl yielded *Gulielmites sedgwicki* (Pratt) ; beneath this was 7 ft. of green-tinged, lead-coloured clay with nodules of earthy limestone, containing reptilian bones, *Belemnites oweni* Pratt and *Cosmoceras stutchburii* (Pratt). A Cosmoceratid, obtained from one of the lumps of earthy limestone, proved to be a new species. It has since been figured by Mr. Buckman under the name of *Anakosmokeras effulgens*.[3]

---

[1] Recorded by Mr. Buckman in ' Type Ammonites,' vol. v, 1925, p. 67, and re-named by him as *Peltoceratoides arduennensis*.

[2] Buckman, S.S., in 'The Geology of the Country between Whitby and Scarborough ' (*Mem. Geol. Surv.*), 1915, p. 87.

[3] ' Type Ammonites,' vol. vi, 1925, pl. dxcvii, A and B.

Nearer Oxford, and close by the railway-tunnel at Upper Wolvercot, there is a deep pit showing the only section of Oxford Clay close to the city. A similar section was at one time exposed in the Pear Tree Hill brickyard, now disused. In the Wolvercot brickyard the following beds may be seen :—

		Ft.	In.
	Gravel (*see* p. 124)		
	6. Lead-coloured clay with fossils. *Cosmoceras proniae, C.* cf. *ornatum distractum, C.* cf. *subnodatum* and *Peltoceras subtense* in upper beds, *Peltoceras athletoides* and *Cosmoceras* cf. *ornatum annulatum* at base	16	0
Proniae Zone	5. Pale cement-stone of inconstant thickness, sometimes replaced by clay. Many fossils : *Cosmoceras proniae, C. ornatum compressum, C.* cf. *gemmatum, Peltoceras* cf. *annulare filatum* and *P.* cf. *subtense,* up to	1	6
	4. Lead-coloured clay with *Cosmoceras proniae* and *C.* cf. *subnodatum*	2	0
	3. Similarly-coloured clay with *Peltoceras athleta, P. annulare,* etc.	2	6
Athleta Zone	2. Thin pale cement-stone of inconstant thickness. Upper surface is often encrusted with shells preserved in pyrites. *Aulacothyris bernardina, Rhynchonella spathica* and *Gryphaea bilobata*	0	6
Duncani Zone	1. Lead-coloured clay with *Cosmoceras duncani;* occasionally exposed to the depth of 4 ft. ..	4	0

At one time this pit was worked to a depth of 40 ft., but at present about 20 ft. of clays are exposed, so that the floor roughly coincides with the clay-band containing *Peltoceras athleta* (Phill.). Frequently, however, a thin irregular cement-stone with shell-encrusted surface is uncovered, and in it, and in clay occupying the same stratigraphical level, the shells of *Aulacothyris bernardina* (d'Orb.) are found in association with *Rhynchonella spathica* (Lam.). The terebratelloid *A. bernardina,* which is characteristically preserved in black shining phosphate, has an exceedingly narrow vertical range, and is practically confined to the horizon of the stone-layer, though at times it may be found along with *Peltoceras athleta.* In this pit the base of the Athleta Zone has been drawn so as to include the cement-stone, and the occurrence of this brachiopod in sections elsewhere may be taken as indicating the lower part of the zone in the absence of ammonites. The underlying clay yields *Cosmoceras duncani* (J. Sow.), but the beds are now rarely exposed.

The clay between the cement-stone bands has been divided into two beds on palaeontological grounds, but no lithological distinction is observable. The lower portion forms the Athleta Bed, and numerous specimens of the zone-fossil are found during digging operations, in association with *Peltoceras annulare* (Rein.) and *P. annulare oblongum* (Quenst.). A species of *Cosmoceras,* closely allied to *C. duncani,* also occurs in the bed. But in the upper part of the clay *Cosmoceras proniae* enters and becomes the dominant fossil, ranging upwards to nearly the top of the section. It seems appropriate, therefore, to adopt this species as the name-fossil for the zone of *Cosmoceras proniae* in order to emphasize the range of Cosmoceratids above the Athleta Zone.

The higher cement-stone, Bed 5, is a fairly constant horizon and can be traced along the northern face of the pit. In addition to numerous species of *Cosmoceras* this stone-band yields many fragments of a degenerate Perisphinctid showing gerontic laevigation. Some of the bits of shell have a strong resemblance to *Proplanulites koenigi,* and this no doubt accounts for the wrongly recorded occurrence of that species at Wolvercot. A specimen brought into comparison with *Longaeviceras longaevum* (Bean) was found loose in the pit, but it probably came from this layer.

Throughout the remaining part of the section the clays are somewhat poorly fossiliferous. At about 6 ft. from the top, however, there is a layer that yields numerous crushed and fragmentary specimens of *Cosmoceras proniae* preserved in pyrites. This species is accompanied by Cosmoceratids of the *subnodatum*-type which appear to have similar range, and *Peltoceras subtense* (Bean). The on-coming of the zone of *Quenstedtoceras lamberti* may be indicated by a fragment of *Quenstedtoceras* collected from the highest bed by Mr. C. C. Gaddum.

The *Cosmoceras*-zones and higher beds were at one time also exposed in the now disused pit adjoining the Keble College cricket ground at Summertown, where the clay was dug to the depth of 40 ft. Many specimens obtained from this brick-pit are to be found in public collections, and in the Museum of Practical Geology the following ammonites are preserved :—

Cosmoceras compressum (*Quenst.*)
,, decoratum (*Zieten*)
,, duncani (*J. Sow.*)
,, *cf.* elizabethae (*Pratt*)
,, hylas ? (*Rein.*)
,, jenzeni *Teisseyre*
,, proniae *Teisseyre*
,, rimosum (*Quenst.*)
,, spinosum (*J. de C. Sow.*)
,, *cf.* subnodatum *Teisseyre*
,, transitionis *Nikitin*
Grossouvria subtilis (*Neumayr*)
Lunuloceras submatheyi (*Lee*)
,, suevum *Bonarelli*
Peltoceras athletoides *Lahusen*
Siemiradzkia rjasanensis *Teisseyre*
,, variabilis *Lahusen*

An additional list, given on p. 32, includes *Creniceras crenatum, C. renggeri* and many species of *Quenstedtoceras* that characterize the Renggeri and Quenstedtoceras Zones. From these lists of ammonites it would appear that the section exposed a complete sequence of clays from the Duncani Beds to some part within the Quenstedtoceras Zones. Mr. C. J. Bayzand informs me that he himself has collected specimens of *Peltoceras athleta* near the base of the pit. It is evident, therefore, that the whole of the clays exposed in the Wolvercot pit were also worked at Summertown within 40 ft. of the surface. The occurrence of these zones at a relatively shallow depth in the disused Summertown pit proves that the south-easterly dip of the formation has been modified by the Islip disturbance, the effects of which are also to be seen in the structure of Corallian Rocks in the Wytham and Seacourt Hills to the west.

The clays of the Scarburgense Zone were at one time exposed in brick-pits at St. Clement's, at the workhouse on the Cowley road, and by the road-side between Magdalen Bridge and Marston, but unfortunately all of the sections have disappeared. The Scarburgense Beds are occasionally penetrated in borings for water which have passed through the Corallian Rocks. They are present also in a well which was sunk to the depth of 90 ft. in clay at the foot of Cumnor Hill, where Mr. C. J. Bayzand collected and identified the following fossils :—*Gryphaea dilatata* Auctt., *Belemnites hastatus* Blainv., *Cardioceras cardia* S. Buckman, *Peltoceras annulare* (Rein.), *Perisphinctes perisphinctoides* Sinzov, *Quenstedtoceras lamberti* (J. Sow.) and *Q. mariae* (d'Orb.). A shallower well excavated at a site above the Witney road at Oaken Holt yielded a similar fauna, indicating the presence of zones from the Scarburgense Zone down to about the Renggeri Beds.

In excavations made at the railway-bridge over the Thames, near Kennington, clays were exposed below the alluvium, and yielded numerous specimens of *Gryphaea dilatata* Auctt. and *G. discoidea* Kitchin. Similar shells, encrusted by *Serpula tricarinata* J. de C. Sow. and *Webbina irregularis* d'Orb. were obtained from a boring at the Morris Works at Cowley, where the Oxford Clay was entered at a depth of 59½ ft. from the surface.

In the great tract of Oxford Clay south-east of Ot Moor, there is only one section to record. This is the small brickyard by the roadside half a mile south-east of Studley. Here, about 10 ft. of blue clay is exposed, and in addition to the characteristic shells of *Gryphaea dilatata* yields the following ammonites, mostly preserved in the form of brown ochreous casts : *Cardioceras cardia* S. Buckman, *C. costellatum* S. Buckman, *C.* cf. *praecordatum* R. Douvillé, cf. *C. quadratoides* (Nikitin) and *Poculisphinctes auricularis* S. Buckman. The ammonites were kindly identified by Mr. Buckman, and in a letter he points out that he is inclined to regard the specimen of *Poculisphinctes auricularis* as having been derived from lower beds. Higher beds of clay were exposed in a well at Studley, and from them Dr. A. M. Davies has recorded finely ribbed Cardiocerates of the *tenuicostatum*-type.[1]

Mr. S. S. Buckman has recorded a well-section, north of the road near Field Farm, about one mile north-west of Worminghall.[2] The site of the well is close to the base of the Ampthill Clay, and Mr. Buckman is of opinion that the whitish clay at the top may possibly be equivalent to the Rhaxella Chert (*see* p. 60). The following details of the strata passed through are based on his account :—

		Ft.	In.
5. Whitish clay		3	0
4. Yellow marly sandstone with *Cardioceras* cf. *zenaidae*, *Miticardioceras mite*, *Perisphinctes* cf. *intercedens* and large specimens of *Gryphaea*		0	6
3. Blue clay		4	0
2. Bluish stone band with lignite		0	6
1. Blue clay with occasional stone. A fragment of ammonite suggesting *Neumayriceras oculatum*.. ..		22	0

Mr. Buckman has applied the term Worminghall Rock to Bed 4. It should probably be classified with the Corallian series and may, in reality, form the base of the Arngrove Stone.

Although sections in the Oxford Clay are few in number, the thick shells of *Gryphaea dilatata* occur in such profusion that it is only necessary to walk over lands below the Corallian escarpment to pick them up in abundance from the ploughed fields, ditches and ponds.

---

[1] Davies, A. M., ' The Kimeridge Clay and Corallian Rocks of the neighbourhood of Brill (Buckinghamshire),' *Quart. Journ. Geol. Soc.*, vol. lxiii, 1907, p. 40. *See also* ' Zones of the Oxford and Ampthill Clay in Buckinghamshire and Bedfordshire,' *Geol. Mag.*, 1916, p. 398.
[2] ' Type Ammonites,' vol. v, 1925, p. 54.

CHAPTER IV

MIDDLE OOLITIC ROCKS—(*continued*)

CORALLIAN ROCKS

OVER a considerable part of the area, the Corallian formation consists of a variable series of sands, sandy, oolitic and pisolitic limestones and beds of rubbly coral-rock, well shown in the quarries near Marcham and in the neighbourhood of Oxford ; but to the north-east of Wheatley most of these deposits are replaced by clays with thin argillaceous limestones to which the name Ampthill Clay has been applied. A similar passage into clayey beds also takes place in the direction of dip, and an excellent section is displayed at Littlemore where the coral-rock is represented by clay and thin clayey limestones.

The sandy calcareous rocks are essentially shallow water deposits, and, together with the beds of coral-rag which are often false-bedded, they appear to have been deposited on a sloping sea-floor exposed to strong currents. There is also abundant evidence of erosion and reconstruction at many localities where pebbles of oolite and lime-stone bored by *Lithodomus* are found in association with rolled fragments of lydite and quartz. In a few cases the corals appear to have grown *in situ*, forming lenticular masses of limited extent, and to these the term 'reef' has been applied by some observers, but for the most part the corals have been drifted into the position in which they are now found. The clays, however, in the evenly stratified character of the beds afford evidence of deeper water, less subject to violent current-action, whilst the pale argillaceous limestones appear to have originated from the fine chalky mud washed outwards from the reef. Indeed, the varied assemblage of rocks included within the formation exhibits all the features characteristic of sediments accumulating in the vicinity of modern coral-reefs and islands.

In 1818, Buckland divided the formation near Oxford into Calcareous Grit, Coral Rag, and Upper or Oxford Oolite,[1] but since then our knowledge has been largely amplified by Fitton, John Phillips, Blake and Hudleston, and the more recent researches of Mr. S. S. Buckman, Dr. A. Morley Davies and Mr. W. J. Arkell[2].

---

[1] Table appended to the Outline of the Geology of England and Wales, by William Phillips, 1818.

[2] *See* Bibliography on p. 179. Also ' Type Ammonites,' vols. iv and v, 1922–1925. The reader should also consult Prof. H. Salfeld's ' Die Gliederung des oberen Jura in Nordwesteuropa,' *Neues Jahrb. f. Min.*, Beil. Bd. xxxvii, 1914.

In the calcareous-arenaceous facies two broad divisions may be
recognized : a lower portion consisting mainly of calcareous sandstone and of loose sands with large concretionary masses, and an
upper part comprising beds of oolitic, pisolitic and shelly limestones
with layers of coral-rag and occasional sandy or clayey partings. A
two-fold subdivision may also be made in the equivalent argillaceous
rocks in the north-eastern part of the district, where the lower
portion is represented by a peculiar argillaceous chert, known as the
Arngrove Stone or Rhaxella Chert, and a higher series of clay with
subordinate bands of clayey limestone. In its various lithological
facies, the formation may be grouped as follows :—

Divisions	Buckland's Subdivisions, 1818	Zones: Salfeld, 1914, and others	Headington, Magdalen Pit	North-east of Wheatley
	Oxford	Ringsteadia pseudocordatus	absent	
Upper Corallian	Oolite	Perisphinctes decipiens	? Pendle	
		Perisphinctes wartae	Rubbly Coral-rock, etc.	Ampthill Clay
	Coral	Perisphinctes antecedens	Brown Course	
	Rag	Perisphinctes martelli	Bottom Course (= Trigonia bed)	
			-non-sequence-	—non-sequence—
Lower Corallian	Lower	Aspidoceras biarmatum	absent	absent
	Calcareous Grit	Cardioceras cordatum	Sands with Rhaxella Chert at base	Rhaxella Chert only

From the above table it will be seen that the formation is
incompletely represented. At the top there is no trace of the
Ringsteadia Zone, so well developed in Wiltshire, and it is possible
that the ' Pendle ' of the Headington sections is to be correlated only
with the lower part of the zone of *Perisphinctes decipiens*. No
fossils, however, have been obtained from this bed during the recent
revision. The existence of the stratigraphical break at the top was
made known by the observations of Conybeare, Buckland, John
Phillips and other writers. Sedgwick, who made one of the earliest
attempts to correlate the Oxford sections with the corresponding
beds near Weymouth, was the first to recognize the extent of the
gap in the sequence. Writing 100 years ago, he said :—' May not
therefore the Coral Rag and superincumbent freestone of Headington

Hill together represent the central group of the Weymouth and Steeple Ashton sections? The conjecture seems to be confirmed by the appearance of the beds in Headington Quarries. In that place the top freestone supports the Kimmeridge Clay ; and the separation between the two is as well defined as a geometric line. Now the instantaneous passage from one formation to another frequently indicates the absence of certain beds or deposits. May not then the upper part of the Weymouth section be wanting near Oxford ? '[1]

The sudden termination of the calcareous rock-bands at Wheatley has been attributed by various authors to an unconformable overlap of the Kimmeridge Clay, but H. B. Woodward[2] advanced the view that the Corallian rocks may be largely represented in point of time by sediments of an argillaceous character. It is certain, however, that the clay now termed the Ampthill Clay has overlapped on to the Rhaxella Chert and represents only the Upper Corallian, as pointed out by Dr. A. Morley Davies.[3] He has shown that when the clay-beds are traced farther east, the stratigraphical break becomes greater, and they finally rest on the Renggeri Beds of the Oxford Clay at Sandy, in Bedfordshire.[4] It is obvious, however, that this overlap at the base of the Upper Corallian takes place also in the area of calcareous development. Thus, around Marcham, the Martelli Zone rests with a pebbly basement-bed on the sands of the Biarmatum Zone. Eastwards of Abingdon this zone has been overlapped and the occurrence of derived fossils and pebbles in the base of the Upper Corallian (Trigonia Bed) at Headington and elsewhere shows that the overlap had been preceded by considerable erosion of the underlying sands. The overlap of the Martelli Beds is a phenomenon common to North-East France and Bavaria ; and there is reason to conclude that the inconstant thickness of the Lower Calcareous Grit in the Oxford area is due to slight folding of the beds and subsequent erosion prior to the deposition of the Upper Corallian limestones or their argillaceous equivalents.

North of Headington a brownish cherty rock makes its appearance at the base of the sands, and it has been traced by means of debris from Elsfield, by Beckley and Stanton St. John down almost to Wheatley Bridge. East of the Holton Brook it has been detected at many localities between Worminghall and Boarstall, underlying the Ampthill Clay. The greatest outcrop of the rock, however, is between Studley and Boarstall, where several outliers cap the low escarpment overlooking the plain of Oxford Clay. This chert-bed appears to have been first noticed by Buckland and has been described by John Phillips and A. H. Green, both of whom give lists

---

[1] Sedgwick, A., ' On the classification of the strata which appear on the Yorkshire coast,' *Ann. Phil.*, vol. xxvii, ser. 2, vol. xi, 1826, p. 350.

[2] Woodward, H. B., ' The Jurassic Rocks of Britain ' (*Mem Geol. Surv.*), vol. v, 1895, pp. 133–135.

[3] Davies, A. Morley, ' The Zones of the Oxford and Ampthill Clays in Buckinghamshire and Bedfordshire,' *Geol. Mag.*, 1916, p. 399.

[4] *Op. cit.*, p. 399.

of fossils obtained from the bed.[1]   At a later date, Dr. A. Morley Davies applied the name Arngrove Stone to the chert, as the chief exposures are near Arngrove Farm, and the term has been found convenient for local use.   Dr. Davies has given detailed descriptions of the rock, which was found by him ' to be studded with innumerable minute ellipsoidal bodies, mostly of a translucent hue, but with everywhere some of an opaque white . . . . It is neither calcareous nor purely argillaceous . . . . [and] as a whole is very light and porous, absorbing water very readily.'   Under the microscope he found the grains ' to agree exactly in size and shape with the globate spicules of the tetractinellid sponge, *Rhaxella perforata*, described by Dr. G. J. Hinde, from cherts in the Lower Calcareous Grit of Yorkshire.'   The Arngrove Stone yields numerous fossils, including *Cardioceras cordatum* (J. Sow.) and *Vertebriceras vertebrale* (J. Sow.), characteristic ammonites of the Cordatum or Vertebrale Zone. In the Ampthill Clay area, the chert forms the principal bed of hard rock, and attains a thickness of 6 ft.

Fossil remains are locally abundant in the higher beds of the Lower Calcareous Grit.   In the neighbourhood of Marcham, layers of sand-rock have yielded numerous characteristic ammonites, including *Aspidoceras catena* (J. de C. Sow.), *Aspid. perarmatum* (J. Sow.), *Cardioceras cordatum* (J. Sow.), *Anacardioceras excavatum* (J. Sow.) and *Vertebriceras vertebrale* (J. Sow.).   These occur mainly in the form of casts.   In the pits near Cowley and Headington, Mr. S. S. Buckman has recorded the occurrence of a number of ammonites which he has figured under the generic names *Arisphinctes*, *Chalcedoniceras*, *Goliathiceras* and *Kranaosphinctes*.[2]   It appears, however, that the above-named species of *Aspidoceras* are confined to the Abingdon-Marcham district.   In this area, also, a *Natica*-bed is found at the top of the Calcareous Grit, and in the pits near Sheepstead Farm, specimens of *Natica marchamensis* Blake and Hudleston and *N. arguta* Phill. may be obtained from it.   The bed is also well-exposed in the section near Bradley Farm, but has not been found to the east of this locality.

Corals are plentiful in the Upper Corallian limestone, and of these the most conspicuous are the ' Honeycomb Coral,' *Isastrea explanata* (Goldf.), *Thecosmilia annularis* (Flem.) and *Thamnastrea arachnoides* (Park.), which often occur in lenticular masses.   Specimens of *Montlivaltia dispar* Phill. are locally numerous near the base of the division in the Headington-Cowley district.   The Trigonia Bed of Blake and Hudleston, which is separated into four layers in the Lamb and Flag pit near Kingston Bagpuize, can be recognized throughout the area to Headington.   It yields excellent examples of *Trigonia hudlestoni* Lyc., *T. meriani* Ag., *T. triquetra* Seebach and *T. perlata* Ag., especially in the Sheepstead Farm pits. *Gervillia aviculoides* (J. Sow.) and the thick prismatic shells of *Trichites*

[1] *See* ' The Geology of the Country round Banbury, Woodstock, Bicester and Buckingham ' (*Mem. Geol. Surv.*), 1864, pp. 44, 45.
[2] *See* ' Type Ammonites,' vol. v. 1925, p. 51.

are also characteristic of the bed. But although the corals are the predominating members of the fauna, the deposits also yield a varied assemblage of fossils, as will be seen from the list on p. 55. It is curious that the type of *Pseudomelania heddingtonensis* is stated by Sowerby[1] to have been received from Heddington, near Calne in Wiltshire; though he also mentions that he had found specimens about Shotover Hill [=Headington] in Oxfordshire.

The most abundant fossil in the argillaceous facies of the Upper Corallian is the small oyster *Exogyra nana*, which is often associated with *Serpula intestinalis*. During the revision of the area, several ammonites were obtained from the clayey equivalents of the Coral Rag in the Littlemore cutting. It is probable that while the coral-banks were growing in the western region, many other life-forms were flourishing in the deeper waters, where the accumulation of argillaceous sediment was nearly continuous from the close of the Great Oolite period to that of the Kimmeridge Beds.

LOCAL DETAILS

The Corallian rocks occupy a broad well-cultivated tract in the south-western part of the district, extending along the southern margin of the sheet towards Abingdon and thence northwards to Cumnor, where the outcrop becomes narrower and forms the high ground overlooking the Botley valley. In this area one of the best sections in the formation is that exposed in the well-known quarry, 350 yds. south-west of the Lamb and Flag Inn, about 2 miles west of Kingston Bagpuize. The section has been described by Blake and Hudleston, H.B. Woodward and other geologists; more recently Mr. W. J. Arkell has given an account of the rock-succession displayed in the quarry.[2] In 1925, the section was as follows :—

		Thickness Ft. In.	
	Reddish soil .. .. up to	3	0
	11. Greyish-white false-bedded calcareous sand-stone with grains of oolite	1	9
	10. Loosely coherent buff oolitic sand with streaks of dark clay and small pebbles of whitish limestone : *Nucleolites scutatus* ..	1	0
	9. Laminated brown sand and clay with thin irregular calcareous seams	7	0
	8. Grey oolitic limestone with few fossils. At top is a well-marked eroded surface.. ..	1	4
	7. Soft brown oolitic layer	0	6
Upper Corallian	6. Hard grey oolitic shelly limestone with *Liosphinctes* aff. *apolipon, Perisphinctes antecedens, Vertebriceras dorsale, Belemnites abbreviatus, Astarte ovata, Trigonia meriani, T. perlata, Gervillia aviculoides, Trichites sp., Nucleolites scutatus, etc.*	1	8
	5. Brown oolitic and pisolitic marl with streaks of dark clay : *Exogyra nana*..	0	6

---

[1] ' Mineral Conchology,' vol. i, 1812, p. 86.

[2] Blake, J. F., and W. H. Hudleston, 'On the Corallian Rocks of England,' *Quart. Journ. Geol. Soc.*, vol. xxxiii, 1877, p. 304 ; H. B. Woodward, ' The Jurassic Rock of Britain ' (*Mem. Geol. Surv.*), vol. v, 1895, pp. 122, 123 ; W. J. Arkell *in* ' Type Ammonites,' vol. v, 1925, pp. 57, 58 ; *see also* H. L. Hawkins and J. Pringle, ' Excursion to Swindon,' *Proc. Geol. Assoc.*, vol. xxxiv, 1923, pp. 234, 235.

		Thickness Ft. In.

Upper Corallian —*cont.*

4. Grey oolitic sandy limestone crowded with the casts of *Gervillia aviculoides* and other lamellibranchs 0 7

3. Dirty grey oolitic and pisolitic limestone. At base numerous rolled fragments of limestone, bored by *Lithodomi* and encrusted with *Serpulae,* and small pebbles of lydite and quartz: *Trigonia spp., Perisphinctes* cf. *subrota, Perisphinctes* cf. *biplex, Cymatosphinctes cymatophorus,* and *Anacardioceras excavatum* 2 10

Lower Corallian (Lower Calcareous Grit)

2. Hard grey calcareous grit-stone, inconstant in thickness; lignite fragments; up to .. 3 0
1. Buff sands with streaks of clay 4 6

At the base of Bed 3, a break in the stratal sequence is indicated by a layer of pebbles which includes rounded fragments of quartz, lydite and limestone. Further indications of the pause in deposition are to be seen in the *Serpula*-incrustations on the pebbles and in the borings made in the rounded pieces of limestone by *Lithodomi,* many of which may be found in their crypts. There are also signs of a non-sequence at the base of Bed 9, which rests on a well-marked eroded surface. The further working of the pit has revealed the real nature of the remarkable eroded surface noticed by Blake and Hudleston,[1] beneath a thin clay bed, which they believed to occur at the top of Bed 6 of our section. This clay proves to be of Pleistocene age. Its appearance in the pit at one time must have been highly misleading, and it led Hull to refer certain beds wrongly to the Upper Calcareous Grit.

The ammonites recorded in the above section from Beds 3–6 which form the Trigonia Bed of Blake and Hudleston were in part obtained from the workmen, but the shells were probably found in downward succession in the order stated, since a similar ammonite-sequence has been independently established by Mr. W. J. Arkell.[2] The ammonites link up this section in a satisfactory way with the faunal sequence established in the more condensed hard grey shelly limestone that forms the basement-bed of the Upper Corallian in the area between Littlemore and Headington, *see* p. 55.

The principal fossil-bed, however, is Bed 6, and it yields many characteristic forms, some of which are noted in the details of the section on p. 43. A species of *Trichites,* formerly referred to *T. ploti,* is confined to this level. H. B. Woodward[3] has recorded *Cardioceras cordatum* from this rock-band, but it is highly probable that this fossil, if it were available for examination, would now be referred to the genus *Vertebriceras,*[4] established by Mr. S. S. Buckman for the reception of certain shells formerly referred to *C. cordatum.* This suggestion is supported by the fact that a specimen identified by Mr. Buckman as *Vertebriceras dorsale* has been collected from Bed 6 by Mr. Arkell.

To the south-east the false-bedded oolitic sandstones are followed by a bluish-grey limestone with many corals, including *Isastrea explanata* (Goldf.), *Thamnastrea arachnoides* (Park.) and *Thecosmilia annularis* (Flem.). Specimens of *Exogyra nana* (J. Sow.) are also abundant. The coral-rock is to be seen in an old, almost overgrown pit 450 yds. south of Lower Lodge

---

[1] *Op. cit.,* p. 304.
[2] Arkell, W. J., in 'Type Ammonites,' vol. v, 1925, p. 59.
[3] Woodward, H. B., *op. cit.* p. 123; and 'The Geology of the Country around Oxford' (*Mem. Geol. Surv.*), 1908, p. 27.
[4] *See* 'Type Ammonites,' vol. iii, 1920, p. 16.

Farm, where the stone was formerly burnt for lime. The pit near Pusey Lodge Farm, in which a similar coraliferous limestone was at one time exposed, has now been filled up and ploughed over.

The upper part of the Lower Calcareous Grit is occasionally dug in a shallow pit near the cross-roads, 500 yds. south-west of Woodhouse Farm, a quarter of a mile east of Kingston Bagpuize. This section was described by Hull.[1] The sands, which are here markedly false-bedded, are locally indurated at the top, and are overlain by a grey shelly limestone about 2 ft. thick, containing rounded fragments of hard limestone and polished pebbles of quartz and lydite. The rock is evidently the equivalent of Bed 3 of the Lamb and Flag quarry, but the stone has yielded no ammonites. In the western part of the pit, higher beds of oolite with a seam of coarse pisolite are exposed. Fossils are somewhat rare, but a few fragments of *Trichites* are preserved, and serve to indicate the horizon of the limestone. A similar section was exposed in a pit, now overgrown, half a mile farther on towards Abingdon.

As a rule, the highest layers of Lower Calcareous Grit are exposed in the stone-pits in which the Upper Corallian rocks are quarried, but in the majority of cases only a few feet of sand can be seen. In the field opposite the Dog House Inn, one mile east of Tubney, and in sections in Tubney Wood, lower beds of Calcareous Grit are well displayed ; these are mostly yellow sand, in part the decalcified remnant of calcareous sandstones. In the Dog House Inn pit a hard bluish grit-stone with shale-galls occurs at the depth of 10 ft. from the surface, and has yielded specimens of *Anacardioceras excavatum* (J. Sow.) and *Aspidoceras perarmatum* (J. Sow.) in the form of casts.

White and buff sands with large cylindrical concretionary masses are exposed to the depth of 18 ft. in a large sand-pit in Tubney Wood, 200 yds. north of Woodside Farm. The sands yield fragments of *Exogyra* and *Ostrea*, but no ammonites have been found. The field-evidence suggests that the beds are below the horizon of *Anacardioceras excavatum.* A similar section is exposed in a field on the opposite side of the road, and it is of interest to note that the water-level in this pit is about 10 ft. higher than in the Tubney Wood section. There are no good exposures of the Lower Calcareous Grit in the neighbourhood of Appleton. Temporary sections show fine grained argillaceous sands near the base, and, as has already been remarked on p. 35, it is possible that some portion of the deposits may represent in time the highest beds of the Oxford Clay.

The most complete series of Corallian strata in the district is to be found in the well-known quarries at Sheepstead Farm, near Marcham, and in the partly overgrown pit near Noah's Ark Inn. These sections offer good illustrations of the rapid alternation of sediments that took place in the shallower parts of the seas of the Corallian epoch. At Sheepstead Farm, the Coral Rag is separated from the equivalent of the Trigonia Bed by about 4 ft. of sands at the south end of the pit, but at the north end the intervening deposits have disappeared, so that the coraliferous limestone rests on the Trigonia Bed ; and from here until the Upper Corallian is replaced by clays north-east of Wheatley, the Coral Rag, with the equivalent of the Trigonia-limestone at the base, is a characteristic feature of the plateau overlooking the Oxford plain.

---

[1] Hull, E., ' Geology of parts of Oxfordshire and Berkshire ' (*Mem. Geol. Surv.*), 1861, p. 7.

The section at Sheepstead Farm is as follows (the details were noted at the south end of the quarry, where the fullest development is seen) :—

		Ft.	In.
	9. Rubbly coral-rock and clay	2	0
	8. Soft light brown sand with grains of oolite ; *Pecten (Chlamys) fibrosus*	0	10
	7. Grey thin-bedded sandy oolite and pisolitic limestone with *Cidaris florigemma* (spines), *Nucleolites scutatus*, *Pygaster umbrella* and fragments of *Perisphinctes*	2	0
Upper Corallian	6. Soft greyish-brown oolitic sand with white calcareous streaks	0	11
	5. Grey thin-bedded oolitic limestone with soft brown marly layers. *Trigonia spp.* ..	2	10
	4. Laminated buff sands and clay ; pebbly layer at base when resting on Lower Calcareous Grit	2	0
	3. White gritty oolitic limestone, tapering away to the north and replaced by rubbly oolite and by a conglomeratic band with pebbles of lydite, quartz, oolite and bored limestone. *Trigonia meriani*, *Gervillia aviculoides* and *Natica marchamensis*.. .. 3 inches to	1	0
Lower Corallian (Lower Calcareous Grit)	2. Hard whitish calcareous sandstone (*Natica*-bed of Blake and Hudleston) with *Natica marchamensis* : in some places united to the bed above, in other places separated by a thin layer of shelly sand with *Exogyra nana*, *Gervillia sp.*, *Pecten (Chlamys) fibrosus* and *Ostrea sp.*	0	10
	1. False-bedded buff sands with streaks of clay, pebbles of quartz and lydite. Here and there the sands contain layers of fissile calcareous sandstone, often ripple-marked ; in other parts of the quarry there are only impersistent layers and doggers of sand-stone. Lignite, *Ostrea (Alectryonia) gregaria*, *Pecten (Chlamys) fibrosus*, *Exogyra nana* and *Cardioceras cordatum* .. .. seen to	10	0

The impersistent character of the deposits between the top of the Lower Calcareous Grit and the base of the Coral Rag forms features of interest. When the strata are traced towards the north end of the section, Beds 6 to 8 are seen to thin out, and the white gritty oolitic limestone (Bed 3) passes into a conglomerate. The only constant bed is the coraliferous limestone which extends the whole length of the quarry without variation in thickness or lithology. At the north end it rests on the decalcified lower part of the higher Trigonia Bed and, in turn, is overlain by a platy semi-crystalline limestone that attains a thickness of 6 ft. The beds appear to occupy a shallow synclinal fold. The inconstancy of the rocks was also noted by H. B. Woodward in his diagram of a former working-face, reproduced in Fig. 3.[1]

At this locality the formation is highly fossiliferous, and the type specimens of *Hemipedina marchamensis* Wright, *Natica marchamensis* Blake and Hudleston and *Vertebriceras vertebrale* (J. Sow.) were obtained from this pit. It is probable that Sowerby's type of *Perisphinctes plicatilis* was also obtained

---

[1] Woodward, H. B., ' The Jurassic Rocks of Britain ' (*Mem. Geol. Surv.*), vol. v, 1895, p. 125 ; and ' The Geology of the Country around Oxford ' (*Mem. Geol. Surv.*), 1st Ed, 1908, p. 30.

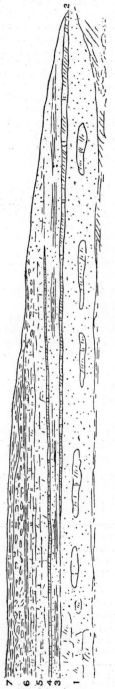

FIG. 3.—*Section at Sheepstead Farm, near Marcham.*

2-7. Upper Corallian.

1. Lower Corallian.

from Sheepstead Farm. He states that the shell was found in a 'sandy stratum containing beds of sandy limestone at Dry Sandford and Marcham, N.W. of Abingdon.'[1] The sands of the Lower Calcareous Grit in this neighbourhood have been famous for fine examples of *Aspidoceras perarmatum* (J. Sow.), many of which occur in the form of casts. Specimens of this kind were named '*Ammonites catena*.' The interior of the ammonite was filled with ferruginous and calcareous mud or sand, and the shell-wall and septa subsequently became dissolved away, leaving only the casts of chambers in a loose form or linked together so as to resemble a rough tapering chain. An excellent example may be seen in the Museum of Practical Geology. In addition to *A. perarmatum*, the sands at Sheepstead Farm have yielded the following specimens, the majority of which are represented in the collections of the University Museum, Oxford :—Lignite, *Carpolithus plenus* Phill., *Ostrea* (*Alectryonia*) *gregaria* J. Sow., *Natica arguta* Phill., *N. felina* d'Orb., *Anacardioceras excavatum* (J. Sow.), *Cardioceras cordatum* (J. Sow.) and *Goliathiceras goliathum* (d'Orb.).

In the Upper Corallian, Bed 5 has yielded some fine examples of *Trigonia meriani* Ag., *T. perlata* Ag., and *T. triquetra* Lyc., and during the re-examination of the section in 1925, a specimen of *Trigonia* was found which appears to belong to an undescribed species. Large forms of *Astarte ovata* W. Smith also occur in this layer. In Bed 3 fragments of the characteristic shell of *Trichites* are present, and, on account of its narrow vertical range, show that Beds 3–5 are the equivalent of the Trigonia Bed of the Lamb and Flag section.

The Lower Calcareous Grit is no longer actively worked in this quarry, but good sections are available a short distance away. In the pit on the east side of Buildings Farm the conglomeratic basement bed of the Upper Corallian is seen to overlie a series of buff sands with beds of bluish-grey gritty calcareous sandstone, containing *Aspidoceras perarmatum* (J. Sow.) *Aspid. catena* (J. de C. Sow.) and *Cardioceras cordatum* (J. Sow.) at the depth of 12 to 15 ft. below the top of the sands. This may possibly correspond to the zone of *Aspidoceras biarmatum*, established by Dr. A. Morley Davies, but during the revision of the area the index-species was not found. The *Natica*-bed appears to be absent, either as a result of local erosion or of overlap by the Upper Corallian rocks.

A section, similar in many respects to that exposed at Sheepstead Farm, was formerly to be seen in the pit near Noah's Ark Inn. It was described by Blake and Hudleston,[2] but is now somewhat overgrown.

Northwards from Abingdon along the Cumnor road, small openings show the Coral Rag with a variable thickness of weathered rock at the top. At Dry Sandford, coral-rock and rubble, 3 ft. thick, rest on buff sands with *Natica marchamensis* Blake and Hudleston, but are not well exposed. At Cothill School the base of the sands was reached in a well, at a depth of about 35 ft. from surface. Sections may also be seen at Cothill and Wooton. At the latter village a shallow quarry, west of the church, shows about 4 ft. of shelly limestone containing many corals, mostly preserved in coarsely crystalline calcite. In parts of the quarry the softer beds are puckered by surface 'creep.'

In the deep hollow at Sunningwell, south of Foxcombe Hill, a narrow outcrop of Upper Corallian appears, but it is not clear whether the rock occurs as an inlier or is connected by the brook-bed with the main outcrop to the south-west. The stone is well exposed in several old quarries, and bears a close resemblance to the limestone quarried at Lyehill and Wheatley (*see*

---

[1] 'Mineral Conchology,' vol. ii, 1818, p. 149.
[2] Blake, J. F., and W. H. Hudleston, 'On the Corallian Rocks of England,' *Quart. Journ. Geol. Soc.*, vol. xxxiii, 1877, p. 305.

p. 59). The following particulars were obtained from the eastern side of the largest excavation :—

		Ft.
Upper Corallian	Hard whitish platy limestone with corals ; up to	3
	Brown pisolitic and oolitic marly limestone with rolled fragments of shells, spines of *Cidaris florigemma*, and a few corals	3½
	Similar rock but harder, with spines of *Cidaris smithi* and fragments of *Isastrea*	3

The hard platy limestone is closely similar to that forming the highest bed in the Sheepstead Farm pit, and is probably the equivalent to the ' Pendle ' in the Headington quarry. It appears to be almost immediately overlain by Kimmeridge Clay. The rock at Sunningwell was formerly quarried on a large scale for building-stone and burning for lime. Some of the beds contain many fragments of corals, few of which appear to have grown *in situ.*

To the south-east of Cumnor, at Bradley Farm, a large quarry shows the following section :—

		Ft.	In.
	Soil .. .. up to	1	0
Upper Corallian	6. Rubbly greyish-white limestone and marl, crowded with *Exogyra nana, Ostrea (Alectryonia) gregaria, Pecten (Chlamys) vimineus, Cidaris florigemma,* etc.	3	0
	5. Greyish-white limestone with *Isastrea explanata,* etc. The corals are bored by *Lithodomus*	2	6
	4. Fine buff sands with thin layers of clay. A whitish calcareous bed occurs near the top and contains nodules. Some pebbles of lydite at junction with Bed 3.. 3 ft. to	5	6
Lower Corallian (Lower Calcareous Grit)	3. Hard grey gritty calcareous sandstone, decalcified in places, with pebbles of clay, lydite and quartz ; crowded with the casts of *Natica marchamensis* and *N. arguta.* It also contains *Anacardioceras excavatum, Perisphinctes* aff. *plicatilis, Vertebriceras vertebrale* and *Aspidoceras perarmatum..* 4 ft. to	5	6
	2. Brown ochreous shelly sand, inconstant in thickness ; probably represents decalcified base of Bed 3 0–	1	3
	1. Fine buff sands .. .. seen to	10	0

This section was described by Blake and Hudleston, who regarded Bed 4 as forming the uppermost member of the Lower Calcareous Grit. They state that it contains '*Ammonites cordatus, Cylindrites luidi, Natica clytia, Gervillia aviculoides, Ostrea solitaria* and *Serpula tricarinata.*'[1] It is more likely, however, that this stratum is the decalcified equivalent of the Trigonia Bed of Sheepstead Farm. At both localities this sand-bed rests on a bed of grit with *Natica marchamensis,* the junction being marked by a pebbly layer. There is thus some justification for assuming that the specimen of *Trigonia triquetra* Seebach, recorded by Lycett from the Calcareous Grit of Cumnor, was found in Bed 4.[2]

In the higher beds, corals are found in an excellent state of preservation and include *Cladophyllia conybeari* M. Edw., *Cosmoseris irradians* M. Edw., *Isastrea explanata* (Goldf.), *Montlivaltia dispar* Phill., *Thamnastrea arachnoides* (Park.), *Th. concinna* (Goldf.) and *Thecosmilia annularis* (Flem.). In

---

[1] Blake, J. F., and W. H. Hudleston, ' On the Corallian Rocks of England,' *Quart. Journ. Geol. Soc.,* vol. xxxiii, 1877, p. 307.
[2] Lycett, J., ' British Fossil Trigoniae ' (*Mon. Pal. Soc.*), 1872, p. 27.

addition, the rocks contain numerous characteristic lamellibranchs and echinoderms.

From the Calcareous Grit of this locality the type of *Carpolithus plenus* Phill. was obtained.

The Upper Corallian rocks appear to have exhibited much lithological variability in the old quarries at the Cumnor cross-roads. These pits are now overgrown, but according to H. B. Woodward the coral-rock appears to be interbedded with tufaceous stone like that at Wheatley.

Coral Rag and rubbly beds are exposed at several localities on Cumnor Hill. Many of the limestones are sub-crystalline, and the corals are usually preserved in coarsely crystalline calcite.

On the Wytham and Seacourt Hills the Corallian rocks form a large outlier, separated from the main outcrop by the deep valley through which the road from Oxford to Eynsham passes. Though this disconnected mass is apparently simple in structure, the rocks in these hills show signs of disturbance when the boundaries are traced on a contoured map. On the slope overlooking the Upper Thames or Isis, the strata are nearly horizontal, for on the western scarp of Wytham and the adjacent tiny outlier of Beacon Hill the base of the Lower Calcareous Grit is at almost the same elevation. But at the col between Wytham and Seacourt Hills the boundary-line rises considerably, and falls something like 100 ft. towards Wytham, and about 200 ft. towards Botley. The dip on the south side of Seacourt Hill is great enough to bring the Corallian

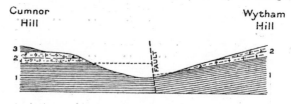

FIG. 4.—*Section across the Botley Valley between Cumnor and Wytham Hills.*

1. Oxford Clay.   2. Corallian.   3. Kimmeridge Clay.

Beds to the river-level between Botley and North Hinksey. Hence it follows that there is a displacement between the Seacourt and Cumnor Hills which cannot be less than 50 ft. and may be nearly 100 ft. Whether this is due to a synclinal fold or to a fault, the evidence in the field is not sufficient to determine, but the latter explanation seems more probable (*see* Fig. 4).

On Wytham Hill the base of the Calcareous Grit is from 100 to 190 ft. below the summit ; that of the Coral Rag 50 to 150 ft. The corresponding figures for Seacourt Hill are 60 to 210 ft., and 25 to 190 ft. The narrow outcrop of the Lower Division in many places along the hillside shows that there cannot be more than 20 to 30 ft. of sand ; but the great vertical range of the Coral Rag above it gives an erroneous impression of its thickness and tends to show that the Wytham and Seacourt Hills are separate anticlinal domes, though the dip of the strata in any direction probably does not exceed 4°. These hills are in line with the inliers of Lower Oolitic rocks extending from Islip towards Buckingham, and the undulations of the Corallian strata are probably the feeble continuation of the sharp folds which bring the older formations to the surface along that region of upheaval.

There are some old quarries at the top of Wytham Hill which were probably worked when the main road from Oxford crossed the high ground, before the present lower road was made. They still show beds of coralline limestone, as also do the other old quarries on Seacourt Hill ; the limestones were recently exposed in an excavation made for a water-tank, south of Little Ash Hill Wood, and were found to contain *Isastrea explanata* (Goldf.), *Thamnastrea arachnoides* (Park.), *Thecosmilia annularis* (Flem.), *Pecten* (*Chlamys*) *fibrosus* J. Sow., *P.* (*Chlamys*) *vimineus* J. Sow. and other characteristic fossils. The ' Honeycomb Coral ' occurred in large masses and showed perforations made by the boring mollusc *Lithodomus*. Near the east side of Wytham Great Wood, the sands of the Lower Calcareous Grit are somewhat poorly exposed in several old pits.

In the main outcrop on Cumnor Hill, the Corallian Rocks swing round in a south-easterly direction and occupy the lower slopes of the high ground, west of the Hinkseys ; but south of Bagley Wood, the outcrop of the formation is confined within narrow limits until the beds pass out of sight under the Kimmeridge Clay of Radley Large Wood.

The formation is exposed at several localities in this area, and the following section, situated a quarter of a mile south-west of North Hinksey, was described by H. B. Woodward.[1] It shows the following beds, now much overgrown :—

		Ft.
Upper Corallian	Rubbly coral-rock with much clay ; spines of *Cidaris*, etc.	8
	Hard sandy oolitic limestone with small pebbles at base ; *Ostrea solitaria*, *Exogyra nana*, *Gervillia aviculoides*, *Pecten* (*Chlamys*) *vimineus* and *Trigonia* spp.	1 to 2
Lower Corallian	Buff sands with beds of calcareous sandstone..	10

Sections of like character may also be seen in the side of the valley, 450 yds. east north-east of Chilswell Farm, and in the old quarry near the brook that runs from Boar's Hill to South Hinksey, not far from where the Abingdon road turns into Bagley Wood. In this stone-pit, about 18 ft. of coraliferous limestones in thick beds are exposed, and contain masses of *Thecosmilia annularis* (Flem.), *Thamnastrea arachnoides* (Park.) and *Isastrea explanata* (Goldf.) in an excellent state of preservation. The corals are associated with other characteristic fossils, such as *Cidaris florigemma* Phill., *C. smithi* Wright, *Nucleolites scutatus* Lam., *Pecten* (*Chlamys*) *vimineus* J. Sow., *Lima* (*Plagiostoma*) *rigida* J. Sow. and *Exogyra nana* (J. Sow.).

Between this locality and Bagley Wood a marked lithological change takes place in the Upper Corallian deposits, the hard coral-limestones passing into argillaceous sediments of Ampthill Clay type in a manner similar to that in which the Corallian deposits are replaced by clays in the area to the north-east of Wheatley. In this wood a small quarry shows a succession of clays and thin clayey limestones occupying the stratigraphical position of the coral-beds. They overlie the equivalent of the Trigonia Bed of Marcham, but this rock-band is poorly exposed. The continuation of the same series of argillaceous deposits in the direction of dip was shown in a pipe-trench excavated along the road from Kennington towards Radley. Here, they were capped by a greyish-white limestone, 3 ft. thick, which in turn was overlain by Kimmeridge Clay. This clayey-facies of the Upper Corallian is exhibited in the railway-cutting near Littlemore station, and a full description of the section is given on p. 52. It is perhaps unnecessary to point out that the passage of relatively porous limestones into clays must have an adverse effect on water-supply.

The grit bands of the Lower Calcareous Grit and the grey sandy limestone equivalent to the Trigonia Bed at the base of the Upper Corallian have been quarried in the Little London pit, now disused. Blocks of grey limestone, containing the characteristic fossils of the Trigonia Bed, may still be examined in the quarry. The limestone can be seen in the road close by the church at Kennington, and immediately below, at the top of the lane leading towards the railway, are large slabs of Calcareous Grit, apparently *in situ*. The next

---

[1] ' The Geology of the Oxford District ' (*Mem. Geol. Surv.*), 1st Ed., 1908, p. 32.

brook to the south, opposite Sandford Pool, also shows sections of both divisions, here and there, and sand with large masses of calcareous sandstone occurs in the adjacent railway-cutting.

On the eastern bank of the River Thames the Corallian plateau is deeply intersected by brooks descending from the high ground of Shotover, so that a part of the Coral Rag is severed and forms an outlier capped by a thin spread of Kimmeridge Clay on the hill between Littlemore and Iffley. West of Littlemore station, part of the cutting, now used as a quarry, shows a magnificent section of Upper Corallian rocks in argillaceous facies, noticed in Bagley Wood and other exposures on the west side of the river. The clays, which are clearly the equivalent of the coraliferous limestones, are here also overlain by a greyish-white limestone as in the pipe-trench south of Kennington, and they have yielded several ammonites which have been identified by Mr. S. S. Buckman. The section is as follows :—

		Ft.	In.
27. Greyish-white sandy limestone, slightly oolitic, with *Perisphinctes* cf. *gerontoides* seen		o	6
26. Brownish-black clay with *Exogyra nana* ..		o	6
25. White weathering argillaceous limestone ..		o	5
24. Brownish-black clay		1	3
23. White weathering argillaceous limestone, 5 in. to		o	10
22. Brownish-black clay		1	5
21. White weathering argillaceous limestone in six layers, separated by thin, irregular seams of brownish-black clay ; crowded with *Exogyra nana, Serpula intestinalis, Perisphinctes* cf. *linki* in top layer ; *Ataxioceras* cf. *bifurcatus* in middle layer, and *Perisphinctes tizianiformis* at base of bed ..		2	10
20. Brownish-black clay		1	o
19. White weathering argillaceous limestone ..		o	5
18. Brownish-black clay		o	7
17. White weathering argillaceous limestone ..		o	3
16. Brownish-black clay		o	10
15. White weathering argillaceous limestone, in five layers, separated by thin seams of clay. *Perisphinctes* cf. *bolobanowi*, at base ..		2	o
14. Brownish-black clay, crowded with *Exogyra nana*. About middle of bed is an irregular band of argillaceous limestone, inconstant in thickness		2	o
13. White weathering argillaceous limestone ..		o	5
12. Brownish-black clay		o	3
11. White weathering argillaceous limestone ..		o	5
10. Brownish-black clay		o	11
9. White weathering argillaceous limestone ..		o	8
8. Brown shelly marl		o	3
7. Shelly argillaceous limestone with *Aspidoceras sp.*		2	o
6. Buff shelly sand, crowded with small specimens of *Pecten (Chlamys) fibrosus* and *Exogyra nana* .. .. .. 10 in. to 1			o
5. Brownish-grey marly limestone, variable in thickness .. .. .. 6 in. to 1			o
4. Brown shelly sand with *Pecten (Chlamys) fibrosus* ; resting on irregular surface of Bed 3		1	3

Upper Corallian

Ft. In.

Upper Corallian —cont.	3. Dark grey gritty limestone, containing in upper part *Perisphinctes* cf. *antecedens* and *Perisphinctes* of *wartae*-style. At base is a shelly layer with small pebbles of chert and quartzite. *Perisphinctes* aff. *martelli* and *Anacardioceras excavatum* ; cemented firmly on to Bed 2 .. .. .. 2 0
	2. Dark grey calcareous sandstone, probably the indurated top of the underlying sands; 0 in. to 0 10
Lower Corallian	1. Buff sands, with spherical and elongated masses of hard grey calcareous sandstone on three levels. The middle band forms a fairly constant layer, 1 ft. to 1 ft. 3 inches thick 15 0

The beds undulate slightly in the cutting, but the general inclination is westward. In 1867, T. Codrington noted that there were numerous small faults in the cutting, but it is possible that some of the peculiar masses of rudely stratified nodular limestone, which interrupt the evenly bedded character of the strata, were then mistaken for dislocations. One of these masses is visible in the present section. (Pl. III.B). The nodular lumps are covered by *Serpula intestinalis* Phill. and *Exogyra nana* (J. Sow.), and in their mode of occurrence they recall the nodules in the large unstratified masses of coralline limestone, known as 'ballstones,' in the Wenlock Limestone at Wenlock.[1]

Bed 3 on account of its thickness and hardness is the most conspicuous bed in the section. It is fossiliferous and contains, in addition to the ammonites, *Gervillia aviculoides* (J. Sow.), fragments of *Trigonia meriani* Agassiz, and other species characteristic of the Trigonia Bed of the Lamb and Flag and Sheepstead Farm sections. It has also a pebbly layer at the base, indicating erosion, and if, as is considered probable, the specimen of *Anacardioceras excavatum* (J. Sow.) has been derived, the stratigraphical break is greater here than in the western part of the area. In fact, the absence of the Biarmatum Zone in the district to the east of Abingdon is probably due to the overlap of the Upper Corallian on to lower zones. Further evidence of an overlap at the base of the Martelli Zone in the neighbourhood of Wheatley is given on p. 60.

The overlying clays yield *Exogyra nana* in abundance, whilst the ammonites, which are rare, are confined to the more calcareous bands. The highest bed in the cutting is poorly exposed and is seen *in situ* only in the shallow undulations, but plentiful fragments of the rock may be found in the field above the quarry. This is probably the equivalent of the 'Pendle' of the Headington Quarry ; it has yielded *Perisphinctes* cf. *gerontoides* Siemiradzki.

A similar limestone was observed by Mr. E. S. Cobbold in excavations made for the sewage-pumping main along the road up Sandford Hill. He states that the limestone was 12½ ft. thick, and was seen to overlie the marls. It was followed upwards by a sandy limestone 2½ ft. thick ; but at the sewage-farm about a mile east of Sandford no trace of these limestones was found in a trial-hole which showed the Kimmeridge Clay resting on argillaceous members of the Upper Corallian.[2] The limestone, therefore, appears to have either been replaced by clay, or to have been overlapped by the Kimmeridge Beds. Mr. Cobbold was of the opinion that the rock had entirely changed its character in the short distance from Sandford, and he suggests that ' the influx of clay may be due to the muddy discharge of some river which might hinder or

---

[1] Murchison, ' Silurian System,' pp. 210–212, 484. *See* also M. C. Crosfield and M. S. Johnston, *Proc. Geol. Assoc.*, vol. xxv, 1914, p. 193.

[2] Cobbold, E. S., ' Notes on the Strata exposed in laying out the Oxford Sewage Farm at Sandford-on-Thames,' *Quart. Journ. Geol. Soc.*, vol. xxxvi, 1880, p. 317, fig. 7.

altogether check the growth of corals, while it was favourable to that of oysters,' and he remarks : ' it seems probable that the Palaeozoic rocks known to exist near London may have been above water in the later Oolitic period, and have had considerable extension to the S.W. and E.[1]

At the western end of the sewage-farm, a disused stone-pit shows Beds 1–5 of the Littlemore section. A few poorly preserved specimens of *Anacardioceras excavatum* (J. Sow.) and *Perisphinctes* cf. *antecedens* Salfeld were found.

When the formation is traced northwards, the coral-beds re-appear, and although no sections are available to show the actual passage of the clays into coraliferous limestones, the proximity of the argillaceous equivalents at Littlemore is indicated by the somewhat clayey character of the coral rag in the pits near the Industrial School, east of Cowley. This is well shown in the pit nearest the road, where the following section is displayed :—

		Ft.	In.
	8. Grey coral-rock, mixed with dark clay ; *Thecosmilia annularis* and *Isastrea* spp. ..	4	o
	7. Grey sandy limestone with a few corals preserved in coarsely crystalline calcite ..	1	6
	6. Brown gritty clay with *Pygaster umbrella* and *Nucleolites scutatus*	o	6
Upper Corallian	5. Grey sandy limestone, decalcified in places..	o	6
	4. Hard grey shelly limestone with *Cymatosphinctes cymatophorus, Gervillia aviculoides, Trigonia meriani, Exogyra nana*, etc. ..	1	o
	3. Soft brown sandy layer with *Perisphinctes antecedens, P.* cf. *biplex* and *Nucleolites dimidiatus*	o	3
	2. Hard grey shelly limestone crowded with *Gervillia aviculoides, Trigonia* spp. and *Pecten* (*Chlamys*) *vagans*	o	8
Lower Corallian	1. Buff sands with concretionary doggers, exposed to	3	o

From the Lower Calcareous Grit, Mr. S. S. Buckman has recorded the following ammonites, *Anacardioceras cordatiforme* S. Buckman, *A. excavatum* (J. Sow.), *Kranaosphinctes kranaus* S. Buckman, and *Goliathiceras ammonoides* S. Buckman[2]; but while their occurrence proves the presence of a varied ammonite-fauna in the sands, it is probable that the specimens were obtained when the beds were worked to a greater depth than is exposed at present. From Bed 2, Mr. Buckman records *Vertebriceras dorsale* S. Buckman, *V. vertebrale* (J. Sow.), *V. rachis* S. Buckman and *V. quadratum* S. Buckman; but with the exception of *V. dorsale*, it is likely that the other species are not indigenous to the bed, but are derived. These species certainly indicate a lower horizon than Bed 2, which is clearly the basal portion of the Marcham Trigonia Bed. He has also recorded in Bed 6 an ammonite formerly referred to *Perisphinctes linki*, which has now become the genotype and holotype of *Liosphinctes apolipon*,[3] a species associated with *Perisphinctes antecedens* at the Lamb and Flag pit. The presence of *linki*-like forms serves to show the general equivalence of the coral-beds with the clays at Littlemore.

A similar section is exposed in the south pit, in which a greater thickness of coral-rag is found as a result of a slight southerly dip of the strata ; and the same beds may also be seen in a quarry on the north side of the road, east of the Roman Way. At this locality, the Trigonia Bed has yielded *Arisphinctes ariprepes* S. Buckman and *Chalcedoniceras chalcedonicum* S. Buckman.[4] In this neighbourhood, the sands of the Lower Calcareous

[1] *Op. cit.*, p. 319.
[2] ' Type Ammonites,' vol. v, 1925, p. 51.
[3] ' Type Ammonites,' vol. v, 1925, pl. dlxvi.
[4] ' Type Ammonites,' vol. v, 1925, p. 51.

Grit are over 60 ft. thick, as proved in a boring at the Morris Works, Cowley. A specimen of *Anacardioceras excavatum* (J. Sow.) was obtained from sands passed through in a shallow well alongside the road to Garsington.

From the Industrial School northwards as far as Headington, the Upper Corallian rocks consist mainly of ' raggy ' limestones largely made up of comminuted shells and corals, with a condensed representative of the Trigonia Bed at the base, overlying the Calcareous Grit. The upper division is variable : in some places it consists of impersistent layers of hard grey shelly limestone alternating with shell and coral-sand ; in other places it comprises irregular bands of coral-limestone and clay, and is often false-bedded. It is exposed in numerous old quarries, many of which, however, are in danger of being filled up. The rocks are highly fossiliferous, and the following specimens, preserved in the collections of the University Museum, Oxford, have been obtained from the Upper Corallian Beds in the area between Cowley and Shotover. The localities are grouped in the list as follows :—1, Cowley, Bullingdon and Horsepath Road, 2, Headington and Shotover.

Isastrea explanata (*Goldf.*), 1, 2.
,, greenovi *M. Edw.*, 1.
Montlivaltia dispar *Phill.*, 1, 2.
Thamnastrea arachnoides (*Park.*), 1, 2.
,, concinna (*Goldf.*), 1.
Thecosmilia annularis (*Flem.*), 1, 2.
Cidaris florigemma *Phill.*, 1, 2.
,, smithi *Wright*, 1, 2.
Hemicidaris intermedia (*Flem.*), 1, 2.
Nucleolites dimidiatus (*Phill.*), 1, 2.
,, scutatus *Lam.*, 1, 2.
Pseudodiadema versipora (*Phill.*), 2.
Pygaster umbrella *Wright*, 1, 2.
Pygurus blumenbachi (*Koch & Dunk.*), 1.
,, costatus *Wright*, 1.
,, pentagonalis (*Phill.*), 1, 2.
Astropecten rectus *M'Coy*, 1, 2.
Serpula sulcata *J. de C. Sow.*, 1, 2.
,, tricarinata *J. de C. Sow.*, 1, 2.
Orbiculoidea radiata (*Phill.*), 1.
Ornithella boloniensis *Rig. & Sauv.*, 1.
Terebratula bucculenta *J. de C. Sow.*, 1.
,, insignis *Schübler*, 1, 2.
,, maltonensis *Oppel*, 1.
Astarte extensa *Phill.*, 2.
,, ovata *W. Smith*, 1, 2.
Corbicella laevis (*J. de C. Sow.*), 1, 2.
Cucullaea oblonga *J. Sow.*, 2.
Eopecten abjectus (*Phill.*), 1, 2.
Exogyra nana (*J. Sow.*), 1, 2.
Gervillia aviculoides (*J. Sow.*), 1, 2.
Goniomya litterata (*J. Sow.*), 2.
Lima elliptica (*Whit.*), 1.
,, laeviuscula (*J. Sow.*), 2.
,, rigida (*J. Sow.*), 1, 2.
,, tumida *Roem.*, 1, 2.
Lithodomus inclusus (*Phill.*), 1, 2.
Lucina sp. [*L. polita* Phill.], 1.
Modiola bipartita *J. Sow.*, 1.
,, perplicata (*Etallon*), 1.
Myoconcha texta *Buv.*, 1.
Opis corallina *Lycett*, 1.
Ostrea (Alectryonia) gregaria *J. Sow.*, 1, 2.
,, solitaria *J. de C. Sow.*, 1.

Pecten (Camptonectes) ' lens ' *J. Sow.*, 1, 2.
  ,,   (Chlamys) vagans *J. de C. Sow.*, 1, 2.
  ,,   ,,   vimineus *J. Sow.*, 1, 2.
Perna mytiloides *Lam.*, 1.
Pholadomya canaliculata *Roem.*, 1.
Pinna ampla *J. Sow.*, 1.
Placunopsis similis *Whit.*, 1.
Pseudomonotis ovalis (*Phill.*), 1.
Pteria expansa (*Phill.*), 1.
Sowerbya deshayesi *Buv.*, 1.
    ,,   triangularis (*Phill.*), 2.
Thracia studeri *Ag.*, 1.
Trichites sp. [*T. ploti* Auctt.], 1, 2.
Trigonia clavellata (*Park.*), 1, 2.
    ,,   hudlestoni *Lycett*, 1, 2.
    ,,   incurva *Benett*, 1, 2.
    ,,   meriani *Ag.*, 1, 2.
    ,,   triquetra *Lycett*, 1, 2.
Alaria seminuda *Heb.* and *Desl.*, 1.
Bourguetia striata (*J. Sow.*), 1, 2.
Cerithium muricatum (*J. de C. Sow.*), 1, 2.
Pseudomelania heddingtonensis (*J. Sow.*), 1, 2.
Pleurotomaria reticulata (*J. Sow.*), 1, 2.
Nautilus hexagonus *J. de C. Sow.*, 1, 2.
Perisphinctes biplex (*J. Sow.*), 2.
    ,,   bolobanowi *Nikitin*, 2.
    ,,   *cf.* chloroolithicus (*von Ammon*), 2.
    ,,   martelli *Oppel*, 1, 2.
    ,,   parandieri *de Lor.*, 2.
    ,,   variocostatus *Buckland*, 1, 2.
Belemnites abbreviatus *Miller*, 1, 2.
Glyphea rostrata *Phill.*, 1.
    ,,   scabrosa *Phill.*, 1, 2.
Asteracanthus ornatissimus *Ag.*, 2.
Pycnodus sp., 2.
Ichthyosaurus sp., 2.

In the pit known as the Vicarage Pit, off Quarry Road at Headington, an excellent section of the beds is exposed. The Trigonia Bed here yielded *Vertebriceras dorsale* S. Buckm., and on its upper surface there is a layer containing large specimens of *Montlivaltia dispar* Phill. The highest beds in the pit, which are in part equivalent to the ' Pendle ' of the Magdalen Quarry, have yielded a Perisphinctid, closely resembling *Perisphinctes chloroolithicus* (von Ammon). This shell is preserved in the University Museum collections at Oxford.

In the Magdalen Quarry, near the workhouse at Headington, the Corallian rocks are being actively quarried for building-blocks and lime-burning, and a good section is seen in the working-face, which shows the following beds (Pl. IIIA) :—

		Ft.	In.
12.	Whitish oolitic limestone, locally called ' Pendle ' ..	5	0
11.	Layers of rubbly limestone with thin marl bands. Corals numerous .. .. 4 to	5	0
10.	Hard grey limestone	1	2
9.	Nodular limestone with marl parting	1	0
8.	Hard greyish-white limestone, known as the ' Headington Hard.' This rock, in passing eastwards, cuts out Beds 3–7 and rests on Bed 2 at east end of quarry ..	1	6

A.—*Upper Corallian Rocks in the Magdalen Quarry, Headington.*

B.—*Section of Corallian Rocks in the railway-cutting at Littlemore.*

Ft. In.

7. Brownish-grey coral-rock and marl. This bed, known as ' *Brown Course* ' is 3 ft. thick at west end of pit ; *Perisphinctes antecedens, P.* cf. *parandieri, Nautilus hexagonus* .. .. 0 to   3   0
6. Thin dark marl with *Pholadomya aequalis* .. 0 to   0   3
5. Hard grey limestone with *Pseudomelania heddingtonensis* .. .. 0 to   1   6
4. Brown marly band .. .. 0 to   0   2
3. Dark grey limestone .. .. 0 to   0   6
2. Hard bluish-grey shelly limestone with lydite pebbles at base. *Perisphinctes biplex.* Known as ' *Bottom Course* ' and occasionally contains derived ammonites   2   6
1. Brown sands .. .. exposed to   3   0

The section shows considerable variation in the details of the beds, largely the result of their false-bedded character. The ' Bottom Course,' however, remains fairly constant throughout the quarry, and it broadly corresponds to Beds 3–6 of the Lamb and Flag section (*see* p. 43). The base of the ' Bottom Course ' is pebbly and frequently contains derived ammonites. One specimen, *Goliathiceras microtrypa*, recorded by Mr. Buckman, appears to have come from a denuded hard band in the sands of the Lower Calcareous Grit.[1]

The highest bed, locally called ' Pendle,' presents an exceedingly irregular surface due to solution, and the hollows are filled with brown clay containing *Elephas antiquus* (teeth fragments).

There are numerous old quarries at Headington, and the junction of the Corallian with the overlying Kimmeridge Clay was at one time well shown in a pit, now overgrown, to the left of the road leading from Oxford to Shotover Hill. The section was as follows :—

Ft.

Kimmeridge Clay	Dark bluish-grey clay Grey racy clay	Saurian bones, *Ammonites*, *Ostrea deltoidea*, large crystals of selenite ..
Upper Corallian	Marly layer .. .. False-bedded sandy rock (decomposed) and passing down into bed beneath ..	1
	Hard grey shelly limestone	1½
	Coral-rock, with bands of hard grey shelly limestone (building-stone) ; few fossils	12

An opportunity to examine the junction occurred when the formations were exposed in a deep trench made alongside the road, east of Shotover Lodge. The markedly eroded surface of the highest Corallian bed then shown confirmed the observations of earlier investigators, and proved the existence of a stratigraphical break between the two formations.

North of Headington the Corallian escarpment is deeply indented by the Bayswater Brook, which, with its tributaries gathered from the rock-beds forms a considerable extent of marsh land at the foot of the slopes. The Calcareous Grit has a narrow outcrop, which becomes still less conspicuous on the opposite side of the valley near Wick Farm ; and it is of interest to note that the thinning-out of the sands at this point coincides with the most westerly occurrence of Rhaxella Chert or Arngrove Stone in the Oxford district. This rock forms the base of the Lower Calcareous Grit, which here is not more than 25 ft. thick, and in a field on the south side of the brook and west of Sand Hill, several fragments of Rhaxella Chert were picked up on mole-hills situated on the junction between the Oxford Clay and the Corallian. From this locality the Chert can be traced by means of debris

---

[1] ' Type Ammonites', vol. v., 1925, p. 50.

in the fields at the base of the formation to the Plough Inn, near Wheatley. Further reference to this characteristic rock is made on p. 60.

At a small pit one-third of a mile N.N.W. of Wick Farm, the Coral Rag consists of limestone-beds full of corals, with *Exogyra nana* (J. Sow.) and other fossils ; and in Wick Copse the thickness of the lower division, with the Rhaxella Chert at its base, can scarcely exceed 20 ft.   Coraliferous and shelly limestones are again seen in a quarry a quarter of a mile west of Stow Wood, on the road to Elsfield.   This pit is close to the line of disturbance mentioned in the account of the Lower Oolites of Islip (p. 25).   The faulting appears to be complicated, but owing to the meagre field-evidence, it could not be deciphered in detail.   The general effect, however, has been to throw down all the beds some 50 ft. on the south-west side of the disturbed area, as may be seen if the escarpment is viewed from the top of Noke Hill, near Islip. The crest is observed to be much higher on the left side of the road to Wheatley than on the right ; this road being coincident with the fault where it reaches the brow of the hill.   If the ground be examined more closely it will be seen that from the corner of Stow Wood, south-eastwards for about a mile, the rising ground on the east side consists of sands belonging to the Calcareous Grit, while at a lower level on the west side is the Coral Rag.   Beyond this the evidence is not so clear, though the fault is conspicuous in the vicinity of Forest Hill.   The rolling character of the surface in the disturbed area contrasts with the prevailing flatness of the Corallian plateau at Headington.

Between Stow Wood and Woodeaton the Upper Corallian is thrown down almost to the bottom of the hill in a trough between the main fault and one close by on the south-west side, the displacement being probably nearly 200 ft. on one side, and upwards of 80 ft. on the other.   At Druns Hill is a small outlier in which the beds have a well-marked inclination to the south, and are cut off abruptly in that direction against the Oxford Clay in the bottom of Woodeaton Wood.   A disused quarry at the top of Druns Hill showed 6 ft. of well-bedded shelly limestone, with partings of marl full of specimens of *Exogyra nana* (J. Sow.).

North-east of the faulted belt some difficulty is experienced in drawing a line between the two Corallian divisions, on account of the sandy character of the whole series.   A thickness of 40 or 50 ft. of Calcareous Grit is shown near Beckley, but there is not more than 30 ft. at Woodperry and Stanton St. John.   In the road-section at Woodperry, now overgrown, A. H. Green observed a 'hard lime-cemented sandstone' at the base of the formation. A small excavation was made by the roadside during the examination of the area in 1924, and when a sample of this rock was obtained it proved to be typical Rhaxella Chert.   The coral limestone, which is here at the base of the upper division, is seen in a small quarry close to Woodperry House, and at the top of the hill, half a mile along the road to Oxford, there is a pit showing higher beds of limestone in which corals are rare or absent.

Upper Corallian rocks have been worked in several quarries at Stanton St. John, but these have all fallen into disuse.   Near the school there is an old stone-pit in which about 10 ft. of rubbly limestones with thin beds of marly clay are exposed.   At the base is a hard sandy limestone which has been worked to a depth of 4 ft., and although no fossil-evidence has been found, it is possible that this bed is the equivalent of the Trigonia Bed of Headington and other localities.   A similar section was noted by A. H. Green in a quarry, now disused, at the south-eastern end of the village, and rubbly limestones, formerly worked for lime-burning, may still be seen on the east side of the road, south of the George Inn.   They are highly fossiliferous and yield an abundance of *Exogyra nana* (J. Sow.), *Gryphaea dilatata* Auctt., and the echinoderms, *Cidaris florigemma* Phill., *Nucleolites scutatus* Lam. and *Pseudodiadema versipora* (Phill.).   Corals are scarce or absent, a fact also noted by Blake and Hudleston.[1]

---

[1] Blake, J. F., and W. H. Hudleston, ' The Corallian Rocks of England,' *Quart. Journ. Geol. Soc.*, vol. xxxiii, 1877, p. 310.

A good section is exposed at Shepherd's Quarry, about 1 mile south-west of the church at Stanton St. John, where the following beds are seen :—

		Ft.
	Brown soil	1
	Brownish-grey rubbly limestone.. ..	3
	Grey clay	1
Upper Corallian	Hard grey shelly limestones with bands of rubbly limestone and marl : *Cidaris florigemma* (spines), *Exogyra nana*, and *Belemnites sp.*	15

The quarry is situated near the line of fault which runs south-eastwards from Islip, and the beds show signs of disturbance. A good deal of 'rock-milk' coats the face of the joints, and tends to obscure the fossiliferous character of the limestones. In the fields to the south-east of the pit, numerous fragments of Rhaxella Chert may be picked up at the base of the Calcareous Grit ; similar fragments may be found by the wood-side east of Stanton St. John.

At Forest Hill coarsely pisolitic and oolitic limestones are exposed in a field north of the Manor House. The beds closely resemble the stone quarried at Lyehill (see below).

On the north-western side of Wheatley there are large quarries in which Corallian limestones are worked for building-blocks and lime-burning. The rock here forms part of the disturbed belt that extends from Woodeaton to the south-eastern base of Red Hill, through Wheatley Village, where the beds are faulted against the Kimmeridge Clay. This fault runs to the north of the railway towards Wheatley Bridge. The Corallian is likewise faulted along its eastern and north-eastern borders between Wheatley and Holton, so that the limestones are preserved by a kind of step-faulting. The throw of the main faults is, however, modified by transverse faulting, as at Forest Hill, where the Portland and Shotover Beds are let down between Kimmeridge Clay and Corallian by normal trough-faulting. Moreover, the general line of fracture and displacement is continued in a south-easterly direction through Great Milton, where an inlying tract of Kimmeridge Clay gives indication of disturbance.

Near to Red Hill are the Lyehill quarries, where about 40 ft. of limestone occurs in massive beds. Hard layers of pale shelly oolitic and pisolitic limestones are interbedded with soft brown layers, and near the surface these are disintegrated into crumbling beds of shell-sand from which fossils may be readily extracted. These include *Serpula sp.*, *Cidaris florigemma* Phill. (spines), *Exogyra nana* (J. Sow.), *Ostrea sp.* and *Pecten (Chlamys) fibrosus* J. Sow. Ammonites are rare, but a large fragment of *Perisphinctes* cf. *parandieri* de Lor. was obtained from a soft brown layer about 12 ft. above the lowest bed exposed. This species probably indicates the Antecedens Zone, which is represented by the 'Brown Course' in the Magdalen Pit at Headington. Higher zones have not been detected, but may be present. The strata are inclined to the north-north-east in this quarry.

In the quarries at Wheatley, the stone is worked to a depth of 30 or 40 ft., and is similar to that of Lyehill. The hard bands are blue-hearted, and are occasionally used for building-purposes. The fossils in this pit include *Cidaris florigemma* Phill., *Exogyra nana* (J. Sow.) and *Belemnites abbreviatus* Miller. A Perisphinctid, doubtfully referred to *Perisphinctes plicatilis*, has been recorded by H. B. Woodward[1] from the layers below the flaggy beds. The remains of a saurian jaw from this locality are preserved in the University Museum, Oxford.

The quarry by the old 'lock-up' at Wheatley is utilized for the reception of village 'refuse,' an unfortunate and ill-advised proceeding, considering that

---

[1] Woodward, H. B., in 'The Geology of the Oxford District' (*Mem. Geol. Surv.*), 1st Ed., 1908, p. 39.

much water is obtained from this mass of limestone. Rubbish has also been shot into a disused pit in the meadow farther west, in proximity to a well.

In Holton Park the Corallian stone lies to the west of the Mansion, which is built partly on made ground. Clay was dug on the island surrounded by the moat, the site of the old Hall. Pieces of cherty sandstone occur in some of the fields to the south of Holton Wood.

The following record of a well sunk to the south of Church Farm Moat was noted by J. H. Blake in 1897 :—

		Ft.	In.
Lower Corallian	Brown sandy and loamy soil	2	0
	Brown sandy oolitic loam with irregular patches and seams of grey clay..	5	0
	Rock band	0	4
	Brown and grey clay	3	0
	Hard yellowish-white speckled cherty rock, called ' Pendle ' by the well sinker : with *Pleuromya*	4	6
Oxford Clay	Blue sandy and shaly clay ,with band of rock 2 ft. thick, and large *Gryphaea dilatata*	6	0

The strata appeared to dip towards the north-east. The cherty rock above noted is evidently the same as the Arngrove Stone.

The boundary of the Corallian and Oxford Clays in the area north-east of Holton is indefinite. The presence of Corallian clays is indicated in many spots by the abundance of *Exogyra nana*, while here and there large examples of *Gryphaea dilatata* are suggestive of the upper part of the Oxford Clay, in which these forms are usually abundant.

Beds of brown clayey Calcareous Grit were exposed in the new road-cutting at the east end of Wheatley village, and in an excavation made for the purpose of diverting a stream near the Plough Inn, the Arngrove Stone was found to overlie blue sandy Oxford Clay as in the Church Farm Moat well. East of Wheatley Bridge there is a narrow tract shown on the Special Oxford Sheet as being occupied by Lower Calcareous Grit ; but no evidence was obtained during the recent revision to confirm the accuracy of the mapping, and the presence of this subdivision must be regarded as doubtful.

North-east of this point, however, it is evident that the Upper Corallian passes into clays which overlap on to the Arngrove Stone, and the effect of the change in lithology is at once apparent in the topographical features of the region. The landscape has now become one of low relief, raised but little above the streams that traverse the area from north to south. The broad valley connecting Ot Moor with the Thame basin is excavated in Oxford Clay, so that to the north-east of Holton and Stanton St. John the ground is practically all clay up to the Portland Beds of Brill and Muswell Hills, the chief hard rock-band being the Arngrove Stone, 6 ft. or less in thickness.

This stone-band is traceable by means of debris from a point south of Parson's Farm through Worminghall northwards to Boarstall,[1] and it is clear from the manner in which the outcrop of the chert runs in V-shapes up the brook valleys that the bed forms a gently inclined plane at the base of the Ampthill Clay. The sands which overlie the chert on the western side of the valley appear therefore to have been overlapped by the clay. The upper

---

[1] A few other places where the same rock may be seen by the side of ponds may be enumerated without further description :—Studley Priory Park, close to the road. Road-side, half a mile north-east of Studley Village, opposite farmhouse. 200 yards south of same farm. Warren Farm. Common by New Arngrove Farm. Half a mile N.N.E. of New Arngrove Farm, near the road. One third of a mile W.N.W. of Boarstall Church. South of Decoy Pond, Boarstall. One third of a mile west of Gravelpit Farm. Holt's Farm. By moat south of Boarstall Tower. Half a mile south-east of Boarstall Church. Pasture Farm near Danes Brook. South-west of Shabbington Wood. At Pasture Farm the rock is thrown down to the south-west by a small fault.

boundary of the Ampthill Clay is more difficult to determine in the absence of sections, and the line on the map separating this formation from the overlying Kimmeridge Clay in the area north and east of Oakley can only be regarded as approximately correct, although it appears to be the most natural position at which to draw the boundary, judging by the nature of the ground.

As already mentioned, there are few sections to record in this clay-area At Worminghall the ground has been dug up in places as if in search of stone-layers, and during the deepening of a pond north of the village fragments of Arngrove Stone were found in abundance in 1925. The soil is in part due to the decomposition of gritty and calcareous layers, and stiff bluish and brown clay with *Exogyra nana* (J. Sow.) and bits of *Gryphaea* were seen along the ditch on the north side of the road from Worminghall to Shabbington, north of Little Ickford. The Serpulite Bed, which is taken as marking the base of the Kimmeridge Clay in the Rid's Hill section, near Brill (*see* p. 74), has been recorded from a well-shaft at Ickford, and from the underlying clays Mr. Buckman has obtained a specimen of *Dichotomoceras dichotomum*.[1] South of Oakley, at the end of the lane east of Shabbington Wood, H. B. Woodward obtained *Exogyra sp., Gryphaea dilatata* J. Sow. and *Ostrea (Alectryonia) gregaria* J. Sow.

Good exposures of the Arngrove Stone are to be found in the neighbourhood of Arngrove Farm, where the rock is dug for ' gravel.' The stone runs with a good escarpment by Arngrove Farm to the north of Gravel Pit Farm and dips gently to the east. It is highly fossiliferous and the following shells were noted at the time of our visit : *Cardioceras cordatum* (J. Sow.), *Vertebriceras vertebrale* (J. Sow.), *Goniomya v-scripta* (J. Sow.), *Pecten (Chlamys) fibrosus* J. Sow., *Pholadomya aequalis* J. de C. Sow. and *Rhaxella perforata* Hind.

Dr. A. Morley Davies states that at a pond near Warren Farm, north of Studley, the chert undergoes a remarkable change, becoming a limestone though still exhibiting the characteristic structure.[2]

At various times the clays below the Serpulite Bed have been exposed in the Rid's Hill brickyard, and from one of these diggings Dr. A. Morley Davies has recorded the following ammonites : ' *Perisphinctes plicatilis* (Sow.), *Perisphinctes decipiens* (Sow.), *Perisphinctes sp.* and *Cardioceras cordatum* (Sow.) '[3] Below the Serpulite Bed the clays appear to pass downwards in unbroken succession, so that the unconformity noted at the top of the Corallian in the Headington district seems to have disappeared.

In the cuttings of the Great Western Railway north and south of Rushbeds Wood, between Ashendon and Ludgarshall, north-east of Brill, about 25 ft. of Ampthill Clay with bands of pale hard marl and argillaceous limestone have been exposed. The lowest layers contained *Exogyra nana* (J. Sow.) and spines of *Cidaris*.[4]

[1] Buckman, S. S., ' Type Ammonites,' vol. iv, 1923, p. 37.
[2] Davies, A. Morley, ' The Kimeridge Clay and Corallian Rocks of the neighbourhood of Brill (Buckinghamshire) ', *Quart. Journ. Geol. Soc.,* vol. lxiii, 1907, p. 38.
[3] *Op. cit.,* p. 34.
[4] See also *Proc. Geol. Assoc.,* vol. xx, p. 184.

CHAPTER V

UPPER OOLITIC ROCKS

THIS group includes the three highest members of the Jurassic Series, namely, Kimmeridge Clay, Portland Stone and Purbeck Beds. South and south-east of Oxford the Kimmeridge Beds occupy a considerable tract of country; but the Portland and Purbeck formations are confined to relatively small areas, and as already pointed out on p. 4, their extension beneath the Upper Cretaceous rocks is extremely limited. In contrast to the corresponding formations in Dorset, the three divisions are greatly reduced. in thickness throughout the Oxford district, largely on account of frequent intraformational erosion and condensed sedimentation, the result being that none of the Upper Oolitic formations is completely represented.

KIMMERIDGE CLAY

The Kimmeridge Clay, overlain directly by Gault, occupies the northern part of the Vale of White Horse, and passes into our region along the Ock Valley at Marcham and Abingdon. Thence it extends to Radley and rises northwards on the flanks of Boar's and Cumnor Hills, where it is cut off by the deep valley of Botley. On the eastern side of the Thames it occupies the banks of Nuneham Park, and rising eastward completely encircles the Shotover Hills, passes into the Thame Valley, and spreads out northward to form the base of Brill and Muswell Hills.

The lower part of the formation consists of dark grey and black shaly clay with septarian nodules and much selenite, but towards the top the clay becomes sandy and in places passes into clayey and gritty sands containing large fossiliferous doggers. As a rule, the clays are darker and more shaly than the Oxford Clay, and in general they owe the dark tint partly to carbonaceous matter and partly to bisulphide of iron.[1] The decomposition of the pyrites by atmospheric agents leads to the formation of selenite, lime being present in the clay as well as in the fossils. In some instances the shells of *Ostrea deltoidea* J. Sow. have been converted into sulphate of lime, as noted by Kidd at Shotover.[2] Dr. A. Morley Davies[3] has

---

[1] Maw, G., 'On the Disposition of Iron in variegated Strata,' *Quart. Journ. Geol. Soc.*, vol. xxiv, 1868, p. 357; *see also* J. D. Kendall, *Trans. N. of Eng. Inst. of Mining Engineers*, vol. xxxv, 1875, p. 156.

[2] *Outlines of Mineralogy*, 1809, vol. i, p. 68.

[3] Davies, A. Morley, ' The Kimmeridge Clay and Corallian Rocks of the neighbourhood of Brill (Buckinghamshire),' *Quart. Journ. Geol. Soc.*, vol. lxiii, 1907, p. 33.

drawn attention to the selenitization of belemnites found in the lower zones of the clay in the old brickyard at Rid's Hill, near Brill. The decomposition of the pyrites also results in the formation of limonite, which is sometimes washed downwards on to the Corallian limestones, and the red earthy layer noted by Mr. E. S. Cobbold at the junction of the Kimmeridge Clay and Corallian at Sandford, may have had a similar origin.[1] The thickness of the Kimmeridge Clay is about 150 ft.

The junction of the formation with the underlying Corallian Beds is rarely seen in sections now available, but previous observers have noted the occurrence of a marked stratigraphical break at the base.[2] During the year 1925, the two formations were exposed in a deep trench made alongside the main road east of Shotover Lodge, and the junction was exceptionally well displayed. It was seen that the upper surface of the Corallian Beds was markedly eroded, and although there was no layer of pebbles or coprolites at the base of the clay, as at Shotover, the Corallian limestone was succeeded abruptly by clays belonging to the zone of *Rasenia cymodoce*. There was no trace of the basement beds which form the zone of *Pictonia baylei* in Dorset, Wiltshire, and in Kent. In the neighbourhood of Brill, however, the Pictonia Zone may be represented by the Brill Serpulite Bed.

As a rule, the clays are highly fossiliferous, some of the layers being crowded with shells, often in a crushed state. In the fossiliferous 'doggers' and in calcareous nodules, however, well-preserved lamellibranchs and ammonites are found. *Exogyra virgula* (Defr.), which makes its appearance in the lowest clays, is characteristic of the lower half of the formation, ranging in Oxfordshire to the top of the zone of *Aulacostephanus pseudomutabilis*, where clusters of large well-developed shells form an irregular hard limy layer in places. Immediately above this zone, the Gravesia Beds being unrepresented in the Oxford localities, *Modiola autissiodorensis* (Cott.) appears in the Virgatites clays and ranges throughout the remaining part of the formation. Reptilian remains are abundant at certain horizons, particularly within the Rasenia and Aulacostephanus Zones.

Until the year 1913, little progress was made in the zonal classification of the Kimmeridge Clay. Indeed, serious study in this direction was liable to be discouraged to a great extent by the unfortunate statement that 'there is no need in this country to divide the Kimmeridge Clay into more than two zones for stratigraphical purposes, and these are intimately blended.'[3] In that year, however, Dr. H. Salfeld, who had studied the deposits of Kimmeridge

[1] Cobbold, E. S., ' Notes on the strata exposed in laying-out the Oxford Sewage Farm, at Sandford-on-Thames,' *Quart. Journ. Geol. Soc.*, vol. xxxvi, 1880, p. 318.
[2] *See* Conybeare's Geology of England and Wales, 1822, p. 189; Sedgwick, *Ann. Phil.* xxvii (ser. 2, xi) 1826, p. 350; Buckland and De la Beche, *Trans. Geol. Soc.*, ser. 2, iv, 1835, p. 26; Phillips, Geol. Oxford, etc., 1871, p. 299; and W. H. Hudleston in Report of Sub-Committee on Classification Internat. Geol. Congress, 1888.
[3] ' The Jurassic Rocks of Britain ' (*Mem. Geol. Surv.*), vol. v, 1895, p. 152.

age at many localities on the Continent, published a brief account of
his researches in England,[1] and in 1914 he issued a work[2] of mono-
graphic scope in which the formation was divided into 11 zones.
These, with some modifications, as noted below, are adopted in this
memoir.   In 1920, Messrs. C. P. Chatwin and J. Pringle, having
concluded that portions of the zonal scheme provided by Dr. Salfeld
were inaccurate in regard to the actual horizon of his *Perisphinctes
eastlecottensis*, undertook a detailed investigation of the Swindon
area, supplemented by visits to the type-section in Dorset.   As a
result, they showed that Salfeld's zones of *Perisphinctes eastlecottensis*
and *Perisphinctes pectinatus* of the so-called Portland Sands of
Swindon are the stratigraphical equivalents of the ' Kimmeridge
Coal ' of Kimmeridge.   They were thus able to confirm independently W. H. Hudleston's correlation of these deposits.[3]   At the same
time it was proved that the Swindon Clay, which overlies the sands
at Swindon, contained a similar ammonite-fauna to that found in
the Rotundum Clays at Chapman's Pool, near St. Alban's Head ;
and it was recognized that the zonal scheme thus emended was
applicable to the whole of the formation as represented in the Midland
Counties.[4]   This conclusion has been confirmed by the subsequent
investigations carried out by Dr. E. Neaverson in Wiltshire,
Oxfordshire and Buckinghamshire.[5]

The fact that a portion of the upper part of the Kimmeridge
formation is present in sandy facies in these counties has given rise
to much confusion, since the sands when overlain by the Portland
Stone were wrongly correlated with the Portland Sands of the Isle
of Purbeck, and were mapped as Lower Greensand when their
stratigraphical relations were obscure, as at Toot Baldon.   The
occurrence of arenaceous Kimmeridge Beds at Culham was first
suggested by John Phillips.[6]

Thus in his notes on the section at Culham brickyard to the south-west of
Nuneham Courtenay, and beyond the limits of our map, Phillips described
a bed of green sand, 9 feet thick, below the Lower Greensand and Gault,
and above the Kimmeridge Clay, from which there were evidences of ' an
easy passage upwards from clay to sand.' He obtained from this sand a
few examples of the ammonite like *A. polyplocus, Cardium striatulum,*

---

[1] Salfeld, H., ' Certain Upper Jurassic Strata of England,'   *Quart. Journ. Geol.
Soc.*, vol. lxix, 1913, p. 425.
[2] ' Die Gliederung des oberen Jura in Nordwesteuropa,' *Neues Jahrb. f. Min.*,
Beil.-Bd. xxxvii, 1914.
[3] Unfortunately Hudleston's statement was hidden away in a report of an excursion of the Geologists' Association and was overlooked at the time ; otherwise attention
would have been duly drawn to his suggested correlation.   See *Proc. Geol. Assoc.*,
vol. xiv, 1896, p. 322.
[4] Chatwin, C. P., and J. Pringle,' The Zones of the Kimmeridge and Portland
Rocks at Swindon,' in ' Summary of Progress for 1921 ' (*Mem. Geol. Surv.*), 1922,
p. 162,   *See also* ' The Concealed Mesozoic Rocks in Kent ' (*Mem. Geol. Surv.*), 1923,
p. 227.
[5] ' The Zonal Nomenclature of the Upper Kimmeridge Clay,'   *Geol. Mag.*, 1924,
p. 148.   *See also* ' Ammonites from the Upper Kimmeridge Clay,' issued by University
Press, Liverpool, 1925.
[6] *Quart. Journ. Geol. Soc.*, vol. xvi, 1860, p. 310 ;   *see also* H. B. Woodward,
' Jurassic Rocks of Britain,' vol. v, pp. 167, 169, 217.

Thracia depressa, Pecten arcuatus, Corbula, and wood ; and he suggested that the bed might be ' perhaps the first stage of a change towards the Portland series, but still to be classed with the clay.'

The sands, which contain large fossiliferous ' doggers,' are well shown in the Shotover brickyard, where they yield a characteristic fauna including *Wheatleyites eastlecottensis* (Salfeld) and *Pectinatites pectinatus* (Phill.); but when the beds are traced in the direction of dip they are found to pass into sandy clays with two hard layers in the tunnel at Horsepath. In the Wheatley brickyard the deposits are sandy and yield the index-fossils ; but here they are seen to be overlain by a clay yielding fragments of ammonites with coarsely biplicate ribbing, closely resembling the shells of *Pallasiceras rotundum* (J. Sow.) from Chapman's Pool. At a slightly higher level within the clays at Chippinghurst, south of Wheatley, the genotype and holotype of *Aposphinctoceras decipiens* was found.[1] This shell, which is now in the University Museum, Oxford, was formerly figured as *Olcostephanus pallasianus* var. nov. by Miss Healey[2] and indicates the Pallasioides Zone of Dr. Neaverson's classification, a part of the Hartwell Clay.

Again, at Brill and in the intermediate area of Red Hill, Forest Hill, these sandy beds are represented by loamy clays, and have not been separated from the Kimmeridge Clay on the Geological Survey Map, although the upper part of the clays was correlated with the Hartwell Clay, at that time regarded as of Lower Portland age.

In the accompanying table of Zones it will be seen that the equivalents of the Hartwell Clay are followed by about 240 ft. of clays and sands near Kimmeridge, where they are well displayed in the cliffs at Chapman's Pool. These strata have no representation in the Oxford district, the beds of the Pallasianum or Pallasioides Zone being overlain by the Portland Stone, as at Chippinghurst. There is thus a marked stratigraphical break at the top of the formation, and this unconformity appears to extend throughout the Midland area from Swindon in Wiltshire towards the north-east as far as the Wash, and thence into Yorkshire.

---

[1] Neaverson, E., *op. cit.*, p. 149.
[2] Healey, M., *Quart. Journ. Geol. Soc.*, vol. lx, 1904, p. 60, pl. xii, figs. 1 and 2.

ZONES OF THE

Salfeld emend. Pringle & Kitchin[2]	Chatwin and Pringle[3]	Neaverson[4]
Kimmeridge	Swindon	Oxford, etc.
'Passage' Beds, zonally unclassified 126 ft.; overlain by Portland Sands, 115 ft.	absent	absent
Pallasiceras 'pallasianum'	Perisphinctes pallasianus	Holcosphinctes pallasioides
Pallasiceras lomonossovi		Pallasiceras rotundum
Pseudovirgatites Subzone of Saccocoma	Perisphinctes eastlecottensis and P. pectinatus	Pectinatites pectinatus
Virgatites	Virgatites	Virgatosphinctoides nodiferus V. wheatleyensis
Gravesia irius	Gravesia	
Gravesia gravesi	Zones	
Aulacostephanus pseudomutabilis	Aulacostephanus	Zones present, but not examined by Dr. Neaverson.
Aulacostephanus yo	Zones	
Rasenia mutabilis	Rasenia	
Rasenia cymodoce	Zones	
Pictonia baylei	Pictonia	

[1] For the chronological sequence as interpreted by Mr. S. S. Buckman (referred
[2] 'The Concealed Mesozoic Rocks in Kent' (*Mem. Geol. Surv.*), 1923, pl. II.
[3] 'The Zones of the Kimmeridge and Portland Rocks' in 'Summary of Progress
[4] 'Ammonites from the Upper Kimmeridge Clay,' University Press, Liverpool, 1925.

KIMMERIDGE CLAY.[1]

Localities.	Some Characteristic Fossils
Chippinghurst	Holcosphinctes pallasioides *Neav.* Aposphinctoceras decipiens *Neav.* Astarte hartwellensis *J. de C. Sow.*
Shotover Hill ; Wheatley	Pallasiceras rotundum (*J. Sow.*) and forms with prominent 'biplex' ribbing
Shotover Hill ; Horsepath ; Wheatley ; Garsington and Toot Baldon	Wheatleyites eastlecottensis (*Salfeld*) Pectinatites pectinatus (*Phill.*) P. aulacophorus *S. Buckman*
Chawley Brickyard ; Shotover Hill ; Wheatley and Brill	Virgatosphinctoides nodiferus *Neaverson* and other ammonites Modiola autissiodorensis (*Cott.*) enters
Absent in Oxfordshire	Exogyra virgula (*Defr.*) disappears
Chawley Brickyard ; Shotover Hill ; Brill and Wheatley	Aulacostephanus eudoxus (*d'Orb.*) Physodoceras longispinum (*J. de C. Sow.*) Trigonellites latus *Park.* (abundant)
? lowest beds in Wheatley Brickpit	Physodoceras acanthicum (*Oppel*) Aulacostephanus contjeani *Salfeld*
Bagley Wood ; Shotover ; Brill	'Involuticeras' desmonotus (*Oppel*) Rasenia mutabilis (*J. de C. Sow.*) Reptilian remains abundant
Rid's Hill, Brill	Rasenia stephanoides (*Oppel*) Amoeboceras kitchini (*Salfeld*)
? Rid's Hill, Brill (Serpulite Bed)	Exogyra virgula (*Defr.*) enters In Dorset, Pictonia normandiana (*Tornq.*) and P. densicostata *S. Buckman*

to on p. 72) *see* ' Type Ammonites,' vols. iv and v, 1922–1925.

for 1921 ' (*Mem. Geol. Surv.*), 1922, p. 163.

LOCAL DETAILS

There are few sections of Kimmeridge Clay in the western part of the area. Clay with *Rhynchonella inconstans* (J. Sow.) was at one time dug in the small outlier west of Marcham, but the pit is now overgrown. The formation is frequently pierced at Abingdon and Radley by wells sunk to the water-bearing Corallian Beds below, but for the most part this low-lying tract is covered by river-deposits. From an excavation made in the Kimmeridge Clay near the viaduct over the Thames immediately south of Abingdon Junction, the following fossils were collected in 1907 : *Arca longipunctata ?* Blake, *Exogyra virgula* (Defr.), *Protocardia morinica* (de Lor.) and *Aptychus sp.* The beds probably fall within the zone of *Aulacostephanus pseudomutabilis*. A section of the Kimmeridge Clay exposed in the Culham brickyard, outside our area, is given on p. 102.

In pits now overgrown, on the west side of Foxcombe Hill, the clay was exposed beneath the Lower Greensand. On Boar's Hill, the thickness of the formation appears to be about 90 ft., but the highest beds are absent. At Cumnor Hurst a good section is exposed in the Chawley Brickyard, where the Kimmeridge Clay is overlain by Lower Greensand, Lower Gault and Drift in upward succession (*see* Fig. 7). The beds are remarkably disturbed and the sequence of the Jurassic clays is greatly confused by slips. The Greensand fills deep hollows in the Kimmeridge Beds, and extends down the slopes of Hurst Hill with a dip amounting to 30° in one instance. In its turn the Lower Greensand is cut into to a depth of about 15 ft. by Lower Gault and Drift (*see* p. 99). The following section gives only the approximate thickness of the different strata :—

			Ft.
Drift	..	Bedded gravel of quartzite, flint, etc., with sand	10
Lower Gault		Dark bluish-grey clay with phosphatic nodules and fragments of *Hoplites dentatus*. A sandy basement-bed is sometimes exposed; up to	10
Lower Greensand		Coarse brown false-bedded quartzose sand with concretionary ironstone	20
Kimmeridge Clay		Bluish sandy clay weathering white to a depth of 3 ft. below junction, with a few small irregularly-shaped grey nodules which weather brown .. .. about	14
		Dark shaly clays with large cement-stones, containing *Modiola autissiodorensis*, *Lucina minuscula*, ? *Aulacosphinctes contiguus*, *Allovirgatites sp.* and numerous other ammonites seen	8
		Dark clays with *Exogyra virgula*, *Aptychus latus*, *Aulacostephanus eudoxus* and reptilian bones. At top is a seam of brownish clay with large shells of *Exogyra virgula*	10

If the section given above be compared with that recorded by Prestwich in 1880,[1] some noticeable differences will be observed in the details. Higher beds appear to have been exposed at the time of his visit, but are now no longer visible. Confirmation of the occasional occurrence of the sandy clays of the Pectinatus Zone is to be found in the ammonites collected from this pit and now preserved in the collections at the University Museum, Oxford. These include the zone-fossil and other characteristic species.

Reptilian bones are numerous in the lower beds which fall within the zone of *Aulacostephanus pseudomutabilis*, and the following genera are represented : *Camptosaurus, Dacosaurus, Ichthyosaurus, Plesiosaurus* and

---

[1] Prestwich, J., 'Note on the occurrence of a new species of Iguanodon in a brickpit of the Kimeridge Clay at Cumnor Hurst, three [miles W.S.W. of Oxford,' *Quart. Journ. Geol. Soc.*, vol. xxxvi, 1880, pp. 430-432.

Pliosaurus. The type of *Camptosaurus prestwichi* Hulke was obtained from this brick-pit. The shells of *Exogyra virgula* (Defr.) are abundant in this zone and occasionally form peculiar irregular masses in a seam of brownish clay at the top.

In 1924, the junction of the Pseudomutabilis Zone with the overlying clays was exposed on the north side of the pit, but a few feet to the south the Virgula Beds are thrown down by a fault, and are not again exposed. The floor of the pit is occupied by dark shaly clays with cement-stones. These are highly fossiliferous, and yield numerous ammonites including *Virgatosphinctoides wheatleyensis* Neaverson, showing the beds to be equivalent to the Virgatites Beds of Salfeld's classification as emended by Pringle and Kitchin.[1] At this horizon the lamellibranchs which characterize the Hartwell Clay make their first appearance, and numerous specimens of *Astarte hartwellensis* J. de C. Sow. may be found in the higher beds, associated with somewhat poorly preserved ammonites bearing a close resemblance to *Virgatosphinctes biplicatus* Uhlig. Further reference to this pit is made on p. 72.

At Sandford, according to Mr. E. S. Cobbold, 'a peculiar bright red earthy layer from 4 to 6 inches thick ' occurred at the junction of the Kimmeridge Clay with the Corallian Beds. From the clay he recorded vertebrae of *Pliosaurus*, good specimens of *Rhynchonella inconstans* (J. Sow.) and numerous crystals of selenite.[2] The red colour may be due to the decomposition of pyrites in the overlying clays (*see* p. 63). Mr. Buckman has suggested that this layer may be equivalent to the iron-ore of Westbury in Wiltshire, but the field-evidence does not support this view.[3]

Although sands and sandy clays with *Pectinatites pectinatus* are occasionally exposed beneath the Lower Greensand in the Chawley Brickyard, Kimmeridge Beds in arenaceous facies are not seen in the area included in the map until the neighbourhood of March Baldon is reached ; and perhaps partly on account of their proximity to sands of Lower Greensand age, they were for some time regarded as Lower Cretaceous deposits. During the revision of the Cretaceous rocks made in connexion with the issue of the Special Oxford Sheet, Mr. Lamplugh observed that the buff or greyish sands in the district around March Baldon were of finer grain than the coarse and pebbly Lower Greensand of Culham and Clifton Hampden, and of a great portion of Nuneham Park, and it was later ascertained by the present writer that in the fields east of March Baldon and at Baldon Row, highly fossiliferous ' doggers ' of sandstone were frequently met with at a depth of 6 to 8 ft. from the surface. He noted that these contained fossils of the same species as those found in the ' doggers ' of Shotover Hill and preserved in an identical matrix. The sands were therefore separated from the Lower Greensand and are now correlated with the arenaceous Kimmeridge Beds.[4] The fossils which are included in the Survey Collections are as follows :—

Garden of house 400 yds. W.S.W. of St. Lawrence Church, Toot Baldon. [Pr. 3978–3984].

Astarte rugosa ? (*J. de C. Sow.*)	Lucina portlandica *J. de C. Sow.*
Corbicella ?	Pecten (Camptonectes) *cf.* morini *de Lor.*

Field 900 yds. N.E. of Post Office, March Baldon. [Pr. 3989–4000].

Astarte rugosa (*J. de C. Sow.*)	Pecten (Camptonectes) morini *de Lor.*
Cyprina ?	,, (Syncyclonema) nitescens *Phill.*
Leda ?	Pecten sp.
Ostrea sp.	Perna sp.

---

[1] ' The Concealed Mesozoic Rocks in Kent ' (*Mem. Geol. Surv.*), 1923, pl. ii.

[2] Cobbold, E. S., *op. cit.*, p. 318.

[3] ' Type Ammonites,' vol. iv, 1923, p. 37.

[4] The colour indicating the outcrop of the Lower Portland on the Special Oxford Sheet may be taken as now representing the distribution of the sandy Kimmeridge Beds.

A boring at Baldon House, March Baldon, carried out in 1883, proved the Kimmeridge Clay to be 146 ft. thick.[1]

To the east of Oxford, brickyards on the western side of Shotover Hill at one time showed the Kimmeridge Clay resting on the eroded surface of the Corallian Beds, but the sections are now overgrown and the lower clays of the formation are no longer exposed. From descriptions, however, they appear to consist of bluish-grey and dark blue shelly clay with a few layers of septaria and much selenite. A layer of coprolites occurred at the junction. In one pit Phillips noted that about 15 ft. from the base there is a septarian band yielding *Rhynchonella inconstans* (J. Sow.), etc. ; lower down there are layers of *Ostrea deltoidea* J. Sow. ,and near the base *Thracia depressa* (J. de C. Sow.) and *Exogyra virgula* (Defr.) are fairly abundant. The type of *Ostrea deltoidea* came from this locality, where the shells were known as ' Heddington [Headington] oysters.' The fact that *Exogyra virgula* occurs in some abundance at the base, suggests that the Pictonia Zone is absent here also, as in the excavation near Shotover Lodge (*see* p. 63). In addition to the fossils already mentioned, the following specimens now in the University Museum, Oxford, have been collected from the Shotover Hill Brickyards :— *Aulacostephanus* cf. *eudoxus* (d'Orb.), *Amoeboceras* cf. *krausei* (Salfeld), ' *Involuticeras* ' *lepidulus* (Oppel), *Orbiculoidea latissima* (J. Sow.), *Lingula ovalis* J. Sow. and numerous reptilian remains. The presence of *Rasenia mutabilis* (J. de C. Sow.) at Shotover, has been reported by Salfeld.[2] The ammonites serve to indicate the occurrence of the Rasenia and Aulacostephanus Zones.

The higher zones are displayed in the clay and sand-pits of the Shotover brickworks, where the following section may be seen below the Portland Beds :—

			Ft.
Rotundum Zone	{ 4. Fragile bluish-grey clay with lydite pebbles at base .. .. 0 to		3
Pectinatus Zone	{ 3. Buff sands with large round doggers of coarse grey calcareous sandstone .. .. 12 to		16
	{ 2. Fine grey loamy sand, lilac tinged when wet..		4
Virgatites Zone	{ 1. Bluish-black clay with grey calcareous nodules, containing *Virgatosphinctoides wheatleyensis* .. .. .. seen to		10

The succession in this pit is at times somewhat obscured by slipped masses of sand or clay, so that the thickness of some of the beds can only be estimated. The lowest bed of clay falls within the zone of *Virgatites*, and yields a similar fauna to that obtained from the corresponding clays in the Chawley and Wheatley brickyards. Numerous specimens from this zone are preserved in the collections of the University Museum, Oxford, and these include *Allovirgatites tutcheri* Neav., *Allov. versicostatus* Neav., *Allov.* cf. *woodwardi* Neav., *Allov. sp. nov.*, *Virgatosphinctoides delicatulus* Neav. and *V. wheatleyensis* Neav. Dr. Neaverson has recorded *Virgatosphinctoides nodiferus* Neav. from the clays below the sands.[3]

The most striking bed in the pit, however, is Bed 3, on account of the occurrence of large doggers known as ' sand-ballers ' or ' giant's marbles,' some of which attain a diameter of over six feet (*see* Pl. IVA). They are highly fossiliferous, and from one of them the type of *Pectinatites pectinatus* (Phill.) was obtained. Mr. Buckman has described the bed as ' Shotover Grit Sands '[4] (*see* p. 87). The fossils include the following species :—

Serpula sp.
Astarte rugosa (*J. de C. Sow.*)

---

[1] ' The Water Supply of Oxfordshire ' (*Mem. Geol. Surv.*), 1910, p. 61.
[2] Salfeld, A., *op. cit.*, tab. 1.
[3] Neaverson, E., ' Ammonites from the Upper Kimmeridge Clay,' University Press, Liverpool, 1925, p. 14.
[4] ' Type Ammonites,' vol. iv, 1922, p. 28.

Exogyra bruntrutana ? (*Thurm.*)
Grammatodon *cf.* rhomboidalis (*Contej.*)
Lucina portlandica *J. de C. Sow.*
Ostrea expansa *J. Sow.*
Pecten (Camptonectes) *cf.* morini *de Lor.*
Perna mytiloides *Lam.*
Pholadomya rustica *Phill.*
Cf. Placunopsis lycetti *de Lor.*
Pleuromya tellina *Ag.*
Protocardia morinica (*de Lor.*)
Trigonia   muricata ? (*Goldf.*)
    ,,   pellati *Mun.-Chalm.*
Pectinatites pectinatus (*Phill.*)
' Perisphinctes ' *cf.* devillei *de Lor.*
Shotoverites pringlei *S. Buckman*
Wheatleyites eastlecottensis (*Salfeld*)
    ,,   tricostatulus ? *S. Buckman.*

The highest bed of clay is seldom visible, but when the section was examined in 1925, a bluish-grey clay, containing many small highly polished pebbles at the base was exposed. No fossils were then found. In 1910, however, ' a number of Kimmeridge fossils, including the species usually termed *Am. biplex,* were obtained from this clay-band,' showing it to be

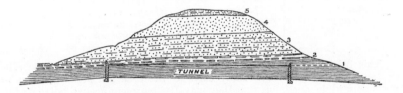

FIG. 5.—*Section along line of railway between Horsepath and Wheatley.*

5. Shotover Sands.   4. Portland Beds.   3, 2, 1. Kimmeridge Beds.

clearly the equivalent of the clay overlying the Pectinatus Zone in the Wheatley brickyard.[1]

The sands of the Pectinatus Beds are easily traceable along the western side of the hill towards Horsepath, and their presence was proved during the construction of the railway-tunnel through the hill between that village and Wheatley. A section of the strata passed through was drawn by T. Codrington, and is reproduced on Fig. 5. Two bands of stone, 4 ft. apart, and $1\frac{1}{2}$ to 2 ft. thick, were constant throughout the cutting, dipping about $\frac{1}{2}°$ to the north-north-west. The upper layer was in parts a loose sandstone passing into compact limestone, and it was overlain by sandy clays. The hard bands were full of fossils and included *Pectinatites pectinatus*; the sands were recognized by Codrington as being continuous with the great doggers of the Shotover section.

The sands, now greatly reduced in thickness and more clayey below, are again exposed in the Wheatley brickpit on the south side of the railway, north-east of Littleworth, near Wheatley, where the following section is seen :—

		Ft.	In.
Rotundum Zone	8. Fragile grey clay with small brown nodules containing fragments of ammonites with coarse ' biplex ' type of ribbing .. .. 10 to	12	0

---

[1] ' The Oxford and Banbury district,' *Geology in the Field*, 1910, p. 206 (footnote).

Ft. In.

Pectinatus Zone	7. Friable sandstone, crowded with shells, including *Pectinatites pectinatus*, *Wheatleyites eastlecottensis*, and a lamellibranch-fauna characteristic of the Hartwell Clay	4 0
	6. Lilac sandy clay, somewhat pyritous and streaked with ferruginous matter. In lower part the clay contains *Aporrhais sp.*, *Modiola autissiodorensis* and *Orbiculoidea latissima*..	5 6
Virgatites Zone	5. Greenish-brown sandy clay, unfossiliferous	1 3
	4. Dark sandy clay with a few isolated nodules near top	4 6
	3. Dark clay with a few crushed ammonites	3 6
	2. Dark clay with thin shaly bands and large cement-stones. Many layers of crushed ammonites, *Lucina minuscula* and *Modiola autissiodorensis*	9 0
Aulacostephanus pseudomutabilis Zone	1. Dark shaly clay with *Exogyra virgula*, large specimens of *Aptychus latus*, *Aulacostephanus eudoxus*, etc. Near base, the clay is less shaly and contains *Physodoceras acanthicum* and *Ph. karpinskii* .. .. seen to	8 0

This brickyard gives a fuller section of the formation than any other exposure in the area. The shaly clays at the base fall mainly within the Pseudomutabilis Zone, but that they may also represent a small portion of the underlying zone of *Aulacostephanus yo* is suggested by the presence of *Physodoceras acanthicum* (Oppel), a characteristic species of this horizon. At the top there are occasionally hard lumps of earthy limestone crowded with the shells of *Exogyra virgula* (Defr.), as at Chawley. This bed marks the limit of the upward range of this species in Oxfordshire. The commonest species of *Aulacostephanus* in the beds is *A. eudoxus* (d'Orb.), and Mr. Buckman appears to have adopted it as the zonal index in preference to *A. pseudomutabilis*. The shales contain a small amount of oil, and when burnt for brick-making will often overheat the kiln.

In the type-section in Kimmeridge Bay, the Pseudomutabilis Zone is followed by the Gravesia Beds, about 60 ft. thick. These deposits, however, appear to have no representation in the Oxford district. There are no signs of unconformity at the junction with the overlying Virgatites Zone at Wheatley, unless erosion is indicated by the sporadic occurrence of the curiously hardened masses of *Exogyra virgula* found at the Wheatley and Chawley brickyards. The palæontological break, however, is well-marked by the sudden incoming of ammonites which characterize the Virgatites Beds in Wiltshire and Dorset. This rich ammonite-fauna has been studied by Dr. Neaverson, and the results of his investigations show that the fauna includes many new genera and species. These he has described, and from the zone of *Virgatites* at Wheatley, he records *Allovirgatites tutcheri*, *Allov. versicostatus*, *Sphinctoceras crassum*, *Sphinct. distans*, *Virgatosphinctoides delicatulus* and *V. wheatleyensis*.[1]

Mr. Buckman, who has also examined the ammonites from this zone at Wheatley, Shotover and Chawley, has recognized two horizons, that of 'dorsoplanus' below and that of 'Aulacosphinctes' above, but, as Dr. Neaverson points out, there seems to be no evidence at present to justify a sub-division

---

[1] Neaverson, E., 'Ammonites from the Upper Kimmeridge Clay,' University Press, Liverpool, 1925.

A.—' *Sand-ballers*' or ' *Giant's Marbles*' in the Pectinatus Sands at Shotover
Brickyard.

B.—*Section of Gault and Kimmeridge Clay in the Culham Brickyard,
Berkshire.*

based on these species. At the top occur fragments of large ammonites bearing a close resemblance to a shell recorded as *Pseudovirgatites scruposus* Vetters[1] from the oil-shale at Corton in Dorset. Similar shells have been noted in the Shotover brickyard by Dr. Neaverson immediately below the Pectinatus Sands, and he states that they apparently have no relation to *Pseudovirgatites*, but are probably a development of an ammonite lineage present in the lower part of the zone.[2]

The passage upwards into the overlying Pectinatus Beds is gradual, and there are no signs of an erosion or non-sequence, as suggested by Mr. Buckman.[3] The lower part of the Pectinatus Zone is best described as a sandy clay, though it clearly represents a portion of the Kimmeridge sands at Shotover Hill. The upper part, which is highly fossiliferous, is sandy, and is directly comparable with the ' doggers ' in the Shotover Grit Sands, since it yields an identical cephalopod and lamellibranch assemblage. The abundant remains preserved in this bed at Wheatley suggest that the deposit here is greatly condensed. At the base, specimens of *Orbiculoidea latissima* (J. Sow.), *Modiola autissiodorensis* (Cott.) and an *Aporrhais* were obtained from beds seldom accessible in the working-face. The gasteropod is probably an undescribed species, but it may aptly be brought into comparison with *Aporrhais piettei* Buv. and is perhaps identical with a shell characteristic of the upper part of the Virgatites Beds and the base of the Pseudovirgatites Beds in Kent and in the Boulonnais.

The Pectinatus Beds are here also overlain by a grey clay, as at Shotover, which can be better studied in this pit, where the lower part is well exposed. It has been termed the Littleworth Lydite Clay by Mr. Buckman,[4] but it contains fewer grains of lydite than at Shotover. In the small brown nodules which occur in the bed, fragments of coarsely biplicate and finely ribbed ammonites have been obtained. These shells have a strong resemblance to *Pallasiceras rotundum* (J. Sow.) which are found in the Rotundum Zone at Chapman's Pool in Dorset, and they have also been recognized by Dr. Neaverson as low in the Hartwell Clay at Hartwell and Aylesbury.[5] Higher beds are concealed in the hill and the junction with the Portland is not exposed. The grey clay occupies the same stratigraphical position as the Swindon Clay, which also yields *Pallasiceras rotundum*. Mr. Buckman is of the opinion that the Hartwell Clay cephalopod fauna should occur below the Pectinatus Beds, but he admits that at Wheatley ' no signs are seen of this fauna.'[6] It is clear, however, from the field-evidence that the Rotundum and Pallasioides Zones represent the highest Kimmeridge Clay in the Midland counties.

In the area south of Wheatley there are few sections to record. Specimens of *Pectinatites pectinatus* (Phill.), now in the University Museum, have been obtained from a sandy clay at Garsington. The Virgatites Beds with large calcareous nodules are to be seen outcropping in a small unnamed stream north of Chippinghurst, and higher beds of clay, equivalent to the Hartwell Clay, were exposed in an excavation made for a water-tank at the farm. It was from Chippinghurst that the type of *Olcostephanus pallasianus*, var. nov., figured by Miss Healey,[7] was obtained. This shell has now been adopted by Dr. Neaverson as genotype and holotype of *Aposphinctoceras decipiens*, a species associated with *Holcosphinctes pallasioides* Neav. in the Hartwell Clay.[8]

---

[1] Dr. Neaverson has since described this shell under the name of *Virgatosphinctoides grandis*. See ' Ammonites from the Upper Kimmeridge Clay,' 1925, p. 13.

[2] Neaverson, E., ' The Zonal Nomenclature of the Upper Kimmeridge Clay ', *Geol. Mag.* 1924, p. 147.

[3] ' Type Ammonites,' vol. iv, 1923, p. 37.

[4] ' Type Ammonites,' vol. iv, 1922, p. 28.

[5] *Op. cit.*, p. 148.

[6] ' Type Ammonites,' vol. iv, 1923, p. 37.

[7] Healey, M., ' Notes on Upper Jurassic Ammonites with special reference to specimens in the University Museum, Oxford,' *Quart. Journ. Geol. Soc.*, vol. lx, 1904, p. 60, pl. xii, figs. 1 and 2.

[8] Neaverson, E., *op. cit.*, p. 149.

F

The following section was noted by Jukes-Browne at a brickyard, now grassed over, by the side of the high road, a mile north of Great Milton :—

		Ft.
Shotover Sand	Sandy soil	3
	Brown loamy sand	0–8
Kimmeridge Clay	Dark blue clay	6
	Grey argillaceous sand	
	Hard blue sandy limestone	3
	Fine grey sand, becoming argillaceous and lilac coloured, and passing down into strong blue clay	¾
		7

According to him, the blue clay contained ammonites and saurian bones, and at its base *Protocardia morinica* and *Exogyra sp.* He stated that the limestone yielded large ammonites and other fossils, but as these were not collected by him it is not possible to determine the zone. The field evidence, however, suggests that the limestone corresponds to the Pectinatus Beds of Wheatley.

Clays included within the zones of *Virgatites* and *Aulacostephanus pseudomutabilis* were proved in well-excavations at Tiddington. From the station well, Mr. Buckman records ' *Perisphinctes dorsoplanus* ' at the depth of 25 ft. ; and from the village well, he found *Aptychus* in clay from the depth of 20 ft.[1]

Reference has already been made to the disused brickyard at Rid's Hill, about one mile north-east of Brill. It lies outside the boundary of our area, but the section is of sufficient importance to justify its inclusion in this memoir. The pit was described by Dr. A. Morley Davies[2] in the year 1906, when the clays were being dug, but before the work was stopped in 1911, higher beds of clay were exposed. The section seen in 1924 is as follows :—

		Ft.	In.
Kimmeridge Clay	Grey-brown weathering clays with many layers of crushed finely ribbed ammonities, as at Wheatley and Chawley ..	8	0
	Gap in sequence ; beds obscured by slipped masses		
	Grey clays with *Aptychus latus, Aulacostephanus eudoxus* and *Exogyra virgula* .. .. .. seen about	12	0
	Pale weathering cement-stone	1	0
	Creamy calcareous clay	2	0
	Pale weathering cement stone	1	0
	Dark grey, brown weathering, seleniti-ferous clay with *Ostrea deltoidea* and *Exogyra virgula* (early forms).. ..	8	0
	Grey shelly limestone crowded with *Serpula tetragona* and containing a rich lamellibranch fauna .. up to	0	6
Ampthill Clay	Black clays with large crystals of selenite and small brown phosphatic nodules : 6 ft. seen, but said to be	14	0
	A band of grey limestone, with *Perisphinctes decipiens*, 6 ft. below floor of pit. *Fide* A. M. Davies, *op. cit.*		

The most interesting bed is the limestone termed the *Brill Serpulite Bed* in Mr. Buckman's classification.[3] It is crowded with a narrow form of *Serpula tetragona* J. de C. Sow, and with a *Cyprina* closely related to, if not identical with, *C. cyreniformis* Blake. In addition to these forms it yields numerous

---

[1] ' Type Ammonites,' vol. iv, 1923, p. 36.

[2] Davies, A. M., ' The Kimeridge Clay and Corallian Rocks of the neighbourhood of Brill (Buckinghamshire), *Quart. Journ. Geol. Soc.*, vol. lxiii, 1907, p. 29.

[3] ' Type Ammonites,' vol. iv, 1923, p. 37.

fossils, including *Astarte ovata* Smith, *Ostrea deltoidea* Auctt., *Exogyra nana* (J. Sow.) and *Prionodoceras superstes* (Phill.), an ammonite of the *Am. serratum*-group. This fauna, and the fact that *Exogyra virgula* (Defr.) is absent, suggests that the limestone lies at or near the base of the Kimmeridge Clay. Actually, it may represent the Pictonia Zone, since at certain localities *Prionodoceras* and *Pictonia* are associated.[1] It would appear, therefore, that the marked stratigraphical break between the Corallian and Kimmeridge formations in the Oxford neighbourhood is less perceptible at Brill. The Serpulite Bed appears to form a slight feature in the clay-area to the west, and Mr. Buckman records it at Ickford in excavations made at some new houses in the village, where the bed has yielded the characteristic ammonite.[2]

The overlying clay yields, in addition to *Rhynchonella inconstans* (J. Sow.) and early forms of *Exogyra virgula* (Defr.), *Rasenia stephanoides* (Oppel), a characteristic occupant of the Cymodoce Zone. The selenitization of the belemnites is an interesting feature in this clay-bed.[3] In the higher beds of cement-stone a few fragments of *Rasenia* were found, but the species cannot be identified, though the general aspect of the shells suggests that the beds represent a portion of the zone of *Rasenia mutabilis*. The overlying clays call for no comment, since the beds may be readily assigned to their respective positions in the Aulacostephanus and Virgatites Zones.

Clays apparently belonging to the zone of *Aulacostephanus pseudomutabilis* were formerly worked in a pit, now grassed over, about 500 yds. south of Brill Station. They yield *Aptychus latus* Park. and *Exogyra virgula* (Defr.)

About 23 ft. of clay, occupying the stratigraphical position of the Hartwell Clay, was formerly exposed in the old brickyard west of Springfield Farm. In this section the clay was unconformably overlain by the basal lydite bed of the Upper Portland. The pit is now grassed over.

---

[1] *See* ' Type Ammonites,' vol. iv, 1923, p. 42.
[2] ' Type Ammonites,' vol. iv, 1923, p. 37.
[3] Davies, A. M., *op. cit.*, p. 33.

CHAPTER VI

UPPER OOLITIC ROCKS—*(continued)*

PORTLAND BEDS

IN the previous chapter it has been shown that the sands and clays hitherto regarded as corresponding to the Portland Sands of Dorset must now be classified with the Kimmeridge Clay. It follows, therefore, that there is a marked stratigraphical break at the base of the Portland Rocks in the area, the strata preserved being equivalent only to the Upper Portland of the type district. Consequently, the actual boundaries of the formation are narrower than those shown on the Special Oxford Sheet, on which the arenaceous Kimmeridge deposits are mapped as ' Portland Sands.' A similar unconformity has been proved at the base of the Portland Stone at Swindon and Aylesbury,[1] and it is evident that the deposition of the Kimmeridge Clay was followed by movements which affected the whole of the South Midlands, causing extensive erosion of the deposits.

The Portland Beds occupy a small area within the sheet, and are confined to the outlying masses of Muswell Hill and Brill to the north-east, to Shotover Hill and the high ground between Wheatley and Garsington, and to the district lying to the east of the river Thame around Great Milton. Although the fact is not demonstrable in any section, these outliers appear to occupy synclinal folds in which the patches of Shotover Sands are similarly preserved. It has been considered by some authors as not improbable that the Portland strata exposed in the Great Milton area are continuous underground with rocks of similar age at Thame and Aylesbury, but so far no evidence in support of this view has been obtained. From the information available it appears that the formation extends only for a short distance beneath the Upper Cretaceous deposits.[2]

There is no section in the district where the whole sequence is visible, but by combining the details obtained from the numerous

---

[1] Chatwin, C. P., and J. Pringle, 'The Zones of the Kimmeridge and Portland Rocks at Swindon,' ' Summary of Progress of the Geological Survey for 1921 ' (*Mem. Geol. Surv.*), 1922, pp. 162–168 ; ' The Geology of the Country around Aylesbury and Hemel Hempstead ' (*Mem. Geol. Surv.*), 1922, p. 6.

[2] *See* 'Summary of Progress of the Geological Survey for 1924 ' (*Mem. Geol. Surv.*), 1925, p. 121.

exposures, the complete rock-succession appears to be as follows, in descending order :—

Ft. In.

			Ft.	In.
Zone of *Perisphinctes giganteus* and *P. bononiensis*	9.	Hard brownish-white limestone with *Trigonia damoniana*, preserved in the form of ferruginous casts	2	6
	8.	White cherty oolitic limestone	0	6
	7.	Fine white sandy oolitic limestone	3	6
	6.	Buff sands with concretionary masses of grey sandy limestone	2	4
	5.	Greyish-white sandy limestone with *Natica ceres*, etc.	1	0
	4.	Buff greenish sands with concretionary masses of stone: *Protocardia dissimilis*, *Trigonia gibbosa*, and fragments of a large Perisphinctid .. .. about	22	0
Zone of *Perisphinctes pseudogigas*	3.	Whitish-grey limestone, marly in places ..	2	6
	2.	Brown weathering glauconitic marl.. ..	2	0
	1.	Rubbly creamy brown glauconitic limestone with layers of brown glauconitic marl containing 'lydite' pebbles at base	3	0

As might be expected, the succession is similar to that observed in the Swindon, Thame and Aylesbury districts, and the zonal scheme of Salfeld's classification,[1] applicable in these areas, can also be applied to the Oxford Portland strata. The zones are as follows :—

3. Zone of *Perisphinctes giganteus* and *P. bononiensis*.
2. Zone of *Perisphinctes pseudogigas* and *P. okusensis*.
1. Zone of *Perisphinctes gorei*.

These zones have been shown by Mr. S. S. Buckman to be made up of the deposits of several *hemerae*, characterized by the presence of species of restricted vertical range ; but the whole succession falls within the ages of Behemothan and Gigantitan of his classification.[2] The presence of the zone of *Perisphinctes gorei* at the base has not been definitely established in the Oxford sections, although it has been recognized both at Swindon and Aylesbury ; but our failure to find it may be due to the rarity and poorness of the sections. Ammonites closely resembling *P. gorei* are abundant in the creamy glauconitic limestones near the base, which yield the fauna characteristic of the 'Cockly Bed' at Swindon.

The giant ammonites *Titanites* and *Briarites* which characterize the highest beds of the Portland Beds at Haddenham and Portland appear to be rare. The corresponding beds are present, but have yielded few cephalopods, and it is possible that these large shells had broken up before entombment. The little gasteropod *Natica ceres* de Lor., which is confined to the Giganteus Zone, is common, and its somewhat narrow vertical range is of value for the purpose

---

[1] Salfeld, H., 'Certain Upper Jurassic Strata of England,' *Quart. Journ. Geol. Soc.*, vol. lxix, 1913, p. 428 ; *see also* 'Die Gliederung des oberen Jura in Nordwesteuropa', *Neues Jahrb. f. Min.*, etc., Beil.-Bd. xxxvii, 1914.
[2] Buckman, S. S., 'Type Ammonites,' vol. iv, 1922, p. 26.

of correlation.   In the Boulonnais it is characteristic of the sand
stones in the highest part of the Portlandien.[1]   The shell is easily
distinguished by its acute spire, strongly impressed suture and
marked transverse ornamental ridges.

   In the northerly part of Shotover Hill and at Coombe Wood,
south of Wheatley, the highest beds of limestone have been greatly
altered by the percolation of water from the overlying Shotover
Sands.   The most usual result is that of partial or more or less complete silicification, or replacement of the calcium carbonate by
ferruginous compounds.   In the latter case the altered rock is not
unlike some of the bands of gritty ironstone in the fresh-water
series, and this resemblance has led to some confusion in the past ;
but the presence of the shells of *Trigonia damoniana* de Lor. is
sufficient to distinguish the altered Portland Beds from the fresh-
water Shotover Series.   Dr. H. H. Thomas has contributed a note
on these changes (*see* p. 79).   At localities where Purbeck clays are
present, as at Brill, the percolation of water downwards has been
prevented, and the Portland limestones are unaltered.

LOCAL DETAILS

   Shotover Hill has afforded some good sections of Portland Beds in the
past, but the formation is now only exposed at a few localities at the north-
west end of the hill.   The rocks are somewhat confused as a result of ancient
landslips, so that it is difficult to make out the general sequence, but the
succession appears to confirm that given on p. 77.   The full thickness is
about 40 ft.
   In the Shotover brickyard, the basement-bed of the Portland is exposed
from time to time, and consists of a thin greenish-brown glauconitic marl,
full of highly polished pebbles of ' lydite.'   The marl passes upwards into a
brownish-green glauconitic clay with nodules of creamy brown limestone
containing *Protocardia dissimilis* (J. de C. Sow.) and other shells.   No
ammonites have been obtained from these marly layers, so that it is not certain
whether they represent the zone of *Perisphinctes gorei*.
   In another part of the same pit, the glauconitic clay is seen to underlie
the following section, displayed in a slipped mass :—

		Ft.
Upper Portland	4. Fine buff sands with concretionary masses of grey sandy limestone	10
	3. Whitish-grey limestone with a marly parting	2½
	2. Brown weathering glauconitic marl ..	2
	1. Rubbly creamy-brown glauconitic limestones with layers of brown glauconitic marl. *Protocardia dissimilis, Ostrea expansa*, etc...	3

   It is highly probable that Bed 2 is the equivalent of the *leucus*-layer of
Long Crendon, from which Mr. Buckman records the ammonite *Leucopetrites
leucus* S. Buckman.   Fragments of a similar species are to be found at Shotover,
but are never well preserved.
   The glauconitic limestones are again exposed in an old pit on the north
side of the hill, close to the reservoir.   Here, they are highly fossiliferous, and
in addition to the characteristic Portland lamellibranchs, yield the following
ammonites, ? *Crendonites leptolobatus* S. Buckman and ? *Glaucolithites lithus*
S. Buckman.   These have been identified by Mr. Buckman, and they clearly
indicate the Pseudogigas Zone of Salfeld's classification.

----

[1] Pruvost, P., and J. Pringle, *Proc. Geol. Assoc.*, vol. xxxv, 1924, p. 37.

A few yards higher up the hill about 10 ft. of buff sands with concretionary bands of grey sandy limestone are to be seen in an old sand-pit. The sands are capped by a silicified ferruginous limestone, 2½ ft. thick, and this bed appears to be followed by a brownish-yellow limestone crowded with the shells of *Trigonia damoniana* de Lor., preserved in the form of ironstone casts. This is the highest bed of Portland exposed. Fitton described this top layer as a hard brown sandstone with a few *Trigoniae*, and it was probably the same bed from which the late Sir J. J. H. Teall long ago obtained a specimen of *Trigonia damoniana*.[1] The ferruginous character of the highest Portland Beds is noteworthy, and because of it they were at one time included with the overlying Shotover Sands, until Mr. G. W. Lamplugh separated the ironstone-beds with fresh-water fossils from those containing marine forms. From an examination of the rock-specimens collected by Mr. Lamplugh, the following notes have been drawn up by Dr. H. H. Thomas.

'The normal Portland Stone is a shelly and oolitic limestone, fairly pure in composition; but under the influence of percolating waters it has locally undergone extensive changes. The most usual change is that of partial, or more or less complete silicification, but in many cases much of the calcium carbonate has been replaced by ferruginous compounds. In the neighbourhood of Shotover Hill remnants of the Portland Stone are met with which have been all more or less changed from their original character by the process of silicification. On the south side of the hill a rock occurs which, under the microscope, is seen to be made up of closely packed oolitic grains set in a matrix almost wholly silicified. The oolitic grains themselves show all stages from partial to complete silicification, but in some of the less altered specimens they still consist in part of carbonate, and retain their original concentric structure. At the same time, in the more completely silicified rock, the outline of the grains is still distinct, being emphasized by dusty iron ores. This change in the oolitic grains seems to have taken place in two ways, both by the replacement of the calcite by chalcedonic silica, and by the growth of quartz, probably on minute clastic grains of that mineral which formed the nuclei of the oolitic structures. The quartz has grown in perfect optical continuity, but not in such a manner as to show crystal outline, the result being an irregularly-shaped mass which often entirely or only partially encloses the oolitic grain. At the same time the original outline of the oolitic structure may be traced through the quartz by means of the ferruginous inclusions.

'Examples of Portland Stone from a sand-pit east of the western brickyard show that nearly all the oolitic grains have been replaced by crystalline quartz, with irregular or subrounded outline. That this silicification has proceeded from the centre is shown by the fact that many of the oolitic grains are not completely replaced, the outer margin, or part of it, being still formed of carbonate.

'From these considerations it is obvious that all the larger quartz grains in these silicified oolites are of secondary and not of clastic origin.

'Occasionally the rock is highly ferruginous, and then it is seen that the iron was introduced, as was the silica, from without, and it is evident that those parts only which had not been previously silicified have been replaced by iron-oxides: it is assumed, therefore, that the iron-bearing waters followed those carrying silica. In some examples it seems that most of the oolitic grains had clastic quartz nuclei, and therefore there was a tendency to the formation of quartz rather than of chalcedonic material.

'In the rock-specimens collected from a sand-pit on the eastern side of the reservoir, most of the oolitic grains are replaced by masses of secondary quartz, and these are set in a matrix consisting chiefly of iron-oxide, causing the rock to present all the appearance of a ferruginous grit. It is evident that in this case we are dealing with a rock which, without regard to less changed

---

[1] Fitton, W. H., *Trans. Geol. Soc.*, ser. 2, vol. iv, 1836, pp. 275, 278; J. J. H. Teall, 'Potton and Wicken Phosphatic Deposits', 1875, p. 32 etc.; H. B. Woodward, 'Jurassic Rocks of Britain' (*Mem. Geol. Surv.*), vol. v, 1895, p. 128.

specimens, would have been classed as original in character, whereas in reality all its components are of secondary origin.

'It is suggested that other so-called ferruginous grits may be altered limestones'.

The outcrop of the Portland Beds is not well exposed on the south-western side of the hill, but the presence of the formation is indicated here and there by debris thrown out of rabbit burrows. To the north-east of Hill Farm, Horsepath, where a spring flows from the base of the Portland, fragments of limestone with *Trigonia gibbosa* J. Sow. and other fossils may be collected.

In the faulted outlier of Red Hill by Forest Hill, traces of Portland Beds are found when graves are dug in parts of the cemetery, and glauconitic limestones were formerly exposed in a trench from which Mr. W. C. Tyndale obtained a fragment of a large ammonite.

South of the railway at Littleworth, near Wheatley, an excellent section is displayed beneath a downwash of Shotover Sands in a field north of the windmill. Here the lower part of the Portland rocks shows the following details :—

	Ft.
Fine-grained buff sands with concretionary masses of greyish sandy limestones with *Protocardia dissimilis*, *Trigonia gibbosa*, and fragments of ' *Perisphinctes* ' spp.	8 to 10
Greyish-white shelly limestone	2½
Buff argillaceous limestone with conspicuous grains of glauconite .. .. seen to	1

The lowest bed passes down into a brownish-green glauconitic clay, but the base is not exposed, so that the junction with the underlying Kimmeridge Clay cannot be studied. The full thickness of the glauconitic limestones was proved to be nearly 7 ft. in the well dug by the windmill in 1893.[1] Mr. Buckman [2] has applied the term Littleworth Sands to the highest beds in the pit. Near Littleworth the downwash of the Shotover Sands extends to the Kimmeridge Clay, and at one time this fact gave rise to the belief that the Lower Cretaceous sands had here overlapped on to that formation.

The highest beds of the Portland were examined during the excavation of a well in the field on the north side of Coombe Wood in 1925, and the top layer was found to be crowded with casts of *Trigonia damoniana* de Lor., preserved in limonite, as at Shotover Hill. The details of the section are as follows :—

		Ft.	In.
	Soil	1	0
Shotover Sands	Brown ferruginous sandstone	1	0
	Fine buff sands	20	6
	Brown cellular ferruginous sandstone with casts of *Cyrena media* and *Unio sp*. .. .. 6 in.	0	8
	Brownish-black and grey clay with traces of plants	0	4
	Hard brown-weathering blue-hearted sandstone resting on irregular surface of	2	6
Portland Beds	Hard brownish-white limestone with streaks of limonite ; crowded with *Trigonia damoniana*, preserved as ferruginous casts..	2	6
	White cherty oolitic limestone	0	6
	Fine white sandy oolitic limestone	3	6
	Buff sands with concretionary masses of grey sandy limestone..	2	4
	Decalcified greyish-white sandy limestone with casts of *Trigonia spp.*, *Lucina portlandica*, *Ostrea expansa*, *Natica ceres*, etc.	1	0
	Buff greenish sands with some hard bands; Water struck at 43 ft. from surface	17	2

[1] ' The Water Supply of Oxfordshire ' (*Mem. Geol. Surv.*), 1910, p. 53.
[2] Buckman, S. S., ' Type Ammonites,' vol. iv, 1922, p. 28.

Beneath the Shotover Sands the Portland limestones are traversed by wide open fissures which extend downwards into the buff greenish sands yielding water.

South of Coombe Wood, in the neighbourhood of Garsington and Cuddesdon, there are now few exposures of Portland rocks. In Fitton's time the principal stone-pits at Garsington were ' in the western escarpment of the hill north of the village, overlooking the low ground about Langcomb and Cowley ' ; Langcomb being probably the valley between Easington and Horsepath. At a later date, Hull noted a section, one mile north of Garsington, showing a white oolitic Portland limestone overlain irregularily by the Shotover Sands.[1] The stone, which was much eroded on the upper surface, contained *Trigonia sp.*, *Pinna sp.* and *Ostrea expansa* J. Sow.

During the revision of the area in 1925, the formation was exposed in a number of temporary excavations dug for the purpose of obtaining a building-sand in a field about 400 yds. south of City Farm ; and from these holes the following details of the rock-succession were obtained :—

		Ft.	In.
Shotover Sands	Dirty-white sands with ferruginous layers resting on an eroded surface of the underlying Portland limestone ; seen to	1	6
Upper Portland	Greyish-white sandy shelly limestone, slightly glauconitic, crowded with casts of *Trigonia spp.*, *Natica ceres* and *Ostrea expansa*.. ..	1	0
	Buff sands with an 8-inch band of hard sandy limestone .. .. 12 to 15		0
	Buff sandy limestone	2	6
	Soft shelly limestone	0	6
	Hard grey limestone, glauconitic, with a shelly bed at base	1	0
	Dingy-grey marly limestone, speckled with large grains of glauconite. Some lydite pebbles at base .. .. seen to	1	6

The excavations confirm the general succession of the Portland given on p. 77, but it will be noticed that the Shotover Sands rest on the limestone with *Natica ceres* de Lor., a horizon slightly lower than that of the junction at Coombe Wood well or Shotover Hill. In the limestones at the base, numerous fossils were noted, and they included the following characteristic shells ; *Lima rustica* J. Sow., *Ostrea expansa* J. Sow., *Pecten (Camptonectes) lamellosus* J. Sow., *Perna bouchardi* de Lor., *Pleuromya tellina* Ag., *Protocardia dissimilis* (J. de C. Sow.) and fragments of a Perisphinctid closely resembling *Perisphinctes gorei* Salfeld. The ammonites have been submitted to Mr. S. S. Buckman for identification, and he, with some doubt, refers them to *Aquistratites aquator*, a species found in the Waterstone Bed of the Crendon district. The lamellibranch-fauna is identical with that of the ' Cockly Bed ' at Swindon.

Dr. A. Morley Davies has recorded a section, which may still be seen, to the north-west of Garsington, near the ' Red Lion.'[2] The beds comprise yellowish and bluish-green sand, about 16 ft. thick, underlain by a thick layer of sandy limestone, and they appeared to him to occur but little above the Kimmeridge Clay ; but the evidence was not clear at the time of his visit. On further examination in 1924, the strata proved to belong to the lower part of the Giganteus Zone, the sands being equivalent to the Littleworth Sands of Mr. Buckman's classification (*see* p. 80). Although not exposed in the section, the soft buff marly limestone with conspicuous grains of glauconite, at the base of the formation, was passed through in a well in the

[1] Hull, E., ' Geology of parts of Oxfordshire and Berkshire ' (*Mem. Geol. Surv.*), 1861, p. 11.
[2] Davies, A. M., ' Contributions to the Geology of the Thame Valley,' *Proc. Geol. Assoc.*, vol. xvi, 1899, p. 19.

field opposite the section.   It rests on a clay, probably the equivalent of the Littleworth Lydite Clay in Wheatley brickyard.

At Cuddesdon the upper portion of the Portland Beds is exposed in a small quarry in a field north-east of the Palace.   The top bed is a tufaceous-looking oolite, containing *Natica ceres* de Lor., *Trigonia gibbosa* ? J. *Sow.* and *Lucina portlandica* J. de C. Sow.   The bed has been considered by some authors strongly to resemble in character the ' Malm ' above the Portland Stone at Garsington, referred to the Purbeck by Fitton,[1] but the fossils clearly indicate that the limestone is of Portland age, and the occurrence of *Natica ceres* suggests that the bed is equivalent to Bed 5 of the general section, given on p. 77.   As has been already stated, this little gasteropod has a narrow vertical range, and is confined to the creamy limestones in Oxfordshire and Buckinghamshire.[2]

Grey sandy shelly glauconitic limestones crop out in the road about 200 yds. west of Cuddesdon church ; and similar beds cap the small hill at Chippinghurst, forming a small outlier which has hitherto escaped notice.

In the area lying to the east of the river Thame, a mass of Portland Limestone appears from beneath the Cretaceous rocks at Great and Little Milton.   The stone has been worked at Great Haseley and near Great Milton, and an old quarry on the eastern side of the latter village shows the following section :—

		Ft.
Shotover Sand	Brown loam (formerly used for brickmaking)..	4
	Sand with bands of white and ochreous clay ..	4 to 6
	Buff and white false-bedded sand with ferruginous layers and concretions ; at base lydite pebbles and ironstone	4
	resting on eroded surface of	
Portland Beds	Rubbly bed of sand with hard nodular calcareous sandstone and chert. This rock has the appearance of a remanié bed	3 to 4
	Shelly clay with hard nodules	½
	Calcareous sandstone, cherty in places, passing down into grey and greenish sandy oolitic limestone with *Ostrea expansa, Perna bouchardi, Trigonia gibbosa*, etc. .. seen to	6

From the higher rubbly bed Blake obtained *Cerithium portlandicum* J. de C. Sow., and he noted that the rock had ' the appearance of rolled masses of stone, so consolidated by similar material that the separate pieces are scarcely recognizable.'[3]   A similar section appears to have been exposed in an old quarry, now overgrown, on the north side of the village of Great Haseley. The top beds of the oolites were observed by Hull to be contorted and nipped up to a depth of 5 or 6 ft.[4]

Brown sandy limestones are exhibited in an old stone-pit 180 yards northeast of Great Haseley Church.   They are decalcified in places, but contain layers crowded with casts of *Trigonia spp., Perna bouchardi* ? de Lor., *Ostrea sp.*, etc.   The section is capped by a rubbly oolitic and sandy limestone, 2 ft. thick, bearing a close resemblance to the highest bed of Portland Stone at Great Milton.

Between Great and Little Milton the area occupied by Portland rocks shows but few sections.   The ground is flat and open, with large fields mostly

[1] Fitton, W. H., *Trans. Geol. Soc.*, ser. 2, vol. iv, 1836, p. 277.

[2] Blake, J. F., ' On the Portland Rocks of England,' *Quart. Journ. Geol. Soc.*, vol. xxxvi, 1880, p. 225.   *See also* ' The Geology of the Country around Aylesbury ' (*Mem. Geol. Surv.*), 1922, p. 7.

[3] Blake, J. F., ' On the Portland Rocks of England,' *Quart. Journ. Geol. Soc.*, vol. xxxvi, 1880, p. 214.

[4] Hull, E., ' The Geology of parts of Oxfordshire and Berkshire ' (*Mem. Geol. Surv.*), 1861, p. 11.

under cultivation, but where evidence is obtained, the formation is seen to consist of crumbly, oolitic sandy limestone. There were formerly many quarries, but the hollows are mostly covered with soil and overgrown. Pits with much sand and decomposed stone are to be found north-east of Little Milton, some used as receptacles for rubbish, and thereby liable to pollute the underground water.

East of Haseley Court on the left bank of Haseley Brook, between Peg's Farm and Upper Standhill, there are a number of old pits that were opened in Portland Stone.

In the Brill outlier the Portland Beds also rest unconformably on the Kimmeridge Clay, and the junction is marked by the outflow of numerous springs, which issue at the base of the rubbly glauconitic limestones. Sections are scarce, and our information is to a great extent based on published records.

At the old brickyard, west of Springfield Farm, and in an adjoining quarry on the north-western side of the hill, the following section was formerly exposed :—

	Ft.
Oolitic and shelly limestone and marl with *Ostrea expansa* and *Trigonia sp.*	3
Chalky rock with *Lucina portlandica*, etc.	4
Brown clay with *Ostrea*..	$\frac{1}{2}$
Oolitic earthy rock	1
Yellow sand, dark glauconitic sand and marly beds : *Pecten lamellosus*	
Glauconitic marly limestone, becoming sandy in lower part ; highly fossiliferous..	7 to 8
Lydite bed : brown clay with pebbles..	1

The section is now grassed over, but the details, which are based on the account given by Woodward,[1] agree in the main points with those recorded by Fitton,[2] who enumerates a number of fossils.

The pits were visited by the Geologists' Association under the guidance of J. F. Blake in 1893, and he then recorded from the fossiliferous glauconitic bed the following fossils[3]:—

'*Ammonites biplex*	*Pecten lamellosus*
,, *boloniensis*	*Perna Bouchardi*
Cardium Pellati	*Pleuromya tellina*
Lima rustica	*Trigonia muricata*
Mytilus boloniensis	— *Pellati* '

The lamellibranch-fauna set forth in the above list is clearly that of the Pseudogigas Zone. Re-examination of the ammonites would probably show that the identification is faulty, and it may be permissible to suggest that the shells referred to '*Ammonites biplex*' are forms near to *Perisphinctes gorei* Salfeld.

Chalky limestones were exposed in a pit about 100 yds. west-north-west of Mill Cottage on Brill Common in 1924. The section showed about 6 ft. of stone beneath a Purbeck clay.

At the base of the Portland Beds on Muswell Hill, there is a glauconitic limestone with *Protocardia dissimilis* (J. de C. Sow.) and other shells, but the rock is seldom visible. Its outcrop, however, can be easily traced, as copious springs are thrown out beneath the stone at various points around the outlier.

---

[1] Woodward, H. B., 'The Jurassic Rocks of Britain' (*Mem. Geol. Surv.*), vol. v, 1895, p. 221.
[2] Fitton, W. H., *op. cit.*, pp. 280, 283, 299.
[3] Blake, J. F., *Proc. Geol. Assoc.*, vol. xiii, 1893, p. 73; *Quart. Journ. Geol. Soc.*, vol. xxxvi, 1880, pp. 209, 226, etc. ; *see also* H. B. Woodward, *op. cit.*, p. 222.

PURBECK BEDS

At the close of the Portland epoch the marine episode was brought to an end by important changes of level, and the succeeding deposits indicate the establishment of estuarine conditions over a wide area. In this district these Purbeck Beds are found only in some localities overlying the Portland Stone, and can be seen outcropping at intervals from beneath the Shotover Sands in the Brill outlier. Generally, the formation is poorly developed, and the beds are merely remnants that have escaped destruction by erosion that took place prior to the deposition of the fresh-water Lower Cretaceous sediments. Indeed, it is questionable whether there are any representatives of the Upper Purbeck present in the area, although this sub-division has been proved at the Bugle Pit, near Hartwell, and other quarries in the country to the east.[1]

Complete removal of the formation by denudation appears to have been effected in some localities. Thus, there is no evidence of Purbeck Beds on the main portion of Shotover Hill, where the Shotover Sands rest directly upon a hard ferruginous sandstone of Portland age (*see* p. 79). In the south-eastern portion of the Portlandian outlier traces of Purbeck were noted here and there by Fitton,[2] who observed beds like the ' Malm ' of Garsington above the Portland Stone of Coombe Wood, south of Wheatley. They consisted of compact and oolitic limestone and rubble, and yielded remains of *Cypris, Mytilus, Modiola, Paludina elongata* and *Planorbis*. They are overlain by the Shotover Sands. The Purbeck Beds, however, proved to be absent in a well, dug in the field north of Coombe Wood.

The following section of a stone-pit at Garsington is here abbreviated from that recorded by Fitton[3] :—

		Ft. In.
[Shotover Sands]	{ Loamy soil	2 0
	{ Ferruginous brown sand and greenish sand, with yellow ochre and fuller's earth..	8 0
[Purbeck Beds]	Malm, soft limestone and softer marl, much decomposed ; comprising— (a) Light greenish-grey marl with, in the upper part, detached fragments of silicified coniferous wood, like that of Portland, and portions of bone ; (b) Limestone, with some oolitic grains ; *Paludina, Planorbis* ? *Mytilus*, and *Cypris ;* (c) Limestone, in some places like the ' Pendle ' of the pits at Whitchurch, oolitic and botryoidal in places, with *Paludina*, etc.	4 0

Portland Stone

[1] Merrett, E. A., ' Fossil Ostracoda and their use in Stratigraphical Research,' *Geol. Mag.*, 1924, p. 237.
[2] *Trans. Geol. Soc.*, ser. 2, vol. iv, 1836, pp. 272, 275.
[3] *Ibid.*, ser. 2, iv, p. 277.

No sections showing Purbeck Beds were exposed during the recent examination of the area south of Wheatley.

The presence of Purbeck Beds beneath the Shotover Sands of the Brill outlier was first definitely recognized by the Rev. P. B. Brodie, in 1867,[1] though one of the sections (C) at Brill, published by Fitton in 1836,[2] includes the strata since found to belong to the Purbeck series. Phillips,[3] in 1871, gave a generalized section which showed the beds to be 10 ft. thick ; but it is probable that the thickness is overestimated, as the sections on the lower slope of Brill Common, in which these beds are exposed, are obscured by slips, which tend to duplicate the strata. The present exposures seem to indicate, as did the sections examined by Mr. G. W. Lamplugh in 1904, that the total thickness is not more than five or six feet ; but as the series is evidently variable both in composition and thickness, it may have been locally thicker in the excavated part of the Common than in the places where it still remains.

When the district was surveyed in 1904, a good section was seen in a small stone-pit, now overgrown, close to the west side of the road that runs along the eastern margin of Brill Common, 300 yds. north of Temple Farm. The beds were much slipped, and were also disturbed by previous workings, but Mr. Lamplugh was able to record the following succession :—

		Ft.	In.
	Top soil, etc.	1 to 2	0
Shotover Sands	Pale grey clay, with a pimply structure suggestive of ostracoda, and with bits of plants : much slickensided and brecciated by slipping about	1	0
	White and buff fine sand and pale grey clay, with crushed remnants of ironstone concretions : irregularly mixed and confused	3 to 4	0
	Yellow and pale buff fine sand and sand-rock with ironstone concretions at base	1	0
Purbeck Beds	Tough bright-green clay with rusty spots, with some earthy fragments and ironstone concretions : much crushed : called ' peter ' by the quarrymen	0 6 to 0	9
	Brecciated white stone and marl, with broken lumps of hard calcareous grit (' pitchingstone ' of the quarrymen) at the top, and Portland limestone below : all crushed and mixed by slipping .. .. seen for	3	0

The quarrymen stated that the ' pitching-stone ' (which was dug for road-metal) occurred in two irregular beds,[4] with a parting of sandy loam between, the lower and thicker bed averaging 6 in. in thickness. From the heap of this ' pitching-stone ' at the entrance to the quarry, Mr. Lamplugh obtained some obscure and indeterminable fossils apparently fragments of marine lamellibranchs.

[1] *Quart. Journ. Geol. Soc.*, vol. xxiii, pp. 197–199.
[2] *Trans. Geol. Soc.*, ser. 2, vol. iv, 1836, pp, 280–281.
[3] ' Geology of Oxford, etc.,' p. 418.
[4] Compare Fitton's section, *op. cit.*, p. 281.

A similar section was exposed in 1924 in a small pit 100 yds. west-north-west of Mill Cottage. The Purbeck Beds, though much confused by slipping, appeared to be between 4 and 5 ft. thick, and are overlain by Shotover Sands.

Traces of the bright green clay were at one time visible in the deep sand-pit at the more northerly windmill on Brill Common; and there appears to have been a trace of the lower part of the series at the top of the quarry in Portland limestone 80 yds. distant, at the northern edge of the Common. These sections are now overgrown.

In an old pit, now obliterated, on the slope below the Congregational Chapel, Mr. Lamplugh noted that a much-obscured section revealed Purbeck Beds of a different type, consisting of 3 or 4 inches of tough black earth or clay, suggestive of an ancient surface-soil, resting on 4–6 inches of tough dark-grey earthy material speckled with small bits of a paler material like decomposed white stone. An earthy breccia of similar character to the latter bed, but much thicker and coarser, forms part of the Purbeck Beds exposed in the well-known ' Bugle ' Pit at Hartwell; and a similar bed was exposed in a railway-cutting on the Great Central line, ¼ mile west of Haddenham.

Purbeck Beds are traceable only in the above-described sections of Brill Common, and they are consequently indicated on the map only in this quarter; but greenish clay above the Portland Stone was observed by H. B. Woodward to the east of Brill Church, on the scarp below Hampden House. Whether the series is continued northward into Muswell Hill is not known, as no exposures are available. The fossils indicate that the beds are of estuarine origin, marking the transition from the marine conditions of Portlandian times to the fresh-water conditions indicated by the Shotover Sands.

CHAPTER VII

LOWER CRETACEOUS ROCKS

SHOTOVER SANDS

THE Upper Jurassic rocks in some parts of the area are capped by isolated patches or outliers of sand with subordinate bands of clay to which the general term ' Ironsands ' has been applied on account of the prevalence of ferruginous material in some of the beds. These Ironsands form the top of prominent hills that rise boldly to a height of 100 to 150 ft. above the surrounding plain of Middle and Upper Jurassic clays, and from the conspicuous development of the series on Shotover Hill, near Oxford, the name Shotover Sands has been given to these deposits.[1]

The Shotover Sands are evidently the relics of an originally extensive deposit of which the greater part has been removed by denudation, and the remnants, like those of the Purbeck and Portland Beds, owe their preservation to the fact that they lie in shallow synclines, the axes of which run centrally to the major direction of the outliers. Although it is not possible to determine the dip from particular exposures on account of the prevalence of current-bedding and lenticular stratification, a gentle inclination of the Sands towards the south-south-east is brought out by the mapping, the base of the group falling from the 600-ft. contour-line at the northern end of the Muswell Hill outlier to about the 300-ft. line, where the formation disappears beneath the Gault near Great Haseley. The underlying Portland Beds show a corresponding inclination, so that the unconformity deducible from wider evidence is not so apparent in this district.

The ferruginous sands of Shotover, along with those of the similar outlier at Brill, were originally considered as forming part of the marine Lower Greensand Series, but the discovery by the Rev. H. Jelly, of Bath, that fresh-water shells belonging to the genus *Paludina* [*Viviparus*] occurred in the Shotover Beds, first made known

---

[1] By Prestwich and others. Unfortunately the term has been applied by J. F. Blake and other authors to the marine so-called Portland Sands now ascertained to be of Kimmeridge age. *See* J. F. Blake, ' On the Portland Rocks of England,' *Quart. Journ. Geol. Soc.*, vol. xxxvi, 1880, Plate viii. Mr. S. S. Buckman has also adopted Blake's term, which he further divides into Shotover Grit Sands and Shotover Fine Sands, *see* ' Type Ammonites,' 1922, pp. 26–28. Dr. A. Morley Davies has described Cretaceous sands in the Bishopstone-Haddenham area under the name of Bishopstone Beds which he correlates with the Shotover Sands (*Proc. Geol. Assoc.*, vol. xvi, 1899, p. 48). This title is unsuitable since De la Beche applied the term Bishopstone Beds to all the strata exposed at Bishopston, near Swansea, above the top of the highest [Carboniferous] limestone (*Mem. Geol. Surv.*), vol. i., 1846, p. 134.

by H. E. Strickland[1] in the year 1834, showed that these deposits could not have been accumulated under marine conditions; and in 1836 Strickland[2] classified them as doubtfully Wealden.

At a later date, Phillips added considerably to our knowledge of the Shotover Sands[3], and described and figured the fossils, which he found to be all fresh-water forms ; he concluded that the deposits ' may at present, with much probability, be referred to the Hastings Sands ; it is, however, possible that they may be an estuarine deposit of the Lower Greensand age.' The occurrence of species of Ostracoda in the Shotover Ironstone was afterwards recorded by Prof. T. Rupert Jones[4] ; and Prestwich also at a later period accepted the view that the Shotover Sands were of Wealden age. The fossils from the Ironsands on Shotover Hill and Wheatley, preserved in the University Museum collections at Oxford, are as follows :—

Pecopteris sp.
Coniferous wood
Cyrena media *J. de C. Sow.*
Unio mantelli *J. de C. Sow.**
,, martini *J. de C. Sow.*
,, porrectus *J. de C. Sow.*
,, stricklandi *Phill.**
,, subtruncatus *J. de C. Sow.**
Viviparus elongatus (*J. de C. Sow.*)
,, ornatus (*Phill.*)*
,, subangulatus (*Phill.*)*
,, sussexensis (*Mant.*)*
Candona phillipsiana *Jones**
Cypridea aculeata *Jones**
,, austeni *Jones**
,, bispinosa *Jones**
,, granulosa *Jones**
,, verrucosa *Jones**

Figured specimens are marked with an asterisk.

Up to 1875 it was recognized that the fauna of the Shotover Sands was wholly fresh-water ; but a few marine fossils that were found subsequently in a matrix of sandy ironstone seemed to imply the association of a marine bed with the sequence. One of the fossils, mentioned by the late Sir J. J. H. Teall (*see* p. 79), was a cast of *Trigonia damoniana*, and it was suggested that this might indicate a gradual passage from Portland Beds to Ironsands conditions. Others, including *Perna* and *Modiola* ?, are preserved in the Oxford University Museum. It was found later, however, that there has been an alteration in places of the uppermost part of the Portland

[1] *Proc. Geol. Soc.*, vol. ii, 1836, p. 6.
[2] In a note contributed to Fitton's celebrated memoir, ' On the Strata between the Chalk and the Oxford Oolite,' etc., *Trans. Geol. Soc.*, ser. 2, iv, 1836, p. 527.
[3] Phillips, J., ' On the Estuary Sands in the upper part of Shotover Hill,' *Quart. Journ. Geol. Soc.*, vol. xiv, 1858, pp. 236–241 ; *see also* ' Geology of Oxford,' etc., 8vo., Oxon, 1871.
[4] *Geol. Mag.*, 1878, pp. 103–110 and p. 277 ; *see also Quart. Journ. Geol. Soc.*, vol. xli, 1885, p. 320.

Beds into ironstone and into a cherty rock, probably through the percolation of water charged with ferruginous matter derived from the overlying Shotover Sands ; so that the presence of marine fossils in an ironstone matrix on Shotover Hill may be thus explained. The petrological characters presented by the altered rock have been described by Dr. H. H. Thomas (*see* p. 79).

In fact, like the Brill outliers, the ironsands of Shotover and Wheatley appear to be entirely of fresh-water origin and the occurrence of remnants of Purbeck Beds at the base of the Ironsands, at Brill, Coombe Wood, and Garsington, has an important bearing upon the question of the age of the Shotover series.   These Purbeck Beds indicate the change from the purely marine conditions of the underlying Portland Beds to the brackish-water and variable conditions following upon a recession of the sea ; and in the Shotover Sands there are indications of the succeeding stage, when the district rose entirely above sea-level and the only deposits were those of fresh-water origin.   This stage presumably followed upon the estuarine episode ; and the deposits are therefore only slightly newer than the Purbeck, *i.e.*, they represent the lowermost part of the Wealden Series of Kent and Sussex, and may be correlated with the Hastings Beds, but are probably older than the Weald Clay.   The fresh-water fossils are, unfortunately, so few in species, and these so little known, that the evidence for this correlation must rest mainly upon the stratigraphical relations of the Shotover Sands. On these grounds the fresh-water ironsands have been separated on the Special Sheet from the sands of Lower Cretaceous age that are considered to be of marine origin, and the two groups are distinguished by different colours.

LOCAL DETAILS

Shotover Hill owes its prominence to a thick capping of more or less ferruginous sand, with some interbedded clay-beds, and much concretionary ironstone, the latter being especially abundant in the upper part of the series. These beds form the flat crest of the long narrow ridge that extends E.S.E. for over 1½ miles nearly to Wheatley.   South of Littleworth the Ironsands are cut out for 300 yards or so by a depression in the ridge, but they reappear in the rise of the ground beyond this space, and are then prolonged in another ridge which sweeps round southward from Wheatley for about two miles , nearly to Garsington.   These ridges form two separate outliers of the Ironsands, surrounded by the Portland Beds which occupy their slopes, while a third outlier is formed by a small patch of the ironstones and sands that occupies the summit of Red Hill, one mile north of Wheatley.

On Shotover Hill the ironsands were formerly dug on an extensive scale for ochre, but this industry has long since died out, and the old pits are now either obliterated or greatly obscured.   The largest workings seem to have been on the site of the present ' allotment gardens,' ½ mile north of Horsepath, and in the park-land north-west of these gardens 100 yds. north of the old coach-road.   In the latter locality there is still a partly exposed section showing several feet of yellow sand with intercalated ironstone and traces of clayey beds below ;   some further account of these sections, compiled from early descriptions, will be given (*see* p. 91).   The best exposures at present available occur in small pits at the western end of the hill, of which some details will be found in the context, and there are also small pits at the eastern edge of Horsepath Common and on the hill south of Wheatley, besides some, more or less obscure, road-cuttings. By combining all the available data, the following generalized section of the series on Shotover Hill in downward succession has been deduced :—

GENERAL SECTION OF THE IRONSANDS ON SHOTOVER HILL

Description	Where best seen	Average thickness
Top soil, brown sandy loam full of fragments of ironstone	—	1 to 3 ft.
1. Rusty sand with much tabular concretionary ironstone, forming the top of the plateau, mixed with and passing down into yellow and orange sand, no fossils seen	Old ochre pits north of Horsepath Common	15 ft. seen, but may be thicker.
2. Grey or white clay, like fuller's earth, probably impersistent : causes slipping on the hillsides	Pit on western crest of Shotover Hill, 80 yds. N. of road	3 to 5 ft.
3. Very fine white or greyish sand and silt, sometimes stained buff, yellow or orange, occasionally streaked with clay: though variable, is fairly persistent as a whole	Ditto	12-15 ft.
4. Coarser sand, white, yellow or brown, with hard purple ironstone concretions, sometimes containing casts of freshwater shells and bits of plants : with occasional streaks or bands of grey or ochreous clay up to 1 ft. in thickness, including unfossiliferous claystone nodules	Sand-pit at E. side of Horsepath Common, 200 yds. south of " Rough Barn " ; also poorly exposed in old pits at west end of Shotover Hill, and at slipped section mentioned below	8-10 ft. seen, but may ʎbe thicker.
5. Coarse speckly sand, with crumbs of white earth (? decomposed clay-pellets) and decayed ironstone concretions : resting on stained Portland Beds (see p. 88)	Small sand-pit east of reservoir on western spur of Shotover Hill (perhaps slipped)	1-2 ft.

Total thickness, about 50 ft.

The pit on the western crest of Shotover Hill deserves particular mention, because of the somewhat exceptional character of the beds and the presence of fossils. The following was the section exposed in 1904 :—

Ft.

1. Ferruginous soil, with many fragments of ironstone ; shattered flaggy ironstone at base in places   ..   .. 2 to 3
2. Ochreous yellow sand, streaked with fine pale yellow silt with dark lamina, indurated to sand-rock in places; about 3
3. Smooth pale grey or whitish clay, with ochreous streaks at base ; thickness variable   ..   .. 1 to 3
4. Fine greyish-white silt, almost like clay, passing imperceptibly into loam ; with large fossiliferous concretions of purple ironstone at base   ..   .. seen to 5

The fossils in Bed 4 occur in the form of sharp empty casts in the hard ironstone, chiefly of *Viviparus ornatus* (Phill.) and *Viviparus sp.* with an occasional *Unio* and some obscure plant remains. It is noteworthy that this assemblage is different from that of the fossiliferous ironstone of the same series near Wheatley, where *Cyrena* is the most abundant shell.

The fine white silt of the above section was formerly dug and sent out of the district for use in some manufacturing process (*see* p. 178).

Conybeare[1] gives the following section of the ' Ochre pits, Shotover Hill,' probably those north of Horsepath, to which reference has been already made (*see* p. 89) :—

	Ft.
Beds of highly ferruginous grit, forming the summit of the hill	6
Grey sand	3
Ferruginous concretions	1
Yellow sand	6
Cream-coloured loam	4
Ochre	$\frac{1}{2}$

' Beneath this is a second bed of ochre separated by a thin bed of clay then succeeds an interval of nearly 40 feet occupied by various alternations of ferruginous and sometimes cherty and argillaceous loams of a deep cream colour.' This section is reprinted by Phillips,[2] who estimates the total thickness of the series at 80 ft., but it is more probable that the maximum does not exceed 60 ft., the apparently greater thickness being due to slipping and downwash on the slopes. Phillips mentions that the fossil-casts are not confined to one horizon but occur throughout the series except possibly in the uppermost 20 ft. It is now considered likely that the cherty layers are of Portland age.

The Ostracoda recorded by T. Rupert Jones were found in association with *Unio, Cyrena, Paludina,* and bones of fish[3] in some pieces of ironstone picked up by Mr. H. Caudell in the vicinity of old stone pits at the western end of Shotover ' Common ' [Plain]. In 1904 Mr. Lamplugh obtained from a similar ironstone casts of shells, including *Cyrena media* J. de C. Sow., *Unio* cf. *cordiformis* J. de C. Sow., and *Viviparus sp.* These were collected from the debris of the old pits in the Allotment Gardens north of Horsepath and on the spur of the hill east of Horsepath Common, 300 yds. N. of Westhill Farm.

The exposures of the Ironsands at present available in the outlier south of Wheatley are confined to a few small pits and road-cuttings, none showing more than a few feet of sand with ironstone. An old wall on the western side of the high road at the margin of Coombe Wood, ½ mile S. of Wheatley Station, is built of flaggy ironstone, probably obtained from an old pit in the Wood, now sloped. This ironstone is crowded with the casts of fresh-water shells,[4] chiefly *Unio* (an elongate form), and *Cyrena media* J. de C. Sow., with occasional *Viviparus* (*see* p. 92). The fossils of the Ironsand series may be obtained more readily from this place than from any other locality at present available either in these outliers or in those around Brill.

Similar material seems at one time to have been exposed in an old pit 200 yds. E.S.E. of the Windmill at Wheatley, where ochre and iron-ore were dug. Prestwich[5] describes this pit as being about 12 ft. in depth, consisting of beds of rubbly iron-sandstone, impure limonite, and yellow

---

[1] Conybeare, W., and J. Phillips,' Outlines of the Geology of England and Wales,' London, 1822, p. 139.

[2] Phillips, J., ' On the Estuary Sands in the upper part of Shotover Hill ,' *Quart. Journ. Geol. Soc.*, vol. xiv, 1858, p. 238 ; and Geology of Oxford, p. 413.

[3] Jones, T. R., ' Notes on some Fossil Bivalved Entomostraca,' *Geol. Mag.*, 1878, p. 103.

[4] Lamplugh, G. W., *Geol. Mag.*, 1902, p. 574 (letter).

[5] *Geol. Mag.*, 1879, p. 194. Since the above was written a new pit has been opened on the eastern side of the windmill.

ochre, and ' at the depth of about seven or eight feet a thin seam of iron sandstone, at the base of the main bed, six or eight inches thick, was literally full of casts and impressions of these shells—chiefly *Cyrena* and *Paludina ;* while another thin band was covered with ripple-markings and matted with indeterminable plant impressions.' Casts of *Cyrena media* and *Unio* were also noticed during the recent survey in ironstone fragments on the surface of a field 600 yds. west of Slay Barn, on the slopes south-east of Hill Farm, and in the ironstone built in the garden-wall at Littleworth windmill. The section in Coombe Wood, described by Fitton, in which Purbeck Beds were seen below the Ironsands, has been previously referred to (p. 84).

Toward the southern end of the Wheatley outlier the beds appear to become more clayey, but the boundaries are difficult to trace, and may have been extended a little too far on the map. In an earlier memoir (' Parts of Oxfordshire and Berkshire,' p. 11, Fig. 2), a section exposed in a road-cutting one mile north of Garsington is figured and described, in which beds of variegated sands and clays with bands of ironstone were seen to overlie an eroded surface of Portland limestone. Fitton (*op. cit.*, p. 277) also described a stone-pit at Garsington which showed 8 ft. of ferruginous sand with bands of clay and ochre, resting on Purbeck Beds (*see also* p. 84).

The base of the series, as a whole, shows a gradual and almost imperceptible dip toward south-east. In view of the similarity now known to exist between these beds and the stained top of the Portland Beds, there is no satisfactory evidence for the supposed overlap of the series northward on to the Kimmeridge Clay that was represented on the previous geological map ; on the Special Oxford Sheet, therefore, the Portland Beds are represented beneath the Shotover Sands in every part of the Shotover and Wheatley outliers.

On Muswell Hill, the most northerly of the outliers, the Shotover Sands occupy an irregularly oval area having an extreme length of 1,400 yards and an average breadth of about 500 yards. On the south-east, this tract extends to within 500 yds. of the north-western edge of the Brill outlier, being separated from it only by a shallow gap of erosion in which the Kimmeridge Clay is exposed. The picturesque little town of Brill stands on the well-marked plateau formed by the Ironsands of the second outlier, which owes its level summit to the cementation of the sands into tabular concretions of ferruginous grit in the uppermost remaining beds of the group. This little plateau is deeply indented on all sides by short steep-sided combes or valleys, excavated by the springs which well out from the Ironsands or from the underlying pervious Portland strata resting upon the Kimmeridge Clay. The outlier is elongated in the same direction as that of Muswell Hill, from N.W. to S.E., and is close upon one mile in its greatest length.

In composition, the Sands show much local variation, while maintaining their general characters with a fair degree of constancy. This is well seen in the excavations on Brill Common which occupies the steep northerly slope of the Brill outlier, where the sands have been dug for building and other purposes, and the clays and silts for making bricks and tiles. Only a small portion of the group is seen in any particular section ; but as the excavations ranged from top to bottom of the hill, almost the whole sequence was at one time exposed here, though the lowermost portion is confused by slipping. By combining this evidence, the following generalized section of the

Brill Ironsands in downward succession was obtained by Mr. Lamplugh.

GENERAL SECTION OF THE IRONSANDS ON BRILL COMMON

Description	Average thickness
	Ft.
Top soil, brown sandy loam full of fragments of ironstone ..	1 to 3
1. Loamy ferruginous sand and sand-rock, with tabular concretions of ironstone, and much streaked with smooth whitish clay	5
2. Fine buff or white sand, with ferruginous bands and incipient ironstone concretions, and a few clayey streaks, passing down into	10
3. Ashy-grey and brown fine loamy sand, silt and grey silty clay, with traces of plants	5
4. Very fine sharp white sand with filmy streaks of clay ..	4
5. Shaly brown and lavender clay and loam, with traces of plants	4
6. Fine white or ashy-grey sand and sand-rock, with thin laminae of clay and some hollow ironstone concretions ..	10
7. Ochreous clay, with concretionary ironstone showing obscure traces of fossil shells and plants	4 in. to 6 in.
8. Ashy-grey, lavender and brownish loam with layers of sand showing traces of plants	5 ft.+

Base seen, resting on Purbeck Beds in the stone-pit adjoining high road at west side of Common ; and in old pit on west side of Common. Total thickness, about 45 ft.

During the recent examination of the area there were no openings on Brill Common that exhibit the higher beds of sand, but Beds 5 and 6 were well exposed in several pits on the west side of the Common.

An excellent section of the sands was also seen in a new excavation on the west side of the road, 400 yds. south of Brill House. It showed the following details : soil with many fragments of tabular ironstone, some of which contain casts of lamellibranchs ; fine white sand with seams of greyish-white clay, 7 ft. ; alternations of greyish-white clay and buff sand, 1 ft. ; fine white and buff false-bedded sand, 4 ft. These beds are probably the equivalent of Beds 2, 3 and 4 of the general section on Brill Common.

With the exception of indeterminable fragments of plants, fossils are rare in these deposits, but there is evidence that the beds have been laid down in fresh water. From an ironstone band at Brill, the Rev. P. B. Brodie obtained ' a small *Paludina*, coarsely but strongly ribbed, and apparently distinct from any figured and described by Professor Phillips ' [from Shotover].[1] The only shells found at Brill during the re-examination of the area were obscure indeterminable casts of lamellibranchs in an ironstone at the pit 400 yds. south of Brill House ; but blocks of similar fossiliferous ironstone were collected in 1904 by Mr. Lamplugh at about the same horizon in the banks of the road and in the adjacent ploughed fields on the south-eastern slope of Muswell Hill, within half a mile of Brill Common, and these rock-specimens were frequently crowded with casts of *Cyrena media* J. de C. Sow., and occasionally with *Unio porrectus* J. de C. Sow. Fitton,[2] in his account

[1] *Quart. Journ. Geol. Soc.*, vol. xxiii, 1867, p. 198.
[2] *Trans. Geol. Soc.*, ser. 2, vol. iv, 1836, p. 280.

of the Brill sections, describes the occurrence, in a clayey bed (probably No. 5 of the above section), of an entire tree, converted into pyritous lignite, full 40 ft. long, the trunk about a foot in diameter, with branches that extended to about 10 ft. beyond it on both sides.   The position of the clay-pit from which this tree was obtained is given as ' about 20 feet below the road on the south-west [?] of Brill.'

The belt of silty clay that occurs in the section on Brill Common gives rise to small springs in this locality, and it is noteworthy that the Ironsands at Shotover also include a clayey zone which occurs in approximately the same position as at Brill (see p. 90).   Like most river-deposits, the varied sediments tend to arrange themselves in elongated lenticles, and not in regular layers like the sediments of deeper and quieter waters.

On Muswell Hill the Shotover Sands are exposed in a series of small sand-pits dug on both sides of the road leading over the hill, and in the shallow pits at the two farmsteads on its south-western flank.   Streaks of damp clayey soil occur in relatively the same position as at Brill, and the generalized Brill section given above is probably representative for the Muswell Hill outlier also.

With respect to the Lower Cretaceous rocks shown on the map as extending in a narrow strip from Tiddington past Chilworth Farm to Great Milton, there is, in the absence of clear sections, no definite evidence, excepting that supplied by the sandy character of the soil and the presence of brown sand in shallow ponds and ditches.   In this tract the sands appear to rest on Kimmeridge Clay, but to the east of Great Milton there are indications that they pass unconformably over the Portland Beds.   A little farther southward, where a sandy and clayey series is seen to rest directly upon the Portland Stone, the beds are almost certainly of fresh-water origin, as will presently be shown ; but it is possible that the uppermost beds, just below the base of the Gault, may belong to the Upper Cretaceous which in this district overlaps upon the Portland Beds and the Shotover Sands.

At present the best exposure of the sands and clays above referred to occurs at Great Milton, where the outcrop of the Lower Cretaceous beds expands considerably and is probably continuous to Great Haseley, and thence to the eastern margin of the map.   The following section is exhibited in an old stone-pit at the east side of the village, where the strata overlying the Portland Stone show the following details :—

	Ft.	In.
Top soil	0	6
Laminated grey and yellowish clay and loam with streaks of sand, and a lenticle of soft ferruginous stone, passing into	4 to 6	0
Greyish-white and yellow fine-grained sand and sand-rock, streaked with dirty grey and brown loamy beds ..	3	0
Pebbly ferruginous sand, with smooth lydites : greyer below, and with ferruginous concretions at base	1 to 2	0
resting on eroded surface of Portland Stone (p. 82).		

The only traces of organic remains detected in these beds were some obscure fragments of plants in the top clays, but in their general characters these deposits are identical with the clays interbedded with the fresh-water beds of Shotover Hill.   In the south-eastward extension of these sediments at Great Haseley, however, definite evidence for the fresh-water origin is forthcoming.   The old stone-pits east of the Great Haseley Allotment Gardens, about a mile south-east of the above-described section, are now largely overgrown with vegetation, though it can still be seen that, above the Portland Stone, a thick bed of grey clay with ochreous ferruginous concretions has been passed through.   This was visible to a depth of about 3 ft., while at the top there are in places deep ' pockets ' of ironstone-rubble mixed with sand, the remnants of beds that originally existed above the clays.

Fitton saw a clear section in ' the principal quarry at this place ' and illustrated it by the following description, and by the figure (Fig. 6)[1] :—

Ft. In.

' 1. Soil forming a level and uniform surface

' 2. Loam, brown and red ; containing fragments of ferruginous conglomerate (carstone) and of a brown substance, like umber ; passing below into ferruginous sand   3   0 to 0   6

' 3. Thinly stratified firm clay or marl, of a light grey colour, approaching to stone, not effervescent, containing between the folia impressions of plants, and including portions of reddish sand, in horizontal masses of very unequal thickness   6   6

' 4. Dark brown clay ; . . . Some of the masses into which it is easily divided are polished by sliding on each other under pressure.   At the bottom ferruginous sand alternates with the clay   1   0 to 1   6

[' All the preceding beds are much disturbed, and bent irregularly, so as to accommodate themselves to a chasm in the strata below—here called a " Gull " (gully ?) . . .].'

5, 6, 7, 8, Calcareous stone-beds and sands (Portland) see p. 82.

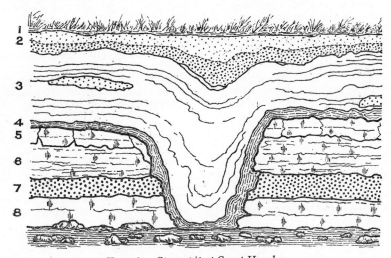

Fig. 6.—*Stone-pit at Great Haseley.*

Fitton does not mention the presence of any fossils, except vegetable remains in the beds above the Portland, but thirty years later Phillips[2] gave a more detailed account of these strata and recorded the discovery of fresh-water shells in the topmost bed.[3] The following is his description of the section :—

' Section at Great Haseley.' (Phillips).

' 12. Soil, uniformly spread, with drift on the surface of chalk flints, and red grit pebbles.

---

[1] ' Observations on some of the Strata between the Chalk and the Oxford Oolite ..' *Trans. Geol. Soc.*, ser. 2, vol. iv, 1836, p. 276.

[2] ' Geology of Oxford,' 1871, p. 417.

[3] The discovery of *Paludina* at Great Haseley appears to have been made by the Rev. P. B. Brodie. *See* Wright, ' Brit. Foss. Echinodermata of Oolitic Formations ' (*Mon. Pal. Soc.*), 1859, vol. i, p. 354.

' 11. Brown sand and laminated ferruginous sandstone or ironstone, with some argillaceous parts. *In this bed* Paludina elongata *and others, lying in separate short tracts or nests, as at Shotover Hill.* Thickness 3 to 5 ft. seen.

' 10. The lower surface is undulated in a surprising manner, and rests on a yellowish or white laminated clay, with thin brown irony bands. Thickness, 3 to 5 ft.   The bottom rests level on the next bed.

' 9.   Brown ferruginous level sands, false-bedded, the lamina dipping N.W.   .   .   .   1 ft. 6 in.

' 8. Dark irony band   .   .   .   3 in.

' 7. White laminated clay   .   .   .   1 ft. 6 in.'

and 6, 5, 4, 3, 2, 1, a succession of white, blue and brown laminated clay-beds with ferruginous and sandy bands, having a total thickness of 7 ft. 3 in.

The general character of the strata above the Portland Stone in these descriptions agrees so closely with that of the beds exposed in the pit at Great Milton, that we must accept the presence of fresh-water shells at Great Haseley as proof of the fresh-water origin of the former also.

Immediately to the south of Great Haseley there occurs an irregular strip of clayey ground, with sandy patches, that is separated from the main outcrop only by a narrow belt of the Portland Beds on which the village itself stands. This is the line of the Wheatley disturbance (*see* p. 6), and probably represents a patch of the Shotover Sands brought in by the slight southward drop at the fault.   Around the village of Little Haseley, whitish clay, overlying sand, was observed, as noted further on.   The composition of these two outliers, as well as their relation to the main outcrop, links them with the fresh-water series.   A third outlier occurs on the low ridge overlooking the Thame, half a mile south-west of Great Milton, which is capped with sandy ferruginous soil containing many fragments of ironstone ; from its position and lithological characters this outlier also probably belongs to the Shotover Sands.

To the east of Great Milton, and south of Silver Cottage, J. H. Blake noted 3 ft. of fuller's earth of whitish colour.   White clays of this character occur beneath the ironstone east of Mill House.

The nature of the ground between Haseley Wood and Little Haseley was shown when a well- dug at the western end of Little Haseley village, proved 8 ft. of whitish clay over sand.   The clay was like that south of Silver Cottage, Great Milton, and in the old stone-pit of Great Haseley.   A similar clay is seen in the banks of the pond at Little Haseley, and west of the ' Sportsman's Retreat.'

Combining the evidence regarding these scattered patches of Wealden fresh-water deposits that lie to the east of Oxford (excluding the independent masses of Brill and Muswell Hill), we find that all the outliers fall within a comparatively narrow belt that runs south-eastward from Shotover to Great Haseley.   The beds in this belt are always underlain by Portland rocks, except in their doubtful extension north of Great Milton, and in a few places where thin lenticles of Purbeck Beds intervene between the two formations.

CHAPTER VIII

LOWER CRETACEOUS ROCKS—(*continued*)
LOWER GREENSAND

BESIDES the Ironsands of Shotover and Brill, there are, within the area of the map, several other outlying patches of sand of the same general character, with interstratified beds of clay, occupying a similar stratigraphical position, between the base of the Gault and the top of the Jurassic strata. A narrow strip of these deposits may also crop out beneath the Gault in the south-eastern part of the map. Unfortunately these beds are in most places devoid of fossils, so that it is difficult (in many instances) to decide whether they belong to the fresh-water series of Shotover and Brill, or represent the sediments laid down during a later marine transgression of Lower Cretaceous age.

At this period the earlier formations that rose above sea-level were planed off by the encroaching sea, so that the marine sands are markedly unconformable to the strata on which they rest. Owing to the low dips that prevail throughout the district, this unconformity can be detected but rarely in any particular section, but it is brought out clearly by the mapping of wide areas. As this marine transgression took place after the deposition of the Shotover Sands, it is highly probable that the original limits of these sands were considerably reduced by erosion at this time. The relationship to the Shotover Sands,[1] however, can only be inferred, as there is no section in which the contact of the marine with the fresh-water beds has been recognized.

With the doubt that must exist in certain places whether the sands belong to the fresh-water or to the marine group, it will be advisable to deal separately with the different areas in which the deposits in question occur, so that the evidence in regard to them may be independently considered.

The long irregular ridge of Boar's Hill, three miles south-west of Oxford, is capped with a thick mass of coarse ferruginous sand containing much concretionary ironstone. Similar material also occupies the crest of Hurst Hill, which lies along the same axis, but is separated from the main ridge by a deep hollow and thus forms a small outlier 600 yards north of the main mass. Smaller isolated patches of red sand, much obscured by gravelly drift, lie on the north-eastern side of the main ridge.

At Hurst Hill the strata are well exposed in the Chawley Brickyard, where the Kimmeridge Clay is dug beneath the sands

---

[1] This view of the unconformable relationship of the marine Lower Cretaceous beds to the underlying strata is clearly brought forward by Dr. A. M. Davies in his paper on the ' Geology of the Thames Valley,' already referred to on p. 87.

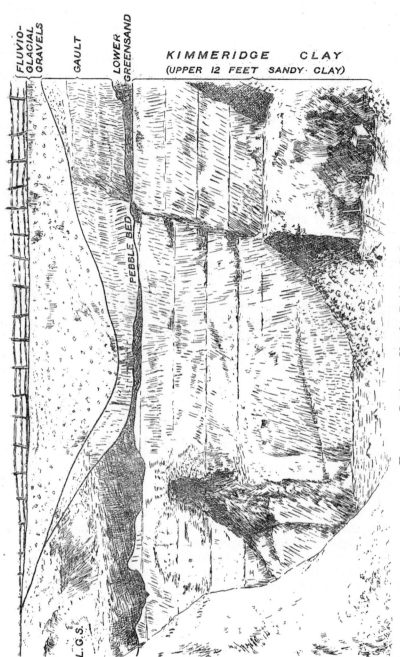

FLUVIO-GLACIAL GRAVELS

GAULT

LOWER GREENSAND

PEBBLE BED

KIMMERIDGE CLAY
(UPPER 12 FEET SANDY CLAY)

L.G.S.

FIG. 7.—*Section at Chawley Brickyard, Cumnor.*
Drawn from a Photograph taken by Mr. C. J. Bayzand.

(Fig. 7). The upper part of this section is much disturbed, either by glacial action or by ancient landslips, or both, so that patches of drift gravel and strips of blue clay, proved by fossil evidence to belong to the Lower Gault (*see* p. 103), as well as portions of Kimmeridge Clay, are curiously entangled among the Lower Cretaceous Sands. Where the latter are comparatively undisturbed they consist of coarse ferruginous sand showing well-worn quartz grains and small pebbles (especially toward the base), up to three-quarters of an inch in diameter. In places they are indurated into lenticular masses of sand-rock, and also contain ironstone concretions of the ' box-stone ' type, *i.e.*, with a hard crust surrounding and enclosing patches of incoherent sand. These beds are exposed to a maximum depth of 16 ft. in the pit. They have as yet yielded no trace of fossils ; but in the coarse grain of the sands, their well-worn aspect, and the presence of small pebbles, they bear a closer resemblance to the beds that are known to be marine[1] than to the fresh-water Shotover Sands. The fact that they rest directly upon an uneven surface of the Kimmeridge Clay, which implies the previous removal of the Portland and Purbeck Beds, lends further support to the view that they were accumulated during the later Lower Cretaceous stage of marine transgression and not during the early stage of fresh-water conditions. On these grounds they are represented as Lower Greensand on the map.

On Boar's Hill the sands are of the same character as in the Chawley section. They may be seen in a disused sand-pit on the north-east side of the road opposite Foxcombe Cottages, and they have been penetrated in numerous wells ; thus, opposite the house named ' Hillcrest,' a well, reported to be 50 ft. deep, was entirely in ferruginous sand with concretionary ironstone ; and in another, about half a mile farther south, adjoining ' Foxcombe ', 35 ft. of the same sand was passed through, and it was stated that the ' blue clay ' (Kimmeridge) would be reached at a further 5 ft. below.

A broad tract of Lower Greensand was shown in the original Geological Survey map as covering Nuneham Park, and extending northward to Toot Baldon. In the new series map Sheet 254, which was colour printed in 1905, Lower Greensand was represented over the area of March Baldon, as surveyed by J. H. Blake.

The mapping of this tract presents many difficulties, owing to the rarity of good exposures, but as elsewhere noted (*see* p. 69) fossil-evidence has now been obtained to show that arenaceous beds of Upper Kimmeridge age occur over parts of the area, probably from the northern margin of the Nuneham Park across the uplands of March Baldon and Toot Baldon, and eastwards towards Chislehampton. Lithologically, these formations are separable : the Lower Greensand locally consists of coarse ferruginous pebbly and quartzose sand, whilst the Upper Kimmeridge comprises sandy clays and fine grained sands and sandstones.

---

[1] This resemblance was commented on in an earlier memoir : on the ' Geology of parts of Oxfordshire and Berkshire ' (Sheet 13), p. 15.

The evidence of fossils, however, indicates conclusively that marine Lower Greensand occurs at Culham and Clifton Hampden, just beyond the limits of the area.   In the section at the entrance to the brickyard at Culham, the formation consists of coarse gritty ferruginous sand with small pebbles, shown at one time to the depth of 12 feet, and it appears to occupy a shallow depression in the Kimmeridge Clay ; but it is cut out about 150 yards farther east by the overlap of the Mammillatus Bed, before the present working-face of the pit is reached.[1]   Unfortunately the intervening ground is overgrown, and the junction of the Mammillatus Bed on the Lower Greensand is not exposed.

That the sand is a marine deposit is indicated by the presence of marine fossils, including *Radiopora sp.* and *Exogyra sinuata* J. Sow,[2] which have been collected for the Geological Survey. Additional species, referred to *Rhynchonella* cf. *parvirostris* (J. de C. Sow.), and *Panopea plicata* (J. de C. Sow.) have been obtained by Mr. C. J. Bayzand, and are now preserved in the collections of the University Museum, Oxford.   But the absence of diagnostic species leaves in doubt the position of the beds within the series.

Similar pebbly greensand is exposed in a low cliff on the banks of the Thames at Clifton Hampden.   The beds in this region are locally indurated into rocky layers ; and in a manuscript description of the neighbourhood, written by Daniel Sharpe,[3] there is a statement that organic remains had been obtained.   These fossils are now pre-served in the collections of the University Museum, Oxford, and are referred to the following species :—*Exogyra conica* J. Sow., *Terebratula ovata* J. Sow., *Rhynchonella parvirostris* ? (J. de C. Sow.) and *Ornithella tamarinda* (J. de C. Sow.).

The late J. H. Blake had noted exposures of Lower Greensand north of Hill Farm, and by Warren Farm, north of Culham ; also eastwards to the railway, where they can be seen in parts of the cutting north of Culham Station.   These sands are similar in character to those exposed at Culham brickyard.   By Rough Lodge, south-east of Nuneham Park, Blake, in 1896, saw in a disused brick-pit 4 feet of coarse quartzose sand resting on a similar thickness of thinly bedded, coarse ferruginous sandy rock, locally known as ' Roach.'   He also observed similar material in Lock Wood, on the western side of Nuneham Park ; there the ' Roach ' has been used for making paths.   Coarse sand is also exposed east and north-east of the Mansion in Nuneham Park, but the difficulties of distinguishing Lower Greensand from the arenaceous beds of Kimmeridge age are here complicated by the presence of Drift sand and gravel, and the absence of good sections.

---

[1] *See also* ' The Cretaceous Rocks of Britain ' *Mem. Geol. Surv.*, vol. i, 1900, p. 268 ; ' Excursion to Culham and Wallingford,' *Proc. Geol. Assoc.*, vol. xviii, 1903, p. 300.

[2] Excellent specimens of *Exogyra sinuata* were collected by J. Phillips at Culham. These are preserved in the collections at Oxford.   *See also* C. G. E. Dawkins, ' Dis-covery of *Exogyra sinuata* in the Lower Greensand of Culham, near Oxford,' *Geol. Mag.*, 1906, p. 94.

[3] Preserved in the Library of the Geological Survey and Museum.

CHAPTER IX

UPPER CRETACEOUS ROCKS

GAULT

THERE is little information to be obtained from the small areas of Gault that are found in the district. As a rule, the exposures are poor, and in the majority of sections it is impossible to decide whether the clays were deposited during the marine invasion that took place at the base of the Lower Gault, or were laid down at the time of the more extensive transgression that ushered in the Upper Gault. In the Culham brickyard, just beyond the southern margin of the sheet, there is definite evidence of an overlap of the Mammillatus Bed upon older rocks; but it is probable that the Gault clay out-cropping between Lower Standhill and Brimpton Farm, south of Tiddington, is of Upper Gault age, and is thus part of the Upper Gault overlap established in the district to the east.[1]

In the Culham brickyard section, the following beds were exposed in the working-face of the pit at the time of our visit (*see* Pl. IV.B) :—

		Ft.	In.
	Soil, up to ..	2	o
	Flint-gravel resting on irregular surface of Gault clay ..	3	6
Zone of *Hoplites dentatus*	5. Dark grey clay with a few white-skinned phosphatic nodules; *Hoplites dentatus* (J. Sow.), *Anahoplites mantelli* Spath, etc...	10	o
	4. Dark grey and brownish-grey clay with numerous specimens of *Hoplites dentatus* and a large, probably undescribed, species of *Inoceramus*. This bed forms a prominent band in the face of the pit .. .. about	4	o
Zone of *Hoplites benettianus*	3. Dark grey clay, slightly glauconitic; *Hoplites* cf. *dentatus* (J. Sow.), *H.* cf. *pseudodeluci* Spath	10	o
	2. Grey finely sandy clay; bedding-planes often dappled with brown rusty films, sometimes iridescent	2	6
Zone of *Douvilleiceras mammillatum*	1. Brownish-black gritty clay with many small pebbles of quartz, chert, ironstone, and rolled phosphatized fossils, including *Pectinatites pectinatus* (Phill.), *Pallasiceras rotundum* (J. Sow.), *Pholadomya rustica* Phill., *Pleuromya tellina* Ag., *Thracia depressa* (J. de C. Sow.), saurian remains, etc., all derived from the underlying Kimmeridge Clay	1	3

---

[1] *See* 'Summary of Progress for 1921' (*Mem. Geol. Surv.*), 1922, p. 112; F. L. Kitchin and J. Pringle, 'On the overlap of the Upper Gault in England and on the Red Chalk of the Eastern Counties,' *Geol. Mag.*, 1922, p. 199, etc.

Ft. In.

resting unconformably on

Kimmeridge Clay ⎰ Dark grey sandy clay.   At top is an indurated
bed of clayey sand, about 10 in. thick, and
its upper surface shows numerous burrows
and narrow fissures filled with clay from the
basement bed of the Gault .. .. seen to   8 0

The Mammillatus Bed which here rests unconformably on the Kimmeridge Clay probably also overlies the Lower Greensand exposed at the western end of the brickyard. This relationship, however, cannot be verified since the intervening ground is wholly concealed. The most notable indigenous fossil that has been obtained from this bed is the zonal ammonite *Douvilleiceras mammillatum* (Schloth.) a fragment of which was found by the writer in 1921. The species has also been recorded from Culham by Dr. L. F. Spath[1] and Mr. H. J. Osborne White.[2]

In the overlying clay-bed, fossils, especially Ammonites, are rare, and there appears to be no trace of the fauna of the Inaequinodus Zone of Dr. Spath's scheme of zonal classification ;[3] but in Bed 3 of the section, Cephalopods characteristic of the Benettianus Zone are abundant, particularly in the upper part of the bed. Dr. Spath, who has examined the specimens collected during the recent revision of the area, states that the top of the zone falls about the base of Bed 4, and the clay a few feet below this level yields *Hoplites* cf. *dentatus* (J. Sow.), *H.* cf. *pseudodeluci* Spath, *H.* cf. *rudis* Parona and Bonarelli, etc. In the University Museum, Oxford, there is a specimen from Culham assigned to *Hoplites benettianus* (J. Sow.), and, although the exact position from which it was obtained is not known, it may be safely referred to Bed 3.

The remainder of the Gault clay in the section is comprised within the zone of *Hoplites dentatus*. Bed 4 forms a prominent band in the working-face of the pit, and on account of its colour it can be easily identified. It is crowded with the remains of a large, probably undescribed, species of *Inoceramus*, somewhat reminiscent of the shells of *Inoceramus crippsi* Mant. from the Lower Chalk. Beds 4 and 5 have yielded the following ammonites : *Hoplites* aff. *bonarelli* Spath, *H. dentatus* (J. Sow.), *H. dentatus* (J. Sow.), var. *densicostatus* Spath, and *H.* aff. *rudis* Parona and Bonarelli.

In its essential features the Culham section is closely comparable with that exposed in the Okeford brickyard in Dorset, where the Mammillatus Bed rests on the Kimmeridge Clay.[4]

---

[1] Spath, L. F., ' Ammonoidea of the Gault,' *Mon. Pal. Soc.*, Pt. 1, 1923, p. 71.

[2] Treacher, L., ' Excursion to Culham and Abingdon,' *Proc. Geol. Assoc.*, vol. xx, 1908, p. 549.

[3] Spath, L. F., ' Excursion to Folkestone,' *Proc. Geol. Assoc.*, vol. xxxiv, 1923, p. 72 ; *see also* his Appendix ' On the Ammonite Horizons of the Gault and Contiguous Deposits ' in ' Summary of Progress of the Geological Survey for 1922 ' (*Mem. Geol. Surv.*), 1923.

[4] Newton, R. B., ' On the identification of the *Acanthoceras mammillatum* and *Hoplites interruptus* Zones at Okeford Fitzpaine, Dorsetshire,' *Geol. Mag.*, 1896, pp. 198–201. *See also* ' The Cretaceous Rocks of Britain ' (*Mem. Geol. Surv.*), vol. i, 1900, p. 162.

The extensive excavation of the Kimmeridge Clay at Chawley Brickyard, near Cumnor, has brought to light a bed of Lower Gault clay above the Lower Greensand, but in a remarkably disturbed condition (*see* Fig. 7).[1] From this clay Prof. W. J. Sollas and Miss Healey[2] obtained specimens of *Hoplites dentatus*, forms similar to those that characterize Bed 4 at Culham. At the base of this remnant of Lower Gault, an irregular pebbly layer can be traced, and in its lithological aspects it shows a close correspondence to those of the Mammillatus Bed, but has yielded no fossils to permit a direct correlation. It is highly probable, however, that this pebbly seam, like the disturbed Gault above it, may be merely a remnant of a bed of greater thickness.

Dark blue clay, probably of Gault age, has also been found in a well at the north end of Boar's Hill, overlying ferruginous sand.

The Upper Gault comprises a series of grey silty marls, belonging to the lower part of the zone of *Schloenbachia rostrata* (J. Sow.), as defined in the older zonal scheme of classification adopted by Jukes-Browne. A species so determined was obtained by J. H. Blake in Clare Brickyard before the closing-down of the pit. At present, exposures of the Upper Gault clays in the area are extremely rare. The full thickness of the Gault is estimated to be about 200 ft.

Gault extends to the borders of the Alluvium, west of Latchford, and thence beyond Latchford Copse. Bluish-grey clay, apparently belonging to the Gault, has been proved in a boring, made in the hill to the north-west of Chislehampton, near the top of the sloping ground opposite Church Farm. The Gault in this area overlies Kimmeridge Clay.

There are tracts of clay on March Baldon Green and around Windmill Hill in Nuneham Park. These are probably Gault, but are too poorly exposed to permit an accurate determination. In the narrow outcrop of Gault east of Great Milton and south of Tiddington, the clay is seldom exposed, but its presence was noted in the banks of the road, south of Sandylane Farm.

UPPER GREENSAND

A small tract of Upper Greensand lies within the area at Easington and Chalgrove.

The lower part of this group consists of malmstone and layers of sandy and glauconitic marl, about 90 ft. thick, beneath which springs are thrown out by the clays of the Gault. The upper part is a green glauconitic sand, 10 or 12 ft. thick. *Pecten (Syncyclonema) orbicularis* J. Sow. and other shell fragments were obtained from the malmstone of Clare Hill, north-east of Easington, where a good section was to be seen in the road-cutting.[3]

---

[1] Attention was first called to these features in 1887, by Dr. F. A. Bather, *Journ. Oxford Univ. Junior Scient. Club*, 1887 (1888), p. 32.

[2] *Proc. Geol. Assoc.*, vol. xix, 1905, p. 57.

[3] Jukes-Browne, A. J., 'The Cretaceous Rocks of Britain' (*Mem. Geol. Surv.*), vol. i, p. 280.

CHAPTER X

PLEISTOCENE DEPOSITS

By K. S. Sandford, M.A., D.Ph.

THERE are two distinct groups of superficial deposits in this district :—

(1) The Plateau Drift, a confused deposit of loam and clay mixed with boulders and pebbles of various sizes, occurring in more or less isolated patches and at high altitudes.

(2) The River Gravels, bedded deposits consisting mostly of pebbles of local limestones, disposed in terraces rising one above another from the present flood plains, almost entirely limited to the present river valleys or immediately flanking them (Figs. 8 & 9).

The distinction was first drawn by Dr. Kidd (first University Lecturer in Geology at Oxford). Further investigation shows that the River Gravels are readily subdivided with some stratigraphical significance, and it is probable that the Plateau Drift may be similarly differentiated. On all grounds it is clear that the Plateau Drift is older than the River Gravels ; therefore the former will be dealt with first, but it may be well to give here a brief historical outline of previous work, the sources of information of the present memoir, and to lay down a plan that will be followed in the systematic study of the ground.

The superficial deposits attracted the attention of Buckland, and in ' Reliquiae Diluvianae ' he gives a clear description of their nature, composition and distribution ; his account has formed the basis of later work.

Three Professors of Geology in the University of Oxford have also helped to elucidate some of the problems—Professors Phillips, Prestwich and Sollas.

Hull and Green also did much towards the study of similar deposits in the districts lying to the north, north-west and north-east, of the area included in the map of the Special Oxford Sheet.

Important papers have been contributed by Osborne White and Davis, the work of the former continuing that of Buckland and of Lucy in the Cotteswolds. Much detailed information was collected by J. H. Blake but was not published, and about 1906, when it was decided that this and other work should be brought up to date and published in a special memoir of the Oxford District, Mr. T. I. Pocock had Blake's notes at his disposal. Finally, all previous work, with the exception of Blake's notes, was at the disposal of the Rev. Charles Overy, who has studied the Plateau Drift, and of the writer during an investigation of the River Gravels ; for the

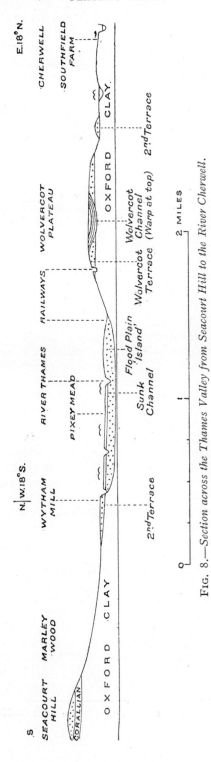

Fig. 8.—*Section across the Thames Valley from Seacourt Hill to the River Cherwell.*

Plateau Drift forms the summit of Seacourt Hill.

latter the valuable collections in the Oxford University Museum were of great importance.

For the present account, therefore, a considerable amount of previous work has been available. Those parts of the memoir of 1908 which dealt with the superficial deposits have been largely rewritten, but portions which needed no alteration have been incorporated.

In describing the actual distribution of deposits, a definite plan has been adopted. The Basin of the Thames above Oxford is first considered and then a traverse is made across each of the northern rivers in turn from west to east—Windrush, Evenlode, Cherwell, Ray ; next the part of the Thames below Oxford is considered and finally the Basin of the Thame—only part of which comes in the area under review. The Thame lies in a position distinct from the other rivers already mentioned and has a somewhat different history ; it is described separately in the case of the River Gravels.

PLATEAU DRIFT

The Plateau Drift is a deposit of rather peculiar character. It is bedded only rarely and then but rudely ; it consists of red-brown clay, loam, occasionally with some sand ; pebbles of all sizes and boulders are set in it without arrangement and locally with their longer axes pointing downwards. As we now see it, clearly it is not a normal fluviatile deposit. The question naturally arises as to whether the calcareous portion of an original gravel has been removed, leaving the present disordered and largely siliceous deposit. Whatever the circumstances of its formation there is no doubt that some calcareous material must have been picked up in its passage over the Oolites on which it now rests ; this has with equal certainty been removed, presumably by solution. The reddish colour of the drift in the north-west of the district is due, at least in part, to fine material derived from the Lias ; but even allowing for the disappearance of lime, and consequent disorder, the drift cannot be described as a normal fluviatile accumulation. It lies scattered over the district in sheets, now dissected by erosion, and at varying heights—many of which may be in correlationship. Most of the boulders, already rounded and smoothed, have undoubtedly been derived from the Bunter Beds of the Midlands ; others have come from East Anglia and the East Coast, and work now in progress tends to show that the rocks of even more distant parts have contributed to the Drift.[1]

Finally, numerous large pebbles and subangular boulders have been found with clearly marked striations on more than one face and in parallel ' sets ' ; only one agent is known which produces exactly this type of striation—moving ice. It is not suggested that in the local Plateau Drift—which from the character of its

[1] A more detailed account of composition is given after distribution has been discussed.

pebbles and boulders has long been termed Northern Drift—we are dealing with a *moraine profonde* of a great ice sheet ; indeed the slight abrasion and smoothing of the scratches on striated boulders —and their partial or complete removal from others—point to wear and tear since the pebbles left such an ice sheet.

Probably the true solution is arrived at if the local drift is considered, as it now lies, as the remnant of a glacial deposit, or in places a boulder clay, transported only a short distance since the disappearance of the ice (otherwise striae would be completely obliterated) by streams which were capable at times of moving heavy blocks. The drift in this district may have originated as a ' fluvio-glacial ' deposit.

Further discussion must now be postponed until the question of distribution has been settled, for it is necessary first to introduce a number of localities and other data.

DISTRIBUTION

The area within the south-west corner of the map is destitute of Plateau Drift ; west of Pickett's Heath (near Wootton, south-west of Oxford) the Corallian escarpment does not appear to have been seriously invaded, or if it was, all but occasional pebbles seem to have been removed by subsequent denudation.[1] Similarly the loop of the Thames valley south of Eynsham is free. There, the river has continually shifted its course southwards and the terraces rise step by step from its northern bank. A patch of Plateau Drift has been found in the Thames valley some miles beyond the western border of the map.

The Windrush Basin within the map is likewise clear of the drift, but near High Cogges, and to the north of it in Cogges Wood, isolated patches are encountered ; and a little farther north, bordering the Evenlode valley on its southern side, occurs the largest spread within the limits of the map. This patch runs from Freeland north-westwards to The Demesnes on the Witney-Woodstock road and extends along that road to the west to North Leigh and to the east until the highest river terrace is met near Long Hanborough (also spelt Long Handborough). It appears that the drift in this patch reaches its highest point in the western corner, north of Eynsham Hall Park, about 200 ft. above the Evenlode, and falls almost to the level of the highest river terrace near Long Hanborough at less than 130 ft. above the Evenlode, the terrace rising to a little above 100 ft. The patches lying to the south also fall and at High Cogges again almost reach the river gravel. To the north the drift is sharply truncated by the Evenlode Gorge, but a small patch occurs on the far side at Combe (just beyond the map) ; to the north-west it is cut off by the Wilcote valley, but as Mr. Pocock has pointed out, ' it reappears on the opposite side in two little outliers, at Wilcote Village and an adjacent hill to the west. There are terraces in the valley itself above the level of the river gravel, perhaps indicating that it was partly excavated before the drift ' (*op. cit.*, p. 96).

Sections have been seen throughout this tract, one of the best being the pits, now disused, at The Demesnes near North Leigh. The clearest section seen recently is situated in the brickyard at Combe,[2] where there was evidence of a small overthrust, but this is beyond the margin of the map, so the account

---

[1] Though on the plateau immediately west of Boar's Hill erratic pebbles are numerous (T. I. Pocock, ' The Geology of the Country around Oxford,' (*Mem. Geol. Surv.*), 1908, p. 100), no signs of drift are to be found on Harrowdown Hill, farther west.

[2] Sandford, K. S., ' The River Gravels of the Oxford District,' *Quart. Journ. Geol. Soc.*, vol. lxxx, 1924, p. 122.

of The Demesnes given by Mr. Pocock may well be used since the deposit at that locality is typical of the drift in the area now being considered.

On the top is an irregular bed of brown mottled loam, a few feet thick, full of stones set at all angles, penetrating the Oxford Clay in irregular hollows. The stones are a very mixed collection, among which occur numerous partially rounded flints a few inches across, and smaller fragments quite unworn. These have originally been derived from the Chalk, but they are so deeply weathered that it is probable that they had gone through more than one stage of transport and deposit before they reached their present position.

Other constituents are liver-coloured quartzites, doubtless from the Bunter Pebble beds of the Midland Counties, white vein quartz and variously coloured quartzites, probably from the same formation, hard sandstones resembling greywethers, also softer sandstones with felspar of the Millstone Grit type, and black lydian stone of unknown origin.[1]

The deposit is unbedded and Mr. Pocock considered that it ' had the appearance of having been disturbed by the action of underground water ';[2] this may be, but it is certain that the lime elements, if ever present, have been removed—which in itself would cause disorder. Careful observation of the pit over a long period has shown that well-striated boulders are by no means rare ; it is curious that those found have been of quartzite—a rock difficult to scratch, which is, however, equally resistant to weathering, preserving any such marks much longer than, say, a limestone.

The section at Combe brickyard has also yielded striated material. Some of the scratched boulders, already smoothed and rounded in the Pebble Beds of the Midlands, have been somewhat waterworn subsequent to their being striated. This, with the general features of the deposit, strengthens the opinion that the Plateau Drift in this area, though probably not a *moraine profonde* of an ice sheet, is at least of glacial origin ; that it has not subsequently suffered much fluviatile erosion (since striae remain) ; and that it may be the outwash of an ice sheet, the general border of which stood at no great distance, though it may well have been laid down in water.[3]

A patch of Plateau Drift occurs also a mile or two to the east, at High Lodge, at about the same altitude.

The variety of rocks yielded by a careful search in these pits is great and the original source of many yet remains to be found. At The Demesnes an angular block of sandstone, closely resembling a sarsen, only slightly waterworn, has been found, which measures 12 in. by 8 in. by 6 in. and weighs 28 lbs.[4] Considering the present position of the Eocene rocks and the bulk of the specimen, it seems clear that some agency other than a river must have transported it. Among many pebbles the tourmalinized rocks or ' schorl rocks ' may be noticed.

At North Leigh and New Yatt there is a greater thickness of drift, and a gravel bed is reported at the base which yields a good supply of water ; no doubt the numerous springs thrown out by the drift here and elsewhere have dissected the larger sheets into isolated patches, and the drift, by thus acting as a reservoir, is accomplishing its own destruction.

A part of the drift, which extends from the east of Eynsham Park by Freeland to Long Hanborough, appears to form a terrace about 350 ft. above the sea, and 120 ft. above the river. There are no good sections, but a pond on the south side of the road from Freeland to Church Hanborough, 300 yds. from the corner, showed three ft. of pebbly loam resting on a foot of mottled sand. It is rudely bedded and may be a part of the drift which was sorted by

---

[1] *Op. cit.,* p. 97.

[2] *Loc. cit.*

[3] The study of a still existing ice sheet and its margin does much to strengthen such beliefs.

[4] Near Combe Brickyard a great block of sarsen has been seen, but at the time of writing it still lies buried. It is believed to be an erratic block, and its size appears to be about 2½ ft. by 2½ ft. by 1 ft.

water on what was then the bottom of the valley. But it is inseparable from the rest of the deposit and is most probably of the same epoch.

Between the Evenlode and the Cherwell there are patches of drift capping Bladon Heath and Begbroke Wood ; no good sections have been seen. The drift rises to a height of 340 ft. above O.D.

East of the Cherwell no Plateau Drift occurs within the area of the map, but the gravels of the Thame, and, to a certain extent, those of the Cherwell and of the Ray, show that the drift is now absent only because it has been entirely denuded—and the clay lowland has been formed since the period of its deposition.[1] It is not known with certainty on Shotover Hill, east of Oxford.

We may now turn to the south bank of the Thames. Drift occurs on Seacourt Hill, south of Eynsham and west of Oxford (Fig. 8). Mr. Pocock reported on it as follows :—' There are several overgrown pits, formerly worked for gravel : the constituents being chiefly quartzite, white quartz, and flint embedded in clay. The drift rests on the slope of the hill, about 270 feet above the river, but does not reach the top. The neighbouring hill of Wytham, which rises 80 feet higher, appears to be destitute of drift.'[2]

An important area lies between the main roads from Oxford to Cumnor and to Abingdon ; the best known sites are :—

(1) Hurst Hill :—immediately south of the Cumnor road, the large pit of Chawley brickworks : hence the site has been known variously as Hurst Hill, Cumnor Hurst or Hill, and Chawley brickworks ; all these terms refer to the same site. A little nearer Oxford is another hill, somewhat lower, called Chawley Hurst.

(2) Pickett's Heath Farm :—almost due south of Hurst Hill, distant about a mile ; about ½ mile to the north of Boar's Hill proper but on the same ridge. References made to Pickett's Heath allude to the farm and its immediate environs.

(1) Hurst Hill is a detached eminence formed by an outlier of Lower Greensand with small patches of Gault clay and drift let down into hollows at the surface, see Fig. 7. At the brick-pit there are two of these depressions which appear to form parts of a trench crossing the top of the hill from north-east to south-west. The drift, which shows traces of stratification, or pseudo-stratification, is about 12 ft. thick in the middle, where it rests on Gault clay, but thins away at the sides, and overlaps on to the Lower Greensand. The stones are well-rounded or subangular and consist mainly of quartzose pebbles and flints associated with other material, including small boulders of a green-grey rhyolite ; the deposit is apparently identical with that of The Demesnes. Similar drift occurs at Pickett's Heath Farm, and at both sites Prof. W. J. Sollas has made extensive collections. Scratched boulders may be found occasionally at both localities.

It is unnecessary to give a complete list of the pebbles found, but here, as at The Demesnes and at Pickett's Heath Farm, they may be classified broadly in the following groups :—

I. Flint. (1) Nodular ochreous flint, with a deep white or brown patina, possibly from East Anglia.
(2) Grey-white nodular flint, which resembles that of parts of East Anglia.
(3) Some nodules of fresh flint from the Chilterns.
II. Quartzites and sandstones, supposedly from the Midlands.[3]

---

[1] Drift occurs at 400 ft. above O.D. on Long Crendon Hill, near Thame, to the east of the map, and on the plateau above the Three Pigeons Inn, near Tiddington, on the eastern border of the map, and there can be no doubt that this area was once invaded.

[2] *Loc. cit.*

[3] Reference should be made to Phillips' ' Geology of Oxford and the Valley of the Thames,' 1871, p. 456 *et seq.*, and particularly to p. 461, where he gives a table of considerable interest.

III. Tourmaline-grits and schorl-rock.
IV. Rare rocks, some of igneous origin.[1]

The matrix contains reddish sand, derived from the Lower Greensand. Numerous small outliers on different parts of the hills are shown by the abundance of pebbles in the soil at certain spots. Probably these patches rest on small areas of Gault, while the adjacent Greensand was not coherent enough to retain the drift.

The occurrence of the channel-like form of the deposit as seen in Chawley brick-pit has been explained by Mr. Pocock as follows[2] :—

' The confusion of strata of different ages, which is so remarkable in the brick-pit, is probably due to several causes. In the first place the Kimmeridge Clay, though less disturbed than the overlying formations, has its bedding arched, as is shown by the lines of concretions. This may be due to the earth movements which gave the strata their present structural forms, but something may have been effected by dissolution of the subjacent Corallian Limestone by underground waters. The Ironsand rests on a denuded arch of the clay in a way that is peculiarly favourable to landslips. Whenever the surface of the clay is wetted by the percolation of water, the overlying sand tends to slip down on both sides of the arch, and much of the material is carried away by the springs thrown out on the hillsides. Fissures and hollows are thus formed into which the Gault clay subsided. The process, though still in operation, had gone on to a considerable extent before the drift was deposited, for it has affected the gravel to a much less extent than the Gault. Some disturbing effect might also be expected from the action of the ice, and this has confidently been appealed to as the cause of all the anomalies,[3] but it is believed that the peculiar phenomena observed in the pit owe their origin in the main to the causes just described.'[4]

This seems to explain the facts ; but it should be remembered that if a deposit could be laid down at this height—520 ft. above sea-level and about 330 ft. above the Thames at its nearest point, possibly not by ice direct but by outwash streams from the ice near by—then it is equally possible for a small channel, such as that exposed on two sides of Chawley brick-pit, to be scoured out and filled. Sections seen recently near by have shown balls and considerable masses of gravel pressed into the underlying clay, with great disorder, which is distinctly suggestive of glacial processes.

On Chawley Hurst there is drift of the same kind, and here it appears to be disposed as a fairly continuous sheet.

(2) The highest drift in the district lies around Pickett's Farm at the north end of Boar's Hill, at a maximum elevation of 540 ft., and about 350 ft. above the Thames at its nearest point. A pit, open at the time of the survey of 1908, is still accessible, though somewhat overgrown and frequently flooded ; it is situated about 300 yds. west of the farm, and Mr. Pocock reports 8 ft. of gravel and sand and gives the constituents as ' principally vein quartz, quartzite and flint, the last being much more abundant and in a fresher state than in the drift of the Evenlode.' He continues : ' A little to the north, another pit now disused showed much smaller gravel of the same materials, totally devoid of bedding, and having at the top an irregular layer about three feet thick of stiff grey clay. In the old pits at Pickett's Heath Farm, where gravel has formerly been obtained in great quantity, there is also a clay bed which has been weathered yellow. The pebbly clay extends southward over the hill a little below the 500-foot contour, but is not connected with the drift

[1] Sandford, K. S., op. cit., pp. 121–122.
[2] Op. cit., p. 98.
[3] Bather, F. A., Journ. Oxford Junior Sci. Club, 1887 (1888), p. 32.
[4] See diagrammatic section, Chawley Brick-pit, by Prof. W. J. Sollas, Proc. Geol. Assoc., vol. xix, 1905, p. 57, and remarks in discussion, Quart. Journ. Geol. Soc., vol. lx, 1904, p. 131.

at lower levels.'[1] The clay has been considered by Prof. W. J. Sollas to be a boulder clay.[2]

There are some other exposures in the immediate vicinity of the farm, many of which are temporary, either being filled with rubbish or water ; one pit, now flooded, is situated close to the farm on the east side and another near by, rather more to the north ; only a few feet of gravel and weathered yellow clay have been seen here, but in general they conform to the description given above. It will be necessary to refer once more to this patch of gravel (*see* p. 112).

Of the remaining patches in the Boar's Hill area Mr. Pocock gives the following account,[3] to which there is little to add, except that close inspection, as at Pickett's Heath Farm and elsewhere, reveals a great variety of pebbles in every good exposure, though the local abundance of rather fresh flint is to be noted. Further, it should be remarked that the deposits in Bagley Wood fall to within about 100 ft. of the Thames, while those in Radley Park and Nuneham Park are at a slightly greater height.

'In Bagley Wood and Radley Park there are numerous patches of drift extending down the slopes from above the 400-foot contour line to below the 300-foot. Along the Oxford and Abingdon road through the wood, the drift was observed to contain pebbles of white quartz, quartzite, flint and lydite stone in reddish clay. In the pits by the roadside it seems to be at least ten feet thick and was probably worked for gravel. Buckland recorded igneous rocks from the drift here, which could have come from no nearer point than Charnwood Forest. At the top of the wood on the road to Boar's Hill there was another obscure section showing pebbly clay.

A section was also open in the Sugwell Farm[4] patch during the building of a house, which showed about four feet of drift on the Kimmeridge Clay. It was of irregular thickness and unstratified. The matrix consisted of clay with a considerable quantity of sand derived from the neighbouring outcrop of Greensand. It was slightly permeable, so that water flowed from the base over the slope of Kimmeridge Clay. At the same time it was sufficiently close-set to allow pools of water to stand on its surface. The pebbles consisted of white quartz, various quartzites, flint and lydite, but not limestone. On the opposite side of the river another group of outliers is found on high ground near the 300-foot contour-line in Nuneham Park. They rise to a height of 130 ft. above the river and are much denuded. The drift consists of loam and clay full of rounded pebbles of quartzite, quartz, lydian stone and flint.'[5]

In the basin of the Thame, as already stated, most of the Plateau Drift has been removed. The composition, when compared with that of the drift in the vicinity of Oxford, is markedly different—owing to the much higher percentage of fresh flint. Mr. Pocock described one small area, quoting from the notes of Mr. Blake[6]:—

'At the top of the hill N.W. of Chislehampton, at a height of 290 feet, 120 feet above the river, are two small patches of drift overlying Gault, in which flints are much more abundant, and the other constituents much less numerous in proportion. In the more southerly of the two patches a small pit was open three feet deep showing irregular gravel and loam much weathered. Mr. J. H. Blake ascertained that the deposit was as much as seven feet in depth at the farm-house close by.'

Farther up the valley, south of Tiddington, is a broad patch of superficial deposits, marked pink on the map, which passes out of the area to the east.

---

[1] *Loc. cit.*
[2] Pres. Address, *Quart. Journ. Geol. Soc.*, vol. lxvi, 1910, p. 57.
[3] *Op. cit.*, pp. 98, 99.
[4] Should read Sugworth.
[5] Blake, J. H., ' Summary of Progress for 1900 ' (*Mem. Geol. Surv.*), 1901, p. 130.
[6] *Op. cit.*, p. 99.

In it an important section was examined by Mr. Pringle and the writer in a large pit between Brimpton Farm and the Three Pigeons Inn at the cross roads to the east. The section, some 100 yds. long, showed peculiar features and will be described in full. The material was well and clearly bedded and non-calcareous; flint, which was abundant, varied from ochreous to fresh, and was splintered and little rolled. There were considerable quantities of small pebbles from the Plateau Drift, including tourmaline rocks. The occurrence of Eocene pebbles was marked and there was a high content of quartz sand (? Shotover) and of Shotover Ironsand. It was noted that Jurassic fossils were entirely absent.

The deposit is unlike most of the Plateau Drift and lacks the clay so often associated with it ; the material is most clearly bedded. It has not been derived mainly from the east, where high ground probably existed at a less distance than it does to-day. Its height, some 150 ft. above the Thame, and the assemblage of pebbles associate it definitely with the Plateau Drift, and it most probably represents a contemporary outwash, with even deposition in a broad belt, from the more normal Plateau Drift to the north. This deposit should be borne in mind in considering the drift as a whole, and its borders.

At the time of the previous survey the deposit was only seen in one small exposure close to the high road near Trindal's Farm. Here the gravel is essentially a mass of unworn flint fragments, without any arrangement. The common pebbles of the Northern Drift are present but in subordinate quantity. According to Mr. J. H. Blake, the gravel has been proved by well-sections to be from ten to twelve feet in thickness.[1]

Mr. Pocock remarks :—' The position of this mass of drift is a striking testimony to the vast denudation which has taken place since its formation. Standing on the plateau, the observer overlooks abrupt slopes on the north and west, leading to the river 150 ft. below. On all sides numerous streams issuing at the surface of the Gault clay, underlying the drift, have cut their valleys far back into the plateau. To the south-east the broad Gault plain extends from Thame along the foot of the ' Greensand ' escarpment, where it might be thought would be an easier course for the river than the tortuous valley through the hills east of Shotover. That the whole depth of 150 ft. has been eroded since the drift was formed must not be inferred, for it is possible that the gravel extended to lower levels, and that only the highest part has escaped denudation' (ibid).

In the area included in the map the division of the Plateau Drift into high and low groups is distinctly noticeable : the patches of Pickett's Heath and Hurst Hill (and Chawley Hurst, though this is rather lower) standing 300 ft. and more above the Thames, while those of Bagley Wood, Radley Wood and Nuneham Park lie within 100 ft. and 150 ft. The latter recall the height of the patch at The Demesnes (general level about 140 ft.). This feature will be referred to again (see p. 115).

With the information available from the foregoing survey it is now possible to discuss the Plateau Drift in greater detail. It has already been shown that the drift may be identified as being originally associated with an ice sheet, the general margin of which probably lay a little to the north ; it will be well now to look into this problem rather more closely.

ROUTES FOLLOWED BY THE DRIFT

Just over a hundred years ago Buckland traced quartzose pebbles up the valleys of the Cherwell and of the Evenlode to deposits at the heads of these rivers, which he definitely recognized as belonging to the New Red Sandstone pebble beds of the Midlands ; the drift was mixed and included material from the Chalk, among which Buckland observed the red chalk of Lincolnshire and Yorkshire, and he inferred that it had been transported to the south-west

---

[1] Pocock, T. I., op. cit., p. 99, and J. H. Blake, 'Summary of Progress for 1898 ' (Mem. Geol. Surv.), 1899, p. 159.

PLATEAU DRIFT. 113

across the Midlands, and had entered the Thames valley by the gaps in the Oolite escarpment near the sources of the Evenlode and Cherwell. He further maintained that, since the drift is found at the tops of isolated hills such as Seacourt and Cumnor, the valleys have been subsequently excavated.[1]

In 1872, Lucy[2] published a paper with a map for which great credit is due. He showed that Northern Drift occurred not only throughout most of the Avon and Severn basins but in isolated patches in the midst of the Cotteswolds as far south and west as Cirencester (near the head of the Thames), north of Fairford (Coln valley), near Northleach and in the upper valleys of the Windrush and of the Evenlode. Twenty-five years later Osborne White showed that red quartzose pebbles may be traced throughout the valley of the Windrush, and, by a gap near Stow-on-the-Wold, into the upper Evenlode valley and thence to the Vale of Moreton ; he, too, noticed Northern Drift in the Coln valley and believed that it has been carried over the much higher gap in the Cotteswolds at the head of that river.[3] Clearly, therefore, there has been a definite transport of material from the north and north-west—mixed with drift which has been brought from the East Coast westwards across the Midland Plain.

There is also evidence of drift from another direction. It has already been noticed that the drift of the eastern part of the area consists mainly of flint ; in that on Boar's Hill there is a predominance of rather fresh flint mixed with Northern Drift—the latter including ochreous and grey nodular flints. Work beyond the limits of the map in the valley of the Cherwell has shown the writer that along the line of this river there seems to be a regional partition of predominant Northern Drift to the west and of flint drift with some constituents of the Northern Drift in it to the east. Traced eastwards from this line (Cherwell-Boar's Hill) the drift contains an increasing percentage of fresh flint, i.e., towards the Chiltern Hills fresh flint becomes predominant, so that there is good reason to suppose that an Eastern Drift entered by way of the Thame valley.

Between the Thame and the Cherwell, north of the area included in the map, lies the Ray-Ouse watershed, which is sprinkled on its southern slope with drift containing numerous pebbles of the type of the Northern Drift, with fresh flint ; the watershed is thickly covered with drift, partly of fresh flint, on its northern (Ouse) side along a line running from Buckingham to Banbury and reaching elevations as great as those near Oxford.[4] As the drift caps the divide there is thus no reason why it should not have entered the Thames Basin. North of Bicester constituents of the Northern Drift are present, as stated above ; nearer Buckingham there is definite evidence of a great proportion of material derived from farther to the east and north ; towards Banbury the percentage of Northern Drift material clearly increases until at that town, or a little west of it, the assemblage is really that of the Northern Drift.[5] There is therefore a north-easterly drift entering the Thames Basin over the Ray-Ouse divide near Bicester.

This survey—part of which must of necessity be conducted outside the area of the map—leads to the definite conclusion that drift material converged on Oxford on lines like the ribs of an opened fan, so that even the remote headwaters of the Thames and of the Coln, in the western part of the Cotteswolds, were not immune from the invasion. There are Eastern passing into North-easterly, true 'Northern' and North Western Drifts ; but the last two include elements brought across the Midlands from the

---

[1] 'Reliquiae Diluvianae,' 1823, p. 250, et seq. ; see also Phillips, 'Geology of Oxford,' etc., 1871, map, p. 1, and p. 456.
[2] 'Gravels of the Severn', etc., Proc. Cottes. Nat. Club, vol. v, 1872, pp. 71–142, and map.
[3] Proc. Geol. Assoc., vol. xv, 1897, p. 157, et seq.
[4] See Green, A. H., 'The Geology of Banbury, Woodstock, Bicester and Buckingham' (Mem. Geol. Surv.), 1864, p. 53, et seq ; and H. B. Woodward, 'Explanation of Horizontal Section, Sheet 140 ' (Geol. Surv.), 1891, p. 10.
[5] Ibid.

East Coast; in addition they contain to a marked degree tourmalinized and other rocks which have come from the west.

Generally, the lines of the river valleys seem to have been followed in the invasion.

MEANS OF INTRODUCTION OF THE DRIFT

Enough has been said to show that the area was invaded by non-local material from various directions, but it would be well now to look further into the problem of the means by which the invasions were effected. That ice was mainly the agent now seems certain, but the task of fixing the southern boundary of an all-covering blanket of ice is more difficult. Striated boulders, however, are found at Boar's Hill and Prof. W. J. Sollas has identified boulder clay there; on this evidence, therefore, it appears that at one time heavy, moving, ice was as far (or very nearly as far) south as Oxford.

It is known that the Midlands north of the Cotteswold escarpment, as well as the Ouse Basin, were submerged by ice which left extensive and unmistakable signs of its passing. The drift material inside the barrier of the Cotteswold escarpment is identical with that outside it, in the Midland Plain, and there is reason to believe that true boulder clay exists in the upper part of the Evenlode valley, and flanking it. At Combe brickyard also there is the small overthrust and striated pebbles and boulders have been found here and at The Demesnes. The deposit at Combe has been declared to be a true boulder clay by more than one highly competent visitor.

Nowhere in the drainage area of the Thames and its tributaries, west of the Chiltern escarpment, is the drift thick; also it is weathered from top to bottom and has been affected by solution and slipping. In this respect a statement made by Mr. Pocock is interesting :—

' A parallel case from another region may not be out of place here. In the Low Peak of Derbyshire there is drift consisting of pebbles from the New Red Sandstone, cherts from the Carboniferous and other stones embedded in clay, and commonly unstriated. The deposit, which is usually thin and deeply weathered, bears much resemblance to the drift of Oxfordshire. But in one of the deep pits on the limestone tract, where the stony clay is abnormally thick, blocks of limestone, beautifully polished and grooved by ice action, were obtained near the bottom. Here there is glacial drift from which all calcareous material in the upper part has disappeared, and which only at a depth of 15 feet shows the characteristic marks of glaciation. No depth so great has been observed in the Oxfordshire drift.'[1]

The evidence for assuming that *at some time* heavy ice reached Oxford and the neighbourhood by the northern, north-eastern, and north-western valleys must be considered as strong. But, as will be seen, the whole of the Plateau Drift is not of necessity the direct deposit of glacial tongues.

VERTICAL RANGE OF THE DRIFT

The reason for the last statement in the above paragraph lies in the work of the Rev. Charles Overy, who has carried out detailed levelling of patches of Plateau Drift, a laborious research which lasted some years. His study was not limited to this district but was continued through Goring Gap into the lower parts of the Thames Basin as well as into the Cotteswolds. As a result, Mr. Overy has formed the opinion that the drift continues the ' terrace system ' of the true river gravels, above their upper limit. He was able to find the base-levels of what appear to be much denuded terraces of Plateau Drift which maintain the same gradient as the present rivers. It may be pointed out that Mr. Pocock suggested the following groups[2] :— (the heights given are those above river-levels).

a. 290–350 ft (Boar's Hill, Cumnor Hurst and Wytham Hill).

---

[1] *Op. cit.*, p. 102.
[2] *Op. cit.*, pp. 103, 104.

b. 200 ft. (top (not bottom) of Bagley Wood and patches along the foot of the Chiltern escarpment. *See* Sheet 237).

c. 130 ft. (the drift sheets of Freeland, and west of Radley).

Mr. Overy has amplified this series and taken the levels of the deposits as follows[1] :—

Evenlode–Isis (Thames) Confluence

345 ft.   300 ft.   265 ft.   250–200 ft.   150–130 ft.

Evenlode Valley

Drift scattered at high level to 280 ft.   230 ft.   200 ft.   130–110 ft. from which, with other figures, he deduces a normal series of

350 ft.   300 ft.   260 ft.   230 ft.   200 ft.   (160–130 ft.)[2]

which, he says, is represented both above and below Goring Gap. (All the heights given above are in feet above present river-level.)

It is in the deposits of the 350 ft. level (Boar's Hill) and of the 160–130 ft. level (The Demesnes, Combe brickyard) that glacially striated boulders have been found.

Mr. Overy discovered in a deserted channel of the Thames near Reading numerous implements lying at depths ranging to 14 ft. in consolidated gravel, and at a height of 140 ft. above the present river-level ; they appear to be of early Chellean type and are mostly well preserved. The discovery is of importance, but a full discussion of it cannot be given in the present memoir.

The following points also arise :—

(1) If the patches of Plateau Drift are graded with the rivers then it is unlikely that they were deposited in their present form and position from beneath an ice cap or from floating ice (*see* p. 108). It seems much more probable that the drift as now seen represents the resorting at definite levels of a portion of a great mass of material, left by ice, here and there preserved intact but mostly resorted.

(2) If the deposits are graded from the Evenlode to the London Basin then the likelihood of a large glacial lake at the foot of the Chiltern escarpment seems to be remote. Certainly the general situation of the Plateau Drift and of the later river terraces seems to give little support to the theory of the ponding of water in this locality over a prolonged period ; the river terraces, being preserved more extensively than the older drift, give positive indication of even grading both above and below Goring Gap.[3]

In referring to this country the work of Professor Déperet and others in the Mediterranean[4] Basin, Professor Sollas has identified the deposit on Boar's Hill (108 metres above the Thames at Oxford and 165 metres above sea-level) as the Sicilian Terrace of the Thames. It was accompanied by glacial conditions which would seem to have been preceded in this country by a great submergence, combined with

[1] Thanks are due to the Rev. C. Overy for placing the whole of his manuscript notes and maps at the disposal of the writer.

[2] *Abstracts Proc. Geol. Soc.*, No. 1095 (January 17th, 1923), p. 28, *et seq.*

[3] *See* Harmer, F. W., on 'Lake Oxford and the Goring Gap,' published in *Abstract Rep. Brit. Assoc.* for 1906 (1907), p. 572 ; also in *Geol. Mag.*, 1906, p. 470. *See also*, by the same author, 'On the Origin of certain Cañon-like Valleys associated with Lake-like areas of depression,' *Quart. Journ. Geol. Soc.*, vol. lxiii, 1907, pp. 470–513.

[4] For a brief account of the original work, and discussion, *see* Prof. W. J. Sollas, *Abstracts Proc. Geol. Soc.*, No. 1095 (January 17th, 1923), p. 21 *et seq.*, and *Nature* March 10th, 1923. The references to the original work are given in 'Ancient Hunters,' 3rd Ed., 1924 (London), p. 36. The application to the Oxford District is found in *op. cit.*, p. 150 *et seq.*

an Arctic climate, so that material could be transported by ice rafts from the West Country eastwards. By suggesting this submergence Professor Sollas revives the conclusions of Phillips and Buckland. He says of Boar's Hill :—

‘ Thus the southern part of England must have been submerged at least to this, and possibly a greater, extent at the time the ice grounded and discharged its load of debris on Boar's Hill. This conclusion finds a partial confirmation in the occurrence on Bowsey Hill, at a height of 145 m., of material brought from the south similar to that already described.’

A subsequent sinking of sea-level to about 100 m. is suggested ; ‘ then the Avon, at that time a tributary of the Thames, brought down from the Midlands vast quantities of quartzite pebbles, and these intermingled with the glacial erratics built up the Sicilian Terrace.’

Professor Sollas considers that after this period the sea-level continued to fall and terraces were formed at 91 m., 81 m., and 71 m. ; at the last stage there was a pause during which a terrace was cut. The sea-level is then thought to have fallen to between 65 and 61 metres ; ‘ at this stage a plentiful deposit of gravel accumulated and a broad terrace was formed which is known as the Tilehurst plateau. It corresponds with the ‘ Milazzian ’ terrace, which in the valley of the Somme contains implements of the Strepyan industry and a fauna resembling that of the Forest Bed of East Anglia. The next terrace is found at a level of 40 m.–50 m. and presents signs of a colder climate ; near Reading it has yielded implements of a primitive Chellean industry to the researches of the Rev. C. Overy. The terrace which succeeds this at 30 m., and thus corresponding with the ‘ Tyrrhenian ’ terrace, was evidently formed during genial conditions ; it contains abundant remains of the warm fauna and typical Chellean bouchers.’

This last terrace, of 30 m., is the Handborough or ‘ 100-foot ’ Terrace of the Thames, the first of the true River Terraces, to which attention will now be turned.

The Plateau Drift is one of the most puzzling of the superficial deposits of this country. The work done by Mr. Overy and adopted by Prof. W. J. Sollas is important. It is indeed significant that the theory of an early invasion of the centre of England by sea, with floating ice, was the considered judgment of Buckland, of Phillips, and now of Professor Sollas. He has, however, made an addition ; he retains the hypothesis of an original submergence but considers that thereafter the material then introduced was resorted and redeposited by fluviatile agency—with the formation of the Plateau Drift.

The existence in this district of material from the West Country may be taken as proved, but in the writer's opinion it yet remains to be shown at what period it was introduced and whether it was first transported to the Midlands. It is debatable if ice-rafts would be capable of transporting the vast amount of non-local material (or that part of it which is referable to the West Country) now found in the Oxford District. The study of existing ice-caps, and of icebergs calved from them, shows that the latter carry much material which the moving ice-cap itself has torn from its bed ; the debris so carried out to sea is deposited over a wide area. On the other hand the ice-cap itself, by definite movement, provides the material which gives rise to the expanses of true boulder clay which often surround it.

CHAPTER XI

PLEISTOCENE DEPOSITS—(*continued*)

RIVER GRAVELS

IN the general introduction to the superficial deposits certain features have already been made clear, notably the main points of distinction between the Drift of the Plateau and the deposits on the River Terraces. Before a particular account of the River Deposits is given it would be well to bring to notice a few points which will be helpful in later discussion, and in following the general relations and significance of the terraces.

It will be shown that of several terraces the highest, which lies between 70 ft. and 100 ft. above the present rivers, is the earliest; it remains, therefore, to consider the relations between it and the Plateau Drift. These relations may be summarized briefly as follows[1] :—

(i) The Plateau Drift is in isolated patches; the terrace, where preserved, is in benches of some length.

(ii) The Plateau Drift is decalcified; the terrace-gravel retains its calcareous matter.

(iii) The terrace-gravel contains a fauna of a warm climate, in association with derived glacially-striated boulders.

(iv) The terrace contains large numbers of erratics derived from places more than 100 miles from the Thames, and in other drainage-basins which could at no time have been invaded by the Upper Thames system or drained by it. These erratics are found in the Plateau Drift at levels higher than the terrace.

(v) Although the Plateau Drift has not been seen resting under the gravels of the Handborough stage [or High Terrace], nor the latter cutting into the former, surveying and levelling show that the terrace-gravels lie round the foot of an isolated patch of glacial Plateau Drift of the stage of 140 ft. above river-level (The Demesnes, near Long Hanborough).

(vi) If the drift were later than the terrace, and of glacial origin, the latter would show signs of considerable pressure or disturbance.

(vii) Plateau Drifts descend into the valley near Ascot in the Moreton Vale, which is covered by low-level gravel. There is no reason why the Moreton Vale and other valleys should not have been partly excavated at this early date; but I know of no other reliable exposure that proves it, except in Bagley Wood, near Oxford, where the Plateau Drifts descend to within 100 ft. of the river.

The above summary of facts leaves little doubt that the highest terrace of the Upper Thames is later than the Plateau Drift. This is a matter of importance; when the gravels throughout the Thames

[1] Sandford, K. S., *op. cit.*, pp. 127, 128.
[2] Hull, E., ' Geology of the Country around Cheltenham ' (*Mem. Geol. Surv.*), 1857, p. 85.

are correlated it seems probable that this terrace will be coupled with the High Terrace of the lower river—as at Swanscombe, Grays and elsewhere, where the same relationship appears to exist,[1] but, owing to the absence of fauna in the critical section, the point could not be proved beyond doubt.

In this district no river gravel older than the High Terrace appears to exist.

Careful levelling establishes another point ; the older terraces of the district, though preserved only in detached benches, undoubtedly present the same gradient as that of the rivers of to-day, which they border ; the parallelism is not exact but the discrepancies are of minor importance. Also, as might be supposed, there is no discontinuity of gradient at the confluence of two rivers.[2]

Lastly, it will be noticed that a name is given in the following pages to each terrace, or other deposit. The terms chosen refer in each case to the locality at which the features of the deposit are best displayed.

Handborough Terrace

The gravels of this Terrace lie between 70 and 100 ft. above the rivers, being preserved mostly in the valleys (or bordering them) of the upper reaches of the rivers which unite near Oxford. In the great valley cut in clay and stretching from Swindon to Aylesbury (Vale of White Horse, Vale of Aylesbury) scarcely a trace of the terrace remains ; it has been removed by denudation. In the Cotteswold country, sheets and patches of gravel crown promontories projecting from the uplands on to the plains of the lower terraces or on to the low-lying clay country.

On the right bank of the Thames above Oxford the gravel of this stage has been removed by the continual lateral erosion of the river and consequent shifting of the course down the dip-slope of the Oolites.

Between the Thames and the Windrush there is an irregular outlier on the hill west of Hardwick : 5 ft. of calcareous gravel with occasional small pebbles from the Plateau Drift were seen in a pit a little outside the boundary of the map (near the cross-roads between Hardwick and Yelford), whence the writer has mapped the superficial deposits as far as the border of Lechlade. The gravel caps a prominent ridge, trenched by later erosion, stretching for about 4 miles to the west of this outlier. On the opposite side of the Windrush are two small patches at High Cogges and another west of Tar Wood. Mr. Pocock saw an exposure in the most westerly of these

---

[1] Holmes, T. V., ' Relation of the Drift to the High Terrace,' *Quart. Journ. Geol. Soc.*, vol. xlviii, 1892, p. 365. *Ibid.*, vol. l, 1894, p. 443 ; and *Essex Naturalist*, vol. vii, 1893, pl. ix, and p. 193.

[2] Sandford, K. S., *op. cit.*, pp. 116–121, and figs. 2 and 3, note, the benches of gravel marked in the figures are those only which were measured by the author ; others, of which at the time it was not possible to obtain the base-level, were omitted.

(Spring Hill) which was similar to that near Hardwick. At South Leigh he found a small pit in which the gravel contains numerous siliceous pebbles at the top and appears to be disturbed at the surface[1]—a common feature in the gravels of this terrace. Mr. Pocock also found a gravelly soil capping a hill north-west of Eynsham ; all the pebbles were derived from the Plateau Drift.

The largest sheet extends from Long Hanborough to Church Hanborough, and flanks the southern side of the valley of the Evenlode. Exposures are numerous and two large pits have been worked for many years but only recently have fossils been found. This is the only known locality west of the Chiltern Hills where the Handborough or High Terrace gravel is fossiliferous.[2]

A large pit worked for gravel and sand is situated on the out- skirts of Long Hanborough on the edge of the Evenlode Gorge, just north of the New Inn. The top 3 ft. are markedly disturbed, especially towards the northern side. The gravel is generally coarse at the bottom, where it is sometimes bleached and loose ; material from the Plateau Drift is abundant, and boulders of quartzite and other hard rocks have been found deeply striated, the striæ being abraded. False-bedding is conspicuous, and there are some bands and lenticles of rather coarse sand. It is possible that the lower bleached gravel is considerably older than the remainder. At the base of the gravel the following fossils have been found :

Elephas antiquus (of archaic type ; molar)
E. antiquus (molar)
E. antiquus *or* antiquus-trogontherii (molar)
E. antiquus trogontherii (molar)
E. trogontherii (molar)
E. sp. (portion of tusk)

From the same level (position unknown): *Equus* cf. *caballus*, (teeth fragments) ; and *Bos* cf. *primigenius*, tooth and limb-bones.[3]

In the pit situated between the fork of the road from Oxford to Witney and that from Oxford to Stonesfield the gravel is 16 ft. thick. It is evenly bedded, with bands of sand and clay, and is composed of small oolitic pebbles. Numerous large pebbles and boulders, often subangular, as well as smaller fragments, of a great variety of rocks (including flint) have been derived from the Plateau Drift at The Demesnes. Large tabular pieces of Forest Marble also occur. The following fossils have been found in this pit, at or near the base, in the gravel itself and not associated with the ' solution pipes ' which descend several feet from the subsoil and in some cases reach the bottom of the gravel : *Elephas antiquus* cf. *trogon-*

---

[1] *Op. cit.*, p. 91.

[2] The exposure at ' The Row,' Long Hanborough, described by T. I. Pocock, *op. cit.*, p. 91, and by E. Hull, ' Geology of the Country around Woodstock ' (*Mem. Geol. Surv.*), 1859, p. 28, is now obscured. *See also* A. E. Salter, *Proc. Geol. Assoc.*, vol. xix, 1905, p. 39.

[3] Sandford, K. S., *op. cit.*, pp. 124, 125. The term *E. antiquus trogontherii* was used by the author with the approval of the late Dr. C. W. Andrews, but it is opposed (on good grounds) by some palaeontologists. See also *Quart. Journ. Geol. Soc.*, vol. lxxxi, 1925, pp. 69–72.

therii, molar ; *Rhinoceros megarhinus* or *leptorhinus,* molar ; and *Cervus* ? *elaphus,* molar.

Pieces of burnt flint, cracked and patinated white in the interstices, have been found *in situ* near the bottom.

The base-level in these pits is about 308 ft. above O.D. while the Evenlode flows near by at 222 ft. above O.D. The solution-pipes are filled with brown gravelly clay ; the cause of their formation is obscure ; they clearly mark localized removal of lime, by solution, as in the soil and subsoil and decayed roots may certainly be found in them from top to bottom[1]. They have been the subject of much speculation, but systematic investigation is required (*see* Plate 11.B).

A single implement of Chellean type, with heavy ochreous patina, is reported from Long Hanborough ; but unfortunately it is not known whether the specimen came from these gravels or from lowlying gravels in the valley nearly 100 ft. below. Prolonged search has revealed no implement in the higher deposit ; the lower is not exposed.[2] At the time of the previous survey no fossils were known within the Oxford district from the gravels of this stage.

It has been proposed that the term Handborough Terrace should be applied to this, the highest river terrace of the Upper Thames system ; hitherto it has been known as the High or the Fourth Terrace and sometimes as the 100-Foot Terrace—though the base-level is generally not more than 90 ft. above present river-level.

Above Long Hanborough, between North Leigh and Wilcote, there are a number of small patches of gravel which probably belong to this terrace, and have given rise to the suggestion that at this time the Windrush joined the Evenlode at this point. The writer has examined the intervening country and has noted a distinct col in the divide, which has been cut into from the Windrush side by a deep combe starting from Hailey (outside the western border of the map). Although a detailed survey is still required it seems that the suggested junction of the two rivers is probable.

Below Long Hanborough there is a patch of gravel on the opposite side of the river facing Church Hanborough, on a small plateau by Purwell Farm, at a height of 300 ft. above O.D., and another northwest of Yarnton. Mr. Pocock saw a section in the latter tract (on the south-west side of the lane leading from Yarnton towards Begbroke Wood) and noted that ' six feet of gravel were seen, of which the upper three feet consisted of a weathered residue of siliceous pebbles in brown loam, the rest being normal Oolite gravel '[3]; the proportion of quartzite material here is greater than at Long Hanborough, probably because weathering has dissolved the calcareous constituents.

In the valley of the Cherwell no gravel of the Handborough stage appears within the limits of the map, but just beyond the northern border, there is an important plateau flanking the eastern

---

[1] *Ibid.,* p. 124.
[2] *Ibid.,* p. 125.
[3] Pocock, T. I., *op. cit.,* pp. 91–92.

side of the incised meanders of the river; the village of Kirtlington is situated upon it. On the western outskirts of the village as much as 20 ft. of gravel occur with base-level at 318 ft. above O.D., the Cherwell flowing at about 218 ft. above O.D. Although the site is outside the limits of the map it would be well to describe certain of its features which are of importance.

(1) Large flags of Forest Marble and of Lias Ironstone are numerous; they are little worn and are found with dimensions up to 2 ft. by 1 ft. and 3 in. thick. The Lias outcrop lies several miles to the north.

(2) Pebbles from the Plateau Drift are scarce and small.

(3) A great deal of solution and surface movement has taken place near the edge of the plateau overlooking the river, and extends to a depth of 5 ft.; but nearer the village the solution-pipes are regular, cylindrical, 10 ft. deep and 5 ft. wide, and are filled with lime-free, pebbly, ferruginous sand. The pebbles retain the lines of bedding, somewhat 'sagged,' of the surrounding calcareous gravel.

(4) Charcoal-like material has been found in patches and along lines of bedding, but it does not appear to have originated from the lignite known to occur in the adjacent Forest Marble. No burnt flints nor implements have yet been found.[1]

In the valley of the Ray, which joins the Cherwell near Islip, no gravel of this stage has been noted, but Mr. Pocock observed rude platforms on the inlier of Great Oolite rocks at Islip; they rise one above the other on the left bank of the river and appear to be independent of the structure of the strata: 'It is possible,' Mr. Pocock says, 'that these are rock ledges formed by the Ray corresponding to the gravel terraces elsewhere.'[2]

On the right bank of the Thames below Oxford one or two small patches of the High Terrace breached by streams from Boar's Hill occur between Kennington and Radley. No sections are open, but Mr. Pocock states that 'in an old pit near the gate of the golf course (opposite Sandford Pool) the deposit was seen to be mainly quartzose gravel and flint embedded in sand derived from the Lower Greensand of Boar's Hill. It is not easy here to separate river gravel from high-level drift; but at Radley the abundance of Oolite pebbles on the surface of the terrace indicates fluviatile origin.'[3] In a well sunk in the terrace at Radley College 8 ft. of gravel were pierced before the Kimmeridge Clay was reached.[4]

South of Oxford no remains of the terrace are preserved on the left bank; the Thames enters the narrow Sandford Gap by which it pierces the Corallian escarpment; the river then swings sharply to the right to Abingdon, the left bank thus being open to denudation —just as the right bank is between Newbridge and Eynsham.

The difference in elevation of the terraces at Yarnton and Radley is over 40 ft., though the river falls only 30 ft. between these points. There is, however, little doubt that the terraces are con-

---

[1] Sandford, K. S., *op. cit.*, pp. 125–127.
[2] *Op. cit.*, p. 93.
[3] *Ibid.*, p. 92.
[4] Note: the well is situated among the buildings at the top of the hill, near the gymnasium: in the details communicated by the Warden to Mr. Pocock, 12 ft. of gravel were quoted, but it is believed that the uppermost 4 ft. were made ground.

temporaneous, and the discrepancy may be due to the slower rate of erosion at the gap in the Corallian escarpment not far above Radley. The terrace here is at about the same distance above the river as that at Standlake.[1]

Wolvercot Terrace

About 50 ft. below the Handborough Terrace, and confined to the present river valleys, lies another deposit, which has hitherto been known as the Third Terrace, but for which the above term is now suggested. It is preserved only in a few isolated patches, and has been extensively denuded. Many of the banks and tracts which have survived are marginal deposits, and a study of their thickness, and of the ground above and beyond them, has shown that they have no connection with, but are undoubtedly later than, the Handborough Terrace (see Fig. 8).

In the Thames Valley above Oxford (apart from Wolvercot) no gravel of this stage occurs within the limits of the map, nor has the writer identified it as far up the river as Lechlade ; neither has it been observed in the valley of the Windrush. In the valley of the Evenlode, however, a considerable tract of this deposit has been found between Charlbury and Chadlington, on the north bank of the river a few miles beyond the border of the map. Here as much as 14 ft. of sand and gravel form a bank, about three miles long, of material largely derived from the Lias Ironstone, with oolitic limestone and debris from the Plateau Drift. The base-level lies at about 50 ft. above the present level of the river, and is thus distinctly higher than at Wolvercot. The gravel at Wolvercot appears to have been formed at a confluence or in the middle of the valley. At Chadlington the deposit is a marginal bank ; it is situated at the upper end of the Evenlode Gorge, a magnificent series of incised meanders of which the inception must date from the close of the period of the Handborough Terrace. In a pit on the Chadlington-Leafield road the gravel was trenched by a channel or rill-bed in which were found two large quartzite pebbles, both of them striated, and doubtless derived from the Plateau Drift.[2]

At Conigree Farm, near Spelsbury, seven feet of gravel were seen, capped by a similar thickness of sand ; a tooth of Horse was recovered from this pit.[3]

The next patch lies within the limits of the map—in Blenheim Park ; here gravel, which probably belongs to this terrace, has been observed. It lies on the narrow neck of land between the Evenlode and the Glyme. Directly opposite the confluence of the Evenlode and the Glyme, and north of Burleigh Wood, is a small crescent-shaped bank of gravel, and farther to the east, north of the high drift-covered ground of Bladon Heath, are small patches of the same terrace with the gravel partially cemented by iron oxide.[4] The

---

[1] Pocock, T. I., op. cit., p. 92.
[2] Sandford, K. S., op. cit., pp. 128–129.
[3] Ibid., p. 128.
[4] Op. cit., p. 90.

disposition of the whole group of gravel patches in this vicinity suggests a confluence near Begbroke of the Cherwell with the Glyme and one branch of the Evenlode.   Part of the Evenlode, however, continued its southerly course, as the whole river together with the Glyme does to-day, for there is a small remnant of gravel situated at the required height at the crossing of the road from Cassington to Bladon and of the Oxford-Birmingham railway line.   It indicates that part of the Evenlode followed the gap now occupied by the railway and joined the Thames near Yarnton.

In the Cherwell Valley there is a large tract of gravel north of Begbroke.   The patch occupies the position of the Wolvercot Terrace, and gravelly soil can be traced over a considerable area to the north and east of Campsfield Farm, but no sections have been seen.

It is probable that the Cherwell followed the course which it occupied until much later times and joined the Thames, with the Evenlode, near Yarnton.   At Wolvercot, about three miles north of Oxford, lying between the Thames and the present course of the Cherwell is an important area of gravel in which numerous sections have recently been seen; hence it is suggested that the terrace now being described should take its name from the exposures seen in the gravel of the Wolvercot plateau (*see* Fig. 8).   The terrace is here separated from the succeeding, lower, deposits to the south by a narrow belt of Oxford Clay which it crowns with about 4 ft. of calcareous gravel, a line of springs being thrown out at its base. The gravel is exposed in the large brick-pit between Wolvercot cemetery and the railway bridge, where it forms the banks of the well-known Wolvercot Channel (*see* p. 136), but clear stratification is not often shown in the gravel itself here.   It has been seen to better advantage in a number of temporary exposures in the cemetery and in house foundations along both sides of Davenant Road.   All the sections showed the same general sequence, though the thicknesses were different.   Along Davenant Road the bottom of the gravel, though uneven, is at about 220 ft. above O.D., *i.e.* 35 ft. above the Thames.   The general section is as follows :—[1]

	Ft.
Fine loose gravel, calcareous, some places with a bed of false-bedded sand and fine gravel	3–4
Disturbed gravel .. .. about	1
Coarse ferruginous gravel with sharp sand	1–2
Loose regular grit and gravel, calcareous : locally ferruginous, especially at base	
Many large pebbles or small boulders from Plateau Drift, at junction with Oxford Clay	about 2

In places the terrace is capped, and hollows in it filled, by stony clay or sand, unbedded and composing the ' warp ' or trail, a nonfluviatile deposit to which further reference will be made.   The localized patches of ' warp ' do not give rise to an uneven surface, and their presence is only revealed in exposures ; their junction with

[1] Sandford, K. S., *op. cit.*, pp. 129–131.

the underlying gravel is distinct and uneven, and their occurrence is sporadic ; they certainly do not appear to be merely the result of decalcification of gravel *in situ*. It is notable that the bottom six inches or so of the warp are often earthy, though very hard when dry, and of a darker brown colour than the remainder.

In one of the exposures in Davenant Road workmen found a large flint flake, with creamy white patina, which may be of Acheulean age ; it is about six inches long and 2 inches wide. The level at which the flake was found is unknown. The flake is now in the University Museum.

An exposure was seen in the south-west corner of the cemetery. Oxford Clay was struck at 9 ft., and it was overlain by 5 ft. of fine ferruginous gravel, dipping steeply to the west, on which lie

(1) lenticles of pebbles, with white limy specks
(2) brown sandy clay above.

At the top was a thickness of 2 ft. of warp sand with numerous quartzite pebbles, covered with six inches of soil.

Recently, excavations for the foundations of the warehouses of the Clarendon Press have been made immediately to the north of the cemetery. These have shown a partition of the gravel into a western part, probably deposited by the Thames, and an eastern, which—since the Cherwell most probably joined the Thames near Yarnton—may be assigned to the Ray. Between them is a knoll of Oxford Clay now known to continue some little distance into the cemetery, but gravel seems to be continuous across the southern side. The western gravels were exposed in a pit in the foundation of the warehouses immediately opposite the custodian's hut in the north-west corner of the cemetery, and the following section was observed. At the base is 3 ft. of fine bedded gravel, mainly calcareous but with some iron oxide, and it is overlain by 7 ft. of ironsand with scattered pebbles (warp) and 3 ft. of soil. Most of the warehouse buildings are situated on the clay knoll ; the eastern gravels are exposed on the other side of the Banbury Road, in shallow pits exhibiting three to four feet of coarse gravel, with some sandy patches. They are disturbed at the top. The actual confluence is probably situated within the bounds of the cemetery. No fauna of any sort is known from any of the exposures yet mentioned (except Horse from the pit at Conigree Farm).

To the north of the Wolvercot Plateau lies Pear Tree Hill, where gravel forms the overburden of an old brick pit in Oxford Clay. Pebbles and small boulders of quartzite, as well as fragments of ochreous flint and other constituents of the Northern Drift are numerous, but the gravels are in a confused state, and seem to have been affected by the processes which produced the warp, and little or no bedding has survived. The small quantities of gravel now remaining appear to have been further disturbed by the digging of the underlying clay, and tongues of unbedded and often highly ferruginous material have been forced down into the soft Oxford

Clay.[1]   Here, as in other places, striated boulders have been found but they appear to have been derived from the Plateau Drift. A. M. Bell found some rough, ochreous flint implements at this locality ; one has recently been submitted to Professor Breuil, who considers it to be Chellean, probably Upper, tending towards Acheulean ; it is abraded and doubtless was derived from an older deposit. Mr. Bell also reported, with probably well-founded reservation, the discovery of a tooth of dog or wolf in this gravel.[2]   There is every reason to suppose that the deposit at Pear Tree Hill, with one or two small and detached patches adjacent to it, is part of the Wolvercot Terrace.[3]

Below Sandford Gap the Wolvercot Terrace reappears in two outliers on Kimmeridge Clay along the road south of Radley Wood. Gravel has been worked there, and also by the roadside near the gates of Radley College, where it is cemented into a hard rock. A pit close to the crossroads south-east of Radley Wood was in-

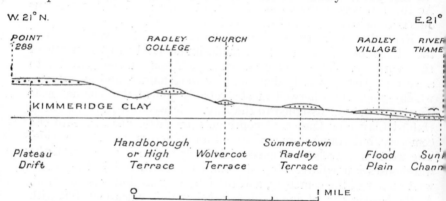

FIG. 9.—*Section showing River Terraces and Plateau Drift, near Radley.*

vestigated by Mr. Pocock ; six feet of gravel were seen and consisted of Oolite pebbles, Coral Rag being abundant, and of material from the Plateau Drift.[4]

In Radley Churchyard the gravel is one foot thick.   On the west side the Kimmeridge Clay rises abruptly from beneath the terrace to the level of the Handborough Terrace in the grounds of Radley College.   On the south and east there is a more gradual but con- spicuous fall of the surface to the succeeding terrace and again to the summit of the Flood Plain gravels ; lastly to the Alluvium. The terrace structure is nowhere more completely demonstrated in the district than between Radley College and Radley Village (*see* Fig. 9).

---

[1] *See also* Woodward, H. B., on ' Underground Waste of the Land, '*Nat. Science,* 1893, p. 126.
[2] Bell, A. M., ' Implementiferous Sections at Wolvercote,' *Quart. Journ. Geol. Soc.,* vol. lx, 1904, p. 120, *et seq.*, and K. S. Sandford, *op. cit.*, pp. 131, 132.
[3] It is coloured as Plateau Drift on the Special Oxford Sheet.
[4] *Op. cit.*, p. 90.

Summertown-Radley Terrace

The ' Second ' Terrace is by far the most extensive, since it is less completely denuded than the older terraces, and is nowhere overlapped by the Alluvium as in the case of the Flood Plain gravel. Its base-level in the district is about 15 ft. above the present river level, though it ranges from about 12 ft. to 20 ft.

Oxford and most of the villages of the Upper Thames Valley stand upon it, as formerly it was of value as a water reservoir.

' Beginning in the west, the rise of the terrace is very conspicuous north of Brighthampton and Standlake, and up the right bank of the Windrush as far as Cokethorpe Park.   The gravel is exposed in pits by the site of the British Village, and at the crossroads close to Hardwick.   At the former it is at least 12 feet thick, and consists of oolitic pebbles, one or two inches in length, with a considerable number of quartzites and other erratics.   Along the bank of the Windrush the base of the gravel can be easily traced by small springs thrown out at the surface of the subjacent Oxford Clay.   Close to Brighthampton, also, there is a spring showing that the gravel rests on a platform of clay, above the level of the adjacent low terrace. On the left bank of the Windrush a corresponding terrace extends nearly three miles in the parish of Stanton Harcourt.   It has been opened in numerous pits, now for the most part disused, which show as much as 9 feet of gravel without reaching the bottom.   Near the village the gravel is cemented with iron into a rock hard enough to be used for building.   The cemented layer, which is a foot or two thick, lies not far below the surface soil, and can still be seen in an old pit S.W. of the village.   The walls of the Norman nave of the church at Stanton Harcourt are built of rough blocks of this material, many of which, after nearly 800 years of exposure, show little sign of decay.

Monoliths of the same rock, six to eight feet high, have been set up in the fields south-west of the church, and are known as the ' devil's quoits.' Farther north the terrace is cut through in two places by branches of the Limb Brook and by the Chil Brook, but with these exceptions it is continuous to the mouth of the Evenlode.   Well-sections near Eynsham show considerable variation in the thickness of the gravel.   Near the railway-station, probably the thickest part, four measurements gave 14 ft., 14 ft., 15 ft. 8 in., and 21 ft. respectively.   At Newfield Cottage, nearer the landward margin, the thickness was only seven feet, while near the edge towards the river five feet and seven feet respectively were recorded.'[1]

Immediately south of Eynsham railway station, and between it and the Stanton Harcourt road, the gravel has been worked extensively for the last two or three years.[2]   The thickness of the gravel was 8 to 12 ft. but it increases south-westwards.   The gravel is even bedded, and consists almost entirely of Oolite debris, with a minor amount of material derived from the Plateau Drift ; the coarse gravel with pebbles about 1–1½ in. in diameter can be screened readily from various fine gravels and sands.

Important discoveries of vertebrate remains have been made.   At the base a foot or so of gravel tends to be ferruginous ; in it have been found many broken bones, probably of *Bos primigenius*.   Some large teeth were

---

[1] *Op. cit.*, p. 85.
[2] *See* Sandford, K. S., *op. cit.*, pp. 139–141.   Work at this pit has almost stopped.

found by the workmen, but unfortunately only one, and part of another, were preserved. The tooth is a molar of *Elephas primigenius*, with rather coarse enamel, and there is little doubt that the other teeth were of the same species. In the autumn of 1925 more teeth of this species were excavated and enough material for study came into my hands, thanks to Mr. Sumner Mariner, of Eynsham. The basement gravel is not separated from the overlying deposits by a well-marked eroded surface. About 1½ ft. from the bottom, one ramus with two teeth in place, of *Cervus megaceros* (Irish Elk) was found—a unique discovery of this animal in the Upper Thames. Throughout the next 7 ft. of gravel unrolled bones and teeth of Hippopotamus were frequent ; parts of at least six " tusks " were saved by the workmen in various parts of the pit, and many more must have been lost. In the same gravel the bones and teeth of *Bos primigenius* were abundant. Horse (*Equus caballus*) and Red Deer (*Cervus elaphus*) also were identified, but their remains were not common. A few shells were found.

This important zone is dissolved and festooned in its top few feet and is overlain by fine false-bedded gravel, resting on a well marked eroded surface. It extends over most of the site of the pit and is still exposed on the western face ; it is not the deposit of a small rivulet. The fact that it is of much later date than the underlying gravel is demonstrated by the fresher state of fragments of bones recovered from it.

Gravel of the same terrace extends from above Church Hanborough to the confluence of the Evenlode Valley with the Thames, but no exposures have been seen. Behind the Bell Inn at Cassington, on the down-stream side of the confluence, a pit has been opened in which 18 ft. of gravel have been proved and the bottom not touched ; the surface level is 220 ft. above O.D. and indicates that the terrace at Cassington is normal to the stage now under review, but that its base is here continued possibly below present river-level. The gravel shallows to the north and more steeply to the south, towards the present course of the Thames.[1]

The above seems to present a cross-section of the river at this period ; near Eynsham station the gravel is at its deepest ; but it shallows both north-wards and southwards (making due allowance for changing surface level, which at Cassington is negligible). A fair idea of the course of the Thames at this time is thus obtained. Similar deep channels are encountered in Oxford (City Brewery) and at Iffley (Cornish Pit)—indicating a continuance of this line.[2]

A good example is thus given of the lateral shifting of the course of the Thames down the dip slope, and of the gradual destruction of the outlier of Corallian rocks at Wytham Hill.

At one time doubtless there was an unbroken bank of gravel between Cassington and Yarnton, but it is now trenched ; each village stands on an isolated patch and between them are two more patches : the river, in the process of cutting back, has deposited alluvium. The confluence of the Thames and Cherwell was formerly at Yarnton, at least during a part of the period of this terrace, and the Cherwell followed the course of the valley, now filled with alluvium, between Kidlington railway station and Yarnton. At the latter place the gravel is from 12–16 ft. thick (in pits, now abandoned, near the railway station).

It was stated by Phillips to be ' formed of many irregular, mostly undulated layers of gravel and sand with stripes of clay ; the stones, mostly oolitic, with admixture of flints, red grits, and white quartz . . . It yielded at and near the bottom, where large pebbles of Northern drift formed an almost solid bed, a profusion of teeth and tusks of *Elephas primigenius*.[3] Teeth of *Rhinoceros tichorhinus* (Woolly Rhinoceros) were found at the same level.

At Kidlington railway station there were formerly extensive gravel pits, in one of which teeth of *Rhinoceros tichorhinus* were found, at an unrecorded

[1] *Ibid.*, p. 147.
[2] *Ibid.*, pp. 145–148.
[3] ' Geology of Oxford and the Valley of the Thames,' 1879, p. 463.

level, many years ago, while in the upper part Phillips obtained a few land and freshwater shells of existing species.[1] *Corbicula fluminalis* was found in gravel near Kidlington but no further details as to its provenance are known. A little to the south-east of the old workings a pit has recently been in use ; about 4 ft. of fine oolitic gravel were seen, but the bottom of the gravel was not then reached.

On the south side of the Thames, at Wytham, opposite the former Thames-Cherwell confluence (at Yarnton), gravel was at one time extensively worked, but now only in small temporary exposures near Northfield Farm.   The site of the old workings can still be found, by the roadside between Northfield Farm and Wytham ; from them was obtained a valuable collection of

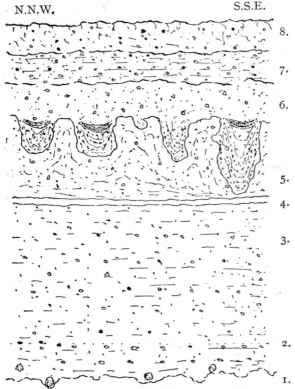

N.N.W.   S.S.E.

Fig. 10.—*Summertown-Radley Terrace, at Webb's Pit (south-eastern corner), Summertown.*

vertebrate remains, now preserved in the Oxford University Museum.   The collection includes the lower jaw of a young elephant (*Elephas antiquus*), with deciduous molars, also a molar tooth of *Rhinoceros leptorhinus*, a part of a tusk of Hippopotamus, and remains of red deer and horse.   Phillips[2] recorded *Elephas antiquus, E. primigenius, Rhinoceros tichorhinus* and *Sus scrofa* (as well as Hippopotamus and others), but the remains preserved in the Museum are identified as above.[3]   Farther south, on the same side of the river, there are remnants of similar gravel near Binsey and at Botley.

---

[1] *Ibid.*, p. 464.
[2] *Op. cit.*, p. 474.
[3] Sandford, K. S., *op. cit.*, pp. 140 and 166 ; and *Quart. Journ. Geol. Soc.*, vol. lxxxi, 1925.

On the left bank a long tract of gravel extends from Summertown to Oxford, occupying nearly the whole of the space between the Thames and the Cherwell. To the north it is bounded by the Wolvercot plateau.[1] An important section is seen in the disused brick-pit on the Woodstock Road (Mr. Webb's Pit). At the south-east corner the following sequence has been observed[2] :—

		Ft.	In.
8.	Soil	1	0
7.	Bedded gravel	1	0
6.	Disordered gravel and loam	1	0
5.	' Solution festoons ' and disturbed gravel	2	0
4.	Clay band, rarely with valves of *Corbicula fluminalis* ..	0	2
3.	Bedded gravel, calcareous (*Bos primigenius*)	5	0
2.	Rubbly gravel, numerous teeth of *Elephas primigenius*..	1	0
1.	Oxford Clay .. .. seen to	40	0

(The beds are numbered as in Fig. 10, p. 129).

Prestwich[3] published a long list of the fauna from this pit, including Mammoth, Woolly Rhinoceros, Red Deer, Roe Deer, Horse, etc., but gave no data as to depth.

About 200 yds. to the east of Webb's Pit, Prestwich saw the following section during the digging of the foundations of St. Edward's School[4] :—

	Ft.	In.
Soil	1	0
Fine gravel (with irregular black and ferruginous veins) ..	3	2
Yellow sand with land and freshwater shells (*Corbicula*		
fluminalis and others numerous, with valves united)..	3	6
Sand	3	0
Hard gravel	—	

In the lower part of the pit, below the level of *Corbicula fluminalis*, remains of *Elephas primigenius* were found.[5]

Corbicula fluminalis has also been found in a similar position in a pit at the rear of the pavilion on the playing fields of the School.

A flint implement, a slightly abraded boucher of Chellean type, has been found in the brick-pit ; it was recovered by workmen when screening gravel, but no details as to level are available. In an exposure in Lonsdale Road the late Mr. Manning obtained an implement at 10 ft., below a skull of the Cave Lion (*Felis leo spelaea*) at 7 ft. He describes the implement as long and pointed, plano-convex, slightly patinated and worn.[6]

In the University Park a large boucher of late Chellean, or Lower Acheulian type has been found, but not *in situ ;* near by, in the foundations of the Dyson Perrin Laboratory, on the south side of the park, 18 ft. of gravel were excavated and part of skull and horn-cores of *Bison priscus*, and teeth of Mammoth, were found at or near the bottom.

In the summer and autumn of 1925 a good exposure was seen in excavations for a boiler house 50 yds. east of the Department of Geology, University Museum, and the following section was noted ; unfortunately no implements, bones or shells were found :—

	Ft.
Disturbed ground	3
Well bedded gravel	4
Fine, false-bedded sand and fine gravel	3
Bedded gravel, fairly coarse	6
Oxford Clay	

---

[1] Sandford, K. S., *Quart. Journ. Geol. Soc.*, vol. lxxx, 1924, fig. 8, p. 131.
[2] *Ibid.*, pp. 141, 142.
[3] Prestwich, J., *Geol. Mag.*, 1882, p. 51.
[4] *Ibid.*, p. 49.
[5] *Ibid.*, ' Fine yellow sand with land and freshwater shells and fossil remains of Elephant, etc. in the lower part,' p. 50.
[6] Notes of the late P. Manning, in the Ashmolean Museum (Library), Oxford.

Water was struck at about 2 ft. above the Oxford Clay and was extremely troublesome, owing probably to the extra depth of the gravel in this exposure—even in a dry summer, and pumping had to be continued for some months until the foundations of waterproof material were completed.

No good sections were seen in other scientific departmental buildings then in course of erection ; generally the foundations were too shallow.

In the foundations of the Girls' High School in Banbury Road[1] two flint implements were found. Many years ago, single specimens were obtained in the foundations of the New Examination Schools in High Street,[2] and near Marston Ferry.[3] All the above, with the exception of Mr. Manning's implement, are preserved in the University Museum and have been identified by Professor Breuil as bouchers of Upper and late Upper Chellean : all are slightly abraded.

Of the gravel under the city of Oxford itself Mr. Pocock gives the following description, which has been confirmed by excavations made during the last few years.

'In Oxford itself there is more sand and clay. Along George Street and Abbot Road the subsoil is nearly all laminated sandy clay, stiff and impermeable, but at the corner of Grove Street in George Street there is five feet of clean gravel. At the top of Walton Crescent nine feet of gravel were seen under four feet of soil and made ground.[4] Pits showing a few feet of gravel are also seen by Holywell Cemetery and in the University Park. The upper surface of the gravel is almost a dead level (210 feet above O.D.) from Summertown to Broad Street. Carfax is higher, having probably been artificially raised. But on either side the terrace inclines gently towards the Cherwell and the Thames. The platform of clay underneath the gravel is shown by wells and foundations of houses to have an uneven surface.[5] Thus, near the brickworks at Summertown, the full thickness of gravel is 15 ft., at Summer Villa 9 ft., North Cottage 6 ft., Blackhall Farm 4 ft. to 6 ft., Bardwell Road 9 ft. In some places the Oxford Clay comes nearly to the surface, in others water is reached at a small depth in gravel, apparently held up in a hollow in the clay. At others again there is no water till the base of the gravel is reached. On the whole the gravel is thinner and cleaner in North Oxford and is bounded by banks of clay which throw out the water into the Thames and Cherwell. In the older part of the city there is more clay in the gravel, which, by preventing rain water from percolating freely through, increases the muddiness of the streets in wet weather, and is conducive to thick fogs.

The base of the Oxford gravel crops out about half-way down St. Aldates, and the lower gravel comes on almost immediately. There may be an outcrop of Oxford Clay between the two terraces near the bottom of the hill, but there were no openings to show this at the time of the survey.'[6]

---

[1] Evans, John, 'Ancient Stone Implements,' 1897, p. 593.
[2] Ibid.
[3] Ibid.
[4] From the notes of Prof. A. H. Green.
[5] The Rev. J. C. Clutterbuck, Journ. R. Agric. Soc., Ser. 2, i, 1865, p. 278.
[6] Op. cit., pp. 86, 87.

An interesting record was obtained from a boring at the City Brewery (*q.v.* p. 174) made in 1898. The surface level is 209 ft. above O.D., and 30 ft. of made ground, sand and gravel were pierced before the Oxford Clay was reached. The surface level, even omitting 7 ft. 6 in. of made ground, is that of the terrace now being reviewed, and it seems most probable that the borehole is in a position analogous to the pit at Cassington—*i.e.*, in the centre of the river channel of this stage.

In the construction of the new Examination Schools, and of the Holywell Drainage, both carried out about fifty years ago, many lower jaws and teeth of *Elephas primigenius* were found[1]; some of these are preserved in the University Museum and from their condition and from available information there is reason to suppose that they came mostly from the junction of the gravel with the Oxford

E.   W.

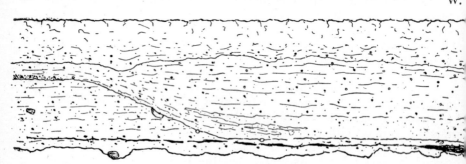

Fig. 11.—*Summertown-Radley Terrace, at Magdalen College Grove*
(Pit about 25 yds. east of the site of the Gallows.)

1. Coarse ferruginous gravel passing eastwards into regular gravel with mammoth; 1 to 3 ft. thick.
2. Shell-sand with *Corbicula fluminalis*; 1 to 1½ ft. thick.
3. Regular gravel with shells and *Bos primigenius*; 2¼ ft. thick.
4. Soil, subsoil, gravel disturbed by roots; 2½ ft. thick.

Clay. One of the mandibles (a broken specimen, with one molar) from the Examination Schools is referable to *E. antiquus*.[2]

A pit opened in the north-west corner of the Deer Park of Magdalen College calls for special notice (Fig. 11); it presents a conclusive explanation of the faunal sequences already observed at Eynsham and Summertown.[3]

On the east side of the pit lay 3 ft. of regular gravel, very coarse and ferruginous at the bottom, crowded with teeth and other remains (mostly decayed) of normal Siberian Mammoth; milk and adult molars were found in good preservation, also parts of two tusks. On the west side the gravel had been eroded to a foot or so and

[1] Prestwich, J., *op. cit.*, p. 50.
[2] Sandford, K. S., *Quart. Journ. Geol. Soc.*, vol. lxxxi, 1925, p. 77.
[3] Sandford, K. S., *Quart. Journ. Geol. Soc.*, vol. lxxx, 1924, pp. 142–143.

replaced by 1 ft.–1 ft. 6 in. of cemented shell-sand and gravel ;
the following shells have been collected from it :—

> Jacosta (Cernuella) virgata (*Da Costa*)
> Fruticicola (Capillifera) hispida (*Linn.*)
> Cochlicopa lubrica (*Müller*)
> Limnaea pereger (*Müller*)
> Limnaea truncatula (*Müller*)
> Bithynia tentaculata (*Linn.*)
> Valvata piscinalis (*Müller*)
> Unio littoralis *Lamarck*
> Unio prestwichi *Kennard & Woodw.*
> Corbicula fluminalis (*Müller*)
> Sphaerium rivicola (*Leach*)
> Sphaerium corneum (*Linn.*)
> Sphaerium radleyense *Kennard & Woodw.*
> Pisidium amnicum (*Müller*)
> Pisidium henslowanum (*Sheppard*)

To the east the shells disappear and give place to fine gravel which
overlaps the older mammoth gravel. In one instance a tooth of mammoth, partly projecting from the lower gravel, was seen to be covered
by *Corbicula fluminalis* and other shells in sand. Above the
cemented shell-band are 2¼ ft. of regular gravel from which remains
of *Bos primigenius* only were recovered. The whole section is covered
by 2½ ft. of soil, subsoil and gravel disturbed by roots and by a surface
of disordered material. A ramus of a Bear, *Ursus anglicus* Gunther[1]
(a rare animal in the local gravels) was found by workmen, who stated
that it was seen in the coarse ferruginous gravel of the older deposit
(mammoth gravel) below the thickest part of the Corbicula Zone.

The above interpretation of the section has been verified by the
opening of a pit a few yards to the north, an analogous section being
observed. Its importance is obvious, since it gives definite illustration of a differentiation of fauna, accompanied by erosion, channel
formation and subsequent deposition—the fauna having changed
in the meantime. With a fuller range of forms, the same important
fact has already been brought to light at Eynsham and Summertown
and will be noted again in the following pages.

Above Oxford the Cherwell Valley is almost free of gravel of this
stage ; indeed it has been swept clear of gravel of all stages ; in the
old course of the river there are the patches at Yarnton and Kidlington
railway station, already described. The present valley of the
Cherwell is flanked on one side by the gravels of the Oxford-
Summertown plateau and two small patches of gravel of this stage
are seen, one at Hill's Farm, the other to the south of it, on which
the village of Marston stands, where 8 ft. of gravel have been noted.[2]

As the Cherwell flowed by Yarnton it is probable that the valley
which it now occupies was at that time the course of the Ray, entering
at Islip.

[1] Gunther, R. T., *Ann. and Mag. Nat. Hist.*, ser. 9, vol. xi, 1923, p. 490.
[2] Pocock, T. I., *op. cit.*, p. 87.

At Cowley (owing to the proximity of the ancient river bank to the east) the gravel is generally not so thick as under Oxford.[1] At the Iffley end of this patch an interesting section was seen between the Thames and a housing estate, south-west of Fairacres House, in a small remnant near the main patch[2] :—

(Cornish Pit). Surface level 193 ft. above O.D. (ignoring 2 ft. of made ground) : level of the Thames near by 179 ft. above O.D. ; 14 ft. of gravel have been proved, bringing the bottom exactly to present river level. The pit was open some years ago, but then—as now—the bottom was usually waterlogged. Dredging was employed, however, and two fine sets of teeth of *Rhinoceros tichorhinus*, fresh and unworn, were recovered. Mammoth was also found.

Manning found flint implements here, and some of them he picked out from the bottom of the gravel when it was dry ; the best account of them is to be found in his notes, now in the Ashmolean Museum. The late A. M. Bell also reports implements of flint and quartzite from the site.[3] Most of the specimens are now missing, but they included Chellean bouchers (one, a fine specimen, is preserved in the Pitt-Rivers Museum), more or less abraded, together with wide flat flakes, some of them trimmed down one edge. Manning also noted Red Deer, Horse, and Hippopotamus ; a large unworn molar of the last was found recently *in situ* at 6½ ft. The deposit in this pit is clearly analogous to that of Cassington and to the gravel passed through in the boring at the City Brewery, but it was thought to belong to the group of the Flood Plain Gravel[4] ; its fauna and the fact that the gravel is continued at greater height towards Cowley point to its being of the same stage as the patch which it adjoins. It would seem therefore that a part of the ancient river bank is exposed on the opposite side of the main road (*i.e.*, opposite Fairacres House). The uppermost few feet of gravel in Cornish Pit are greatly disturbed by ‘ solution ’ festoons and tongues.

The gravel is not seen again till the river reaches the outcrop of the Kimmeridge Clay south of the gap at Sandford. Three small patches separated by tributary streams extend along the right bank to Radley, but these show no sections. On the concave side of the bend between Radley and Abingdon the terrace widens to the extent of a mile, and has been exposed in numerous pits, which show gravel of the same general character as that in the upper reaches of the valley, *i.e.*, small and oolitic with an admixture of quartzites and flints, occasionally cemented into a rock. The abundance of fragments from the neighbouring Corallian rocks and from concretions in the Kimmeridge Clay is notable.

The last important section is seen in a pit near Radley, almost due south of the church, on the road from Abingdon to Radley Village (Mr. Silvester's Pit[5]). The pit, which is 8–10 ft. deep, is worked in two levels ; in summer, when the water-level is low, the lower part can be dug as well as the upper, but in winter the deeper parts are filled with rubble and the upper alone worked. Aided by the above system of excavation, interesting results have been obtained ; from the bottom good specimens of the molars of *Elephas primigenius* have been recovered ; a hard band of gravel, cemented by cal-

---

[1] Note.—The following are some thicknesses give by Mr. Pocock from the notes of J. F. Blake :—

	Ft.
By Iffley Road near James Street	7
At the corner of Bullingdon Road and Denmark Street	3
At the corner of Hurst Street and Leopold Street	6
At Fairacres House	5

[2] Sandford, K. S., *ibid.*, pp. 145, 146.
[3] Bell, A. M., ‘ Implementiferous Sections at Wolvercote,’ *Quart. Journ. Geol. Soc.*, vol. lx, 1904, p. 129.
[4] Pocock, T. I., *op. cit.*, p. 84.
[5] Sandford, K. S., *op. cit.*, pp. 143, 144.

careous material, is sometimes seen here, and a water-worn boulder of this hard rock has been found in the upper part of the pit. In the upper gravel remains of Hippopotamus are not uncommon, some of them quite unabraded, together with teeth and bones of *Cervus elaphus* and *Bos primigenius* and the following land and freshwater shells :—

Jacosta (Cernuella) virgata (*Da Costa*)
Jacosta (Xerophila) itala (*Linn.*)
Fruticicola (Capillifera) hispida (*Linn.*)
Succinea pfeifferi *Rossmässler*
Ancylastrum fluviatile (*Müller*)
Limnaea pereger (*Müller*)
Limnaea palustris (*Müller*)
Limnaea truncatula (*Müller*)
Planorbis leucostoma *Millet*
Valvata piscinalis (*Müller*)
Valvata macrostoma *Steenbuch*
Unio prestwichi *Kennard & Woodw.*
Anodonta anatina (*Linn.*)
Corbicula fluminalis (*Müller*)
Sphaerium corneum (*Linn.*)
Sphaerium radleyense *Kennard & Woodw.*
Pisidium amnicum (*Müller*)
Pisidium henslowanum (*Sheppard*)
Pisidium subtruncatum *Malm*
Pisidium cinereum *Alder*

A skull of Cave Lion was found some years ago in the upper gravel and is now preserved in the Museum of Radley College, together with other specimens from the pit. The upper gravel is capped by as much as 3 ft. of dark humus, in which shallow burial pits, containing fragments of pottery and flint flakes have been dug.

On account of the remarkable faunal successions at Summertown (Webb's Pit) and at Radley, supported by confirmatory evidence from other sites, it has been proposed that the term Summertown-Radley Terrace be applied to the deposits of the stage described in the foregoing pages. It is unfortunate that Hippopotamus has not yet been found at the Magdalen College Grove exposures, but the evidence there is definite enough by itself. *Elephas antiquus* is known from Wytham and from beneath Oxford, and in the Museum of Manchester University there is a tooth of the species marked ' Summertown ', without further data.

Below Radley, on the Radley-Abingdon road, gravel is worked (for the manufacture of concrete bricks) and some acres of it have been removed. On an average the gravel is here about 8–10 ft. thick. In contrast to the pit at Radley, mollusca are missing here and vertebrate remains extremely scanty, a tooth of Horse alone having been identified ; two flint implements, however, are stated to have been found near the bottom ; they are in the possession of Mr. D'Almaine of Abingdon, and were described and figured by Mr. Reginald Smith. They are of ovate form and apparently of Acheulean type ; and they are the only true ovate implements known from the Oxford district.[1]

---

[1] See '*Antiquaries Journal*,' July, 1922, p. 257, and R. A. Smith, '*Archaeologia*,' vol. lxxv, 1923, p. 28.

In the same pit recent digging exposed about four feet of loamy
ferruginous sand, with a few pebbles from the Plateau Drift
apparently formed by the disintegration of the gravel ; the junction
with the underlying gravel is sharp and uneven, but no contortion
is noticeable ; it was exposed along a face of some 30 yds., and after
some weeks of excavation remained constant. The deposit at once
calls to mind the ' warp ' of the Wolvercot Plateau, which it
resembles in a number of its characters. Together with other
features of the top of the Summertown–Radley Terrace, the above
will call for further comment at a later stage[1] (*see* p. 165).

At Abingdon the Ock joins the Thames, and much of the town is
built on gravel of this terrace ; a collection of vertebrate remains
from the gravel in the immediate vicinity is preserved in the Museum
in the Town Hall, but information regarding the specimens is scanty.
Blake found 12 ft. of gravel and clay in a pit just outside Abingdon
on the Faringdon Road, and exposures are frequently to be seen
showing about 8 ft. of gravel.

Wolvercot Channel

In the brick-pit at Wolvercot between the cemetery and the
railway, deposits of a channel later than the Wolvercot Terrace and,
as will be shown, probably later than the Summertown–Radley
Terrace are clearly exposed. The channel is unique in the district—
the much smaller rill-bed at Chadlington being accounted for by
its position on the side of the river valley and on a steep slope
(*see* p. 123), whereas the Wolvercot Channel is cut in an ' island ' of
gravel of the Wolvercot Terrace in the centre of the wide low-lying
valley of the Thames–Cherwell–Ray (former course).

Owing to the important finds of implements here much attention
has been given to the site. Implements and bones were collected
for many years by Messrs. Manning and Bell and the latter published
an account of the pit [2] ; unfortunately, the exact provenance of the
implements has rarely been recorded. Detailed work has been carried
on at the pit for the last few years and the bones and implements
recovered, coupled with other information and former work, have
served to elucidate the stratigraphy.[3]

The channel has been cut through the gravels of the Wolvercot
or ' Third ' Terrace and has penetrated some feet into the underlying
Oxford Clay (*see* Fig. 12). The lowest deposit of the channel is
the most important ; it consists of calcareous gravel, a foot or so
thick, which lines the bottom and both flanks. On the east
side of the present E.–W. section there are numerous pockets or
swirl holes ; the channel is known to turn to the east at this point,

---

[1] Sandford, K. S., *Quart. Journ. Geol. Soc.*, vol. lxxi, 1925, p. 63.
[2] Bell, A. M., *op. cit.*, p. 120 *et seq.*, and *Rept. Brit. Assoc.* (Oxford), 1894, p. 663.
See also W. J. Sollas, Pres. Address, *Quart. Journ. Geol. Soc.*, vol. lxvi, 1910, p. 57,
and K. S. Sandford, *Quart. Journ. Geol. Soc.*, vol. lxxx, 1924, pp. 132–138, and vol.
lxxxi, 1925, pp. 62 *et seq.*
[3] Note : a full account of one section is given as the pit has almost reached its
limit in a southerly direction ; the face here described will probably be available for
study for some years, or if the excavation is completed the description given here is
likely to be generally applicable.

towards the cemetery—where, however, it is missing; it probably
turns to the north again, thus accounting for the swirl holes in the
Oxford Clay at the north end of the east side of the pit—*i.e.*, the
swirl holes are in both cases on the inward side of the course of the
stream. It is particularly in these flanking swirl holes and in the

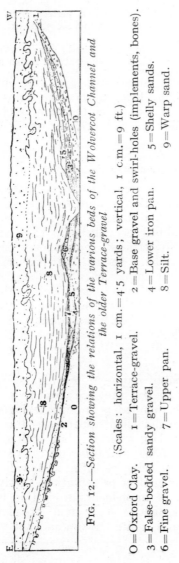

FIG. 12.—*Section showing the relations of the various beds of the Wolvercot Channel and the older Terrace-gravel*

(Scales: horizontal, 1 cm. = 4·5 yards; vertical, 1 c.m. = 9 ft.)

O = Oxford Clay.   1 = Terrace-gravel.   2 = Base gravel and swirl-holes (implements, bones).
3 = False-bedded sandy gravel.   4 = Lower iron pan.   5 = Shelly sands.
6 = Fine gravel.   7 = Upper pan.   8 = Silt.   9 = Warp sand.

gravel filling and immediately overlying them that implements,
bones and teeth have been found. The fauna consists of :—

Elephas antiquus : molars closely analogous to the specimens known from
the Summertown-Radley Terrace and in strong contrast to those of
Hanborough; one specimen is in the University Museum and there are a

number in the Manning Collection in Manchester University Museum. Two of the latter are so perfect that even the delicate cement *cingulum* which marks the position of the tooth in the jaw in relation to the soft gum, is preserved.[1] There can be no doubt, therefore, of the occurrence here *in situ* of *E. antiquus.*

Rhinoceros leptorhinus : a pelvis of rhinoceros is in the Oxford University Museum, and in the Manchester collection part of a tooth of *R. leptorhinus* is preserved.

Cervus elaphus : numerous antlers, perfect in the Oxford Clay on which they often lie but invariably spoilt in process of excavation ; also bones, all of large individuals.

Bos primigenius, Bison priscus (?), and *Equus caballus ;* the last with molars which seem to possess a molar crown pattern rather simpler than usual.

Associated with the above are flint implements[2]—abraded Chellean bouchers and Lower Acheulean forms somewhat abraded ; with these occur others to which the term ' Wolvercot type ' is sometimes applied. They are plano-convex or slipper-shaped[3] and may be divided into :—

(*a*) Small plano-convex bouchers.
(*b*) Magnificent implements measuring up to 10 in. in length.

(*a*) These are highly arched, with a flat base and a trimmed butt.[4] Their colour varies with the flint, but generally is grey or black ; that is, they are made of fresh flint. They are mostly unpatinated, and are barely rubbed or polished. They are so little abraded that they are almost certainly contemporaneous with the sand and gravel in which they lie. The flat base has usually been retrimmed, and the edges of the implements have been retouched. Some at least have been struck from a core ; yet, neither these nor the implements (*b*) described below are normal Levallois flakes, but are comparable to the late Acheulean forms which approach in some respects the Levallois type. They are probably of Upper Acheulean or Acheulean III industry. Prof. Breuil classified one specimen as Upper Acheulean.

(*b*) These probably represent the highest stage of evolution of the type described above ; they are about 10 in. long and nearly 4 in. broad, thin at the rounded point, thickening slightly towards the butt. They were detached apparently, though not certainly in every case, from a larger block ; but both faces are etched with beautiful fish-scale flakes, and this with their size, shape, and finish, precludes them from being classified as Levallois flakes. They are unpatinated, and in perfect preservation. Only four are known.[5]

A small series of implements from this bed is of particular chronological importance ; only four are known ; one, in the University Museum, is quite unworn and not more than 5 in. long,

---

[1] Sandford, K. S., *ibid*, pp. 73, 74.
[2] *See* Sandford, K. S., *Quart. Journ. Geol. Soc.*, vol. lxxx, 1924, Appendix II, p. 168 *et seq.*
[3] Evans, Sir John, ' Ancient Stone Implements,' 1897, p. 594.
[4] In some, portions of the crust remain, however. K. S. Sandford, *ibid*, pp. 169–170.
[5] Three in the Pitt-Rivers Museum (Bell Collection), and one in the Ashmolean Museum (Manning Collection).

of sharp triangular section, slightly asymmetrical, with a partially trimmed butt and a well-finished point. The simplicity and effectiveness of the technique is remarkable. It was identified by Prof. Breuil as of the industry of La Micoque—lowest or 'warm' Mousterian. Recently, an implement of the above type but only $3\frac{1}{4}$ in. long has been found, and is strongly suggestive of the same industry. The basement gravel of the channel is therefore associated with a 'warm fauna'—similar to that of the upper part of the Summertown–Radley Terrace—with (probably) late Acheulean and Micoque industries: an important datum is thus established.

Above the zone already described, a patch of fine calcareous false-bedded gravel, with some iron oxide, occurs on the west side of the channel; it has been eroded from the centre and east side and heavy iron pan caps the lowest calcareous gravel, passing over the fine gravel as iron staining. The pan forms a hard layer, and consists of an oolite gravel, about 6 in. thick, which has been metasomatically replaced by iron compounds, the oolitic structure of the constituent pebbles being reproduced in limonite. This layer of pan serves to 'seal' the lower implementiferous deposits. An implement of Lower or Middle Acheulean type has been found and is ironstained, a condition which, with iron encrustation, is noticed in many of the implements of the earlier collections (Bell and Manning). Between this bed and an upper pan lie shelly sands, containing an assemblage of mollusca, which indicate a temperate climate; *Corbicula fluminalis* is absent. The sands are trenched by a small rill containing shells and overlain in the centre of the channel by the upper iron pan which coalesces with the lower on the eastern side of the pit. The whole of the above deposits were considerably eroded before silt and clay filled the channel. It was at the bottom of this silt ('lacustrine beds') that Bell found a thin layer of peat, probably deposited in running water.[1] It is not seen in the present section. From it were identified 30 species of flowering plants and 35 or 37 of mosses. It was described by Clement Reid as a water-surface, which had caught and deposited in a back-water a number of plant-remains floated down the stream. About two-thirds of the mosses, as well as the flowering plants, are still found in the neighbourhood. But some of the others are exceptional. Thus *Hypnum capillifolium* Warnst. has been found in Britain only in the Arctic freshwater bed at Mundesley, and now occurs in high northern latitudes. *Thuidium decipiens* De Not. is an Alpine species found in the Scottish Highlands but not elsewhere in this country. Five others, *Camptothecium nitens* Schp., *Dichodontium pellucidum* Schp., *Hypnum giganteum* Schp., *H. revolvens* Sow., *H. stramineum* Dicks. are sub-Alpine, not now living in Oxfordshire.[2]

Fragments of elytra of beetles were also obtained, but were not

---

[1] *Quart. Journ. Geol. Soc.*, vol. lx, 1904, p. 120 *et seq.*
[2] The mosses were determined by Messrs. A. Gepp and A. N. Dixon, the flowering plants by Clement Reid.

identified at the time.   Recently they have been examined and are found to be nearly all referable to existing species.[1]

The overlying silt and clay, to a maximum depth of 15 ft., is almost entirely barren ; recently, however, teeth of Horse have been identified from it and part of a Deer's antler.   In the Museum of Manchester University (Manning Collection), however, is part of an antler referable to the Reindeer (*Rangifer tarandus*) from this pit, and its condition and adhering sand and clay give some grounds for referring it to the silt bed.   This is the only definitely established occurrence of Reindeer in the river gravels of the district.   During the last five years implements have been found in the silt—three flakes, all of creamy-white or ' basket work ' patina ; none is typical of any industry.   One, a trimmed scraper, of triangular outline, was found at 9 ft. from the surface : its upper surface is of flint crust, flaked at the border, the lower is a bulbar surface with well-marked flake scar ; part of the striking platform remains, but is damaged, and appears to be facetted.

The whole channel is capped by the ' warp ' which has a contorted junction with the underlying silt :—

' Its junction with the clay is contorted, and masses are driven down into the latter ; balls of sand are found in the clay which could hardly have been forced in, unless they were cemented into a hard lump, as they would be by ice or snow.   The clay is disturbed and forced up between the downward-thrust tongues of the warp.   The whole is superficial : the warp sands have a maximum thickness over the channel of about 5 ft. and disturbance occurs to a depth of about 2 feet into the clays below.'[2]

It has been suggested that the warp indicates a glaciation in the Thames valley at this time, and the discovery of a glaciated pebble in it some years ago by Prof. Sollas[3] appeared to strengthen the suggestion.   But many such pebbles have now been found in the terrace gravels and undoubtedly have been derived from the Plateau Drift, and it seems likely that if a glacier had travelled over the site more impressive signs of its passing here and elsewhere in the river valleys would have been found.

It is probable that the warp is a deposit indicating, by its character, a cold, wet climate ; a simple solution of its origin seems to be that given for rather similar deposits in other areas[4]—a sludgy mass of soil and gravel, frozen solid in winter, liquid or even dried in summer, moving at times over the underlying surface which might be permanently frozen.   The only condition which does not seem to be satisfied is that of the ' tea leaf structure '[5] noticed by Prof.

---

[1] Poulton, E. B., *Proc. Entom. Soc.*, March 23rd, 1923, and K. G. Blair, *Trans. Entom. Soc.*, 1923–24, pts. 3 and 4, p. 55 *et seq.*
[2] Sandford, K. S., *op. cit.*, p. 137.
[3] Sollas, W. J., *ibid.*, p. 137.
[4] Hudleston, W. H., *Quart. Journ. Geol. Soc.*, vol. xlii, 1886, p. 169, and H. B. Woodward, ' Geology of the London District ' (*Mem. Geol. Surv.*), 2nd Ed. by C. E. N. Bromehead, 1922, p. 59.
[5] Discussion on A. M. Bell's paper, *Quart. Journ. Geol. Soc.*, vol. lx, 1904, p. 131.

Sollas in the underlying clay, which would appear to indicate considerable pressure from above.

It will be noted that the fauna of the base of the Wolvercot Channel has much in common with that of the upper gravels of the Summertown–Radley Terrace, and that the implements point to rather a later culture in the former deposit. Above the level of the basement gravels the deposits of the channel appear to indicate conditions decreasing from temperate to sub-arctic, possibly culminating in the warp which, whatever its exact age, is later than the Wolvercot Channel. This question is again discussed on p. 165.

Flood Plain and Sunk Channel Gravels

This group of the river gravels forms in some places a well-marked terrace 5 to 10 ft. above the level of flood ; but locally patches occur, surrounded by alluvium, and within the tract of floods. The surface follows the river valley with a more uniform gradient than the alluvium, lying about 220 ft. above the sea-level in the extreme west of the district, near Shifford, and 180 ft. at Abingdon. Owing to the distribution of the alluvium in flat expanses at different levels, the gravel is sometimes completely overlapped. It is usually separated from the higher Summertown–Radley Terrace by a marked clay-step, along which springs often arise.

In the western part of the district a terrace, 5 to 10 ft. above the alluvium, spreads from Shifford to Stanton Harcourt with two breaks, cut by a small stream near the former village, and by the Windrush at Standlake. A section near New Shifford Farm showed 4 ft. of oolitic gravel on Oxford Clay. Elsewhere the gravel is seen in numerous dykes, but there are no openings showing its full thickness. At the hamlet of Moorton, near the river, the gravel rises in a low bank surrounded by alluvium on all sides and covered during the highest floods. It is said to be cemented into a hard rock. On the opposite side of the river, at Bablock Hythe, it is exposed to a depth of 4 ft. in a shallow pit by the roadside. At Stanton Harcourt the gravel passes under the broad spread of alluvium and does not come to the surface again for several miles, but it is occasionally exposed in the rivulets which cut through the flood-loam. Small banks rise to the surface within the flood-tract near Eynsham, at Lower Wolvercot, Binsey, and on towards Oxford, where the gravel forms the foundation of the low-lying district near Folly Bridge and the suburb of New Hinksey.

A considerable amount of information has recently been obtained during the construction of new bridges over branches of the Thames between Oxford and Botley.[1] Test borings were made at Pacey's Bridge (near Oxford Castle), where a maximum of 12 ft. of gravel and peat were pierced below river-level. On the Oxford side, peat formed the bottom but thinned from 6 ft. to about a foot in the centre boring, and on the west side was replaced by gravel (5 ft.) which was surmounted by blue clay and river silt, passing to river silt and gravel again on the Oxford side. At Bulstake Bridge, at about the middle of the alluvial tract, gravel capped by yellow (and in one case black) clay was found to a depth of 16 ft. below river-level and 5 ft. above it (alluvium). No borings were made at the bridge near the Black Horse Inn at Botley, but a few feet of gravel, cemented in places, was proved ; gravel reappears

---

[1] Sandford, K. S., *op. cit.*, p. 148 *et seq.* The information and plans of these borings were kindly supplied to the writer by Mr. J. E. Wilkes, City Engineer of Oxford.

from beneath the alluvium and rises to about 10 ft. above river-level a
Botley.

At the Oxford gasworks (standing on alluvium) gravel has been found
and the bottom not reached at 20 ft.[1] South of the city the river has cut
through the gravel to a somewhat greater depth, and gravel again appears
as a terrace along the margin of the alluvium. A small pit by North Hinksey
showed 7 ft. of oolitic gravel under 2 or 3 ft. of loam. At another pit in South
Hinksey the gravel was said to be 10 ft. thick.

In the centre of the alluvium belt, along the Abingdon Road, runs an
' island ' of gravel. Recently, a deep trench was carried along the road and
near the One Mile Stone it was turned towards the river. For the greater
part of the distance the trench ran along the ' island ' and then passed into
alluvium. Along the road 17–18 ft. of fine loose calcareous gravel was met
with, and Oxford Clay was usually reached at this depth. The road is almost
flat and the general surface may be taken as 183–185 ft. above O.D. The
river runs parallel to it, about ¼ mile to the east, at 179 ft. above O.D. : there
is therefore a thickness of about 5 ft. of gravel above river-level and 13 ft
below. As the cutting turned towards the river, the gravel thickened rapidly
and at about this point the alluvium, to a maximum depth of 3 ft., was
encountered, lying in patches on an eroded surface of the gravel. So soon
as the road was left, the gravel was not bottomed at 17 ft., and about 100 yds.
nearer the river (at a cottage in Long Bridge's backwater) 20 ft. of gravel
were passed through unbottomed. At this point, then, there is a sunk channel
unbottomed at 15 ft. below river-level.[2]

At Iffley Lock a depth of 25 to 30 ft. of gravel is reported below mean
water-level (the fall of water at the Lock is from 179·72 ft. O.D. to 176·99 ft
O.D.).[3] At the railway bridge on the Oxford-Thame line, which crosses the
river about a mile below Iffley Lock, caissons have been sunk, and nothing
but Oxford Clay encountered. The gravel was struck, but unbottomed at
12 ft., on the Berkshire (south) side of the river. Here, then, the river seems
to have cut into its northern bank, and to have deserted its former course.[4]

The floor of the Cherwell valley is almost completely covered with alluvium
but a small patch of gravel occurs at Kidlington, on which the church is built ;
near Islip the Ray now joins the Cherwell and here, to the east of the faulted
rock-mass on which the village is built there is a patch of gravel standing
above the level of the alluvium, but it is only a few feet thick. South of
Islip, in the Cherwell valley, the gravel is covered by alluvium, but a patch of
Flood Plain gravel comes to the surface on the Oxford side of the river opposite
Marston. In the University Park (near a footbridge spanning the river)
20 ft. of ' silt ' have been reported below the eastern bank.[5] Whether the
silt is to be correlated with the Flood Plain and Sunk Channel gravels or with
the alluvium is doubtful. On the Marston Meadows side of the footbridge
about 100 yds. from the river, gravel has been dug to a depth of about 4 ft.,
but flooding rendered the pit of little use. Below the footbridge, on the
Oxford side, patches of gravel occur above river-level in the University Park
and down-stream in ' Mesopotamia.'

From Kidlington to Yarnton no gravel of the Flood Plain stage appears
in the old Cherwell valley, which is filled with alluvium, and Oxford Clay
outcrops between it and the patch of gravel at Kidlington Church. It seems
probable that the Cherwell made its detour towards Islip at this time and
that part of its water flowed by the former Ray valley between Marston and
Oxford and so to the Thames near Cowley ; it is likely that the old valley
to Yarnton was also used.

[1] *Ibid.*, p. 150.
[2] *Ibid.*, pp. 149–150.
[3] Information supplied by Mr. E. Burnard, District Superintendent of the Thames
Conservancy Board.
[4] *Ibid.*, p. 150.
[5] Information supplied by Mr. J. E. Wilkes.

Below the immediate neighbourhood of Oxford the Flood Plain gravel is lost when the Thames enters Sandford Gap, but it reappears in the meadows at Radley and extends continuously as a well-marked terrace 6 ft. higher than the alluvium to the east of Abingdon, where it is cut through by a small tributary. The same terrace forms the foundations of the lower part of the town and the opposite bank of the River Ock, and also occurs within the alluvial tract on Andersey Island. Sections are shown in a few pits, for the most part disused, *e.g.*, close to the river ¼ mile south-east of Radley Village, where the gravel is dug to a depth of 3 ft. under a loamy soil 1 ft. thick. In other places 6 ft. or more of gravel can be seen.[1]

The banks against which the gravel of this stage was laid down are mostly intact and, beyond the minor deflections of course noted above, only one important change of river bed is to be found, at Shifford, in the extreme west of the district, where the river now flows through a valley a mile long between banks of Oxford Clay, while the old channel filled with gravel lies farther north in a direct line between Standlake and Bampton.

The records of borings and of deep excavations given above establish the following :—

(1) The presence of a ' Sunk Channel,' which seems to deepen down stream.

(2) The Sunk Channel gravels and the so-called First Terrace or, as it is proposed to call them ' Flood Plain Gravels,' are continuous.

It is fairly clear that the upper part of the Flood Plain gravel rests on a ledge on the side of the Thames generally a few feet above normal river-level, but the gravel is continuous over the ledge and fills a much narrower Sunk Channel. The ' islands ' situated in the Flood Plain rise to the height of the gravel of the bounding ledge ; therefore in cutting its deep channel the Thames either paused at the height of the ledge, and then cut its deep channel and aggraded its bed to the previous level (to erode it again to the level of the base of the alluvium)—or it cut the deep channel first and aggradation brought the river back again to the level of the ledge which it then formed.

Owing to the rare occasions available for studying the gravels and the rapid flooding of any excavation, the solution of the above problem is a matter of some difficulty ; but the continuity of gravel from below river-level to some feet above it (as in the Abingdon Road ' island ') points to the latter explanation being the correct one.

No unworn implements are known ; bones and teeth, as well as abraded implements, are occasionally dredged from the river and its backwaters, but they are of no value as indices. Only one tooth has been recovered—a large molar of Siberian Mammoth, which probably came from the bottom of the gravel in Christ Church Meadows, on the south side of Oxford, where one or two small marginal banks of gravel show above the alluvium.[2] Antlers of Red Deer also were found, it is believed at a higher level.

The record of a skull of Hippopotamus from beneath the same meadows is perplexing[3] ; the specimen must undoubtedly have been derived from an older deposit, probably from the Summertown–

---

[1] Pocock, T. I., *op. cit.*, p. 84.

[2] Sandford, K. S., *Quart. Journ. Geol. Sec.*, vol. lxxxi, 1925, pp. 82, 83.

[3] Bell, A. M., *Antiquary*, vol. xxx, 1894, pp. 148 and 192. *See also* K. S. Sandford, *Quart. Journ. Geol. Soc.*, vol. lxxx, 1924, p. 157.

Radley Terrace, the present margin of which lies at about the position of Christ Church Quadrangle.

Alluvium

Along the course of the Thames and its tributaries, slightly raised above the ordinary water-level, is a strip of flat meadow land for the most part uninhabited.   After heavy rains the whole of this tract is often covered by water, but the floods must have been more frequent and protracted before the river-banks were built and the low grounds drained.   For unknown ages at every inundation the fine sediments brought down from higher lands have been spread out upon the flats, gradually raising their levels and filling the hollows worn in the older deposits.   For the most part these sediments consist of fine silt, forming a soil lighter than the tough Oxford Clay.

The alluvium is six or eight feet thick, in the more central parts near the present watercourses.   Locally it extends to the foot of a bank of Oxford Clay ; but elsewhere, as in Ot Moor, it thins out so gradually that no definite boundary-line can be drawn.   Freshwater and land shells occur abundantly in places, as at Water Eaton, on the bank of the Cherwell.   Those hitherto recorded are all species living in the district.

A good section was seen at Iffley during the reconstruction of the Lock—about 4 ft. of silt and sand, with many shells, rested on the gravel of the sunk channel and were capped by about the same thickness of dark platy mud, in which bones of Horse and Ox were found. The shells have been declared by Mr. A. S. Kennard to be of Holocene age ; this is important because no clear line of partition was seen between the silt and sand and the gravel lying below river level, hence the shelly zone might represent the top of the Sunk Channel series at this point.   Elsewhere (as on the Abingdon Road) there is a strongly eroded surface marking the junction of the gravels with the alluvium.

Mr. E. S. Cobbold mentioned that in the vicinity of the Sewage Farm east of Sandford ' the bottoms of the small valleys which intersect the farm are filled with peat from four to six feet deep, in which have been found Roman pottery (at three feet), fresh-water shells, bones of deer, domesticated pig, cow, horse and dog.   Under the peat, patches of gravel of very local character are found, quite unlike that in the Thames Valley.'[1]

The alluvium does not follow the rivers with a perfectly uniform gradient, but tends to form lake-like expansions at slightly different levels along the narrow parts of the valley.   Thus, near the confluence of the Thames with the Evenlode, at the foot of Wytham Hill, the passage is too narrow for the combined flood waters to escape ; in consequence they spread over $2\frac{1}{2}$ square miles of country near Stanton Harcourt and at times stretch far up the valley between the Wytham Hill outlier and Hurst Hill.   No water is known to find its way across this neck to Botley—at any rate at the present day—nor are there fluviatile deposits at any height in the cross valley (*see* p. 172).   The

---

[1] *Quart. Journ. Geol. Soc.*, vol. xxxvi, 1880, p. 319.

alluvium has buried the Flood Plain gravel from Eynsham up the Evenlode and along the Thames as far as Port Meadow; it covers the old Cherwell valley running from Kidlington railway station to Yarnton.

A great expanse of alluvium stretches from Cassington over Port Meadow, continuing south as a broad belt between Oxford and North Hinksey and then narrowing to the funnel-shaped Sandford Gap at Iffley, thereafter running as a narrow tract through the Gap as far as Abingdon, where it begins to expand again.

The present valley of the Cherwell shows a great expansion of alluvium, and the Flood Plain gravel is completely submerged except at Kidlington. Three 'islands' of Oxford Clay project through it, one of them (Marston) being capped by gravel of the Summertown–Radley stage, which may have led to the preservation of the other two, though their gravels are now removed.

The greatest expansion is in the valley of the Ray, where there is the wide depression of Ot Moor, roughly circular in outline, about seven square miles in area, and lying between 193 ft. and 205 ft. above sea-level. This cup-shaped hollow is remarkable and doubtless it owes its origin to the much faulted barrier of limestones running from Islip towards Wheatley, to the east of which the Corallian limestones pass into Ampthill Clay—lying on Oxford Clay. Though only one patch of Flood Plain gravel is visible, the inception of the northern part of Ot Moor dates from much earlier times (*see* p. 171). There are now no fewer than four deep valleys radiating from it, all occupied by alluvium. Three join the Cherwell: the first to the north of Islip, blocked on the inner side by the patch of Flood Plain Gravel; the second, a deep gorge in which Islip stands, occupied by the Ray; the third which runs from Noke to Woodeaton, is a much wider valley flanked by Oxford Clay, but with sides eventually rising sharply on both sides to more than 300 ft. and crowned with limestones; to the north is the faulted inlier of Great Oolite, with Forest Marble and Cornbrash, to the south the Corallian outlier; the valley contains no river.

The fourth valley runs southwards into the basin of the Thame, and is occupied by the Holton Brook in its lower part. It seems probable that this stream, with the Moorbridge and Danes Brooks forming its headwaters, is a brook consequent on the exposure of clay, and is not to be considered as a vestige of an original Ray–Thame watercourse (*see* p. 168).

In times of flood the centre of Ot Moor is submerged and as a result the area, though mostly cultivated, is almost uninhabited. It will be noticed that a Roman Way crosses the Moor from south to north, but attempts to reach Joseph's Stone along this road usually fail, even in summer, since part of the Moor is now virtually a bog.

Close to the present courses of the rivers the alluvium is often at a slightly higher level than it is at some distance away, owing to the sudden check in the velocity of the stream as it overflows its banks, and the consequent deposition of part of the mud in suspension. This is well seen at many points of the Flood Plain in time of flood. The walks of ' Mesopotamia,' south of the University Park in Oxford, have been quoted [1]; and it may be seen also in the belt of alluvium between Godstow and Cassington, and in many other places. In addition, pollard willow trees often flank the rivers and grow on the raised bank, doubtless helping to consolidate it ; hence the ' islands ' of willows sometimes to be seen during floods, as well as the grass-covered alluvium patches.

River Terraces of the Thame

' The Thame joins the Thames at Dorchester beyond the southern edge of the area shown on the map, and there are extensive tracts of gravel overspreading the Gault south of Chislehampton which were laid down at the confluence of the two rivers in the Pleistocene period.   Here, as in the upper reaches of its valley, the Thames has step by step shifted its course to the southward.   A succession of alluvia of different ages may be traced similar to that which has been already described.' [2]

Of the high terrace little remains ; there are four small patches of gravel which correspond approximately in level to the terrace at ' Golden Balls,' south of March Baldon, on Clifton Heath, and to the south-west and $\frac{1}{4}$ mile to the north-west.   No sections have been seen and these patches may be of Plateau Drift ; in any case they might belong to the Thames itself or to the region of its confluence with the Thame.

There are two small remnants of the gravel, one near Tiddington Station, and the other a mile and a half down the river to the west.   There is a third about one mile east of Waterstock and half a mile north of Tiddington which is now being worked and was investigated by Mr. Pringle and the writer.

The composition is mainly flint, much of it ochreous and not greatly abraded, sometimes sharply angular.   Fresh flint and Eocene pebbles occur together with Shotover Ironsand, vein quartz and Bunter quartzite ; the last two are few in number : tourmaline grit is very scarce.   Chalk occurs.   The ochreous flint is often pitted.   The whole forms an irony and disordered deposit, with much solution in the upper part.   Towards the base bedding is marked.   Layers of sharp quartz sand occur.   These patches most probably belong to the High Terrace ; that described at any rate does not belong to the Plateau Drift.

The next lower terrace is particularly well represented and has been described by Mr. Pocock ; recently also a section has been seen at Little Haseley.   It is not present in the region near the mouth of the Thame, but there is a terrace rising with a good feature some 15–20 ft. above the ' second ' terrace and extending from Burcot Farm a mile and a half to the north-east ; ' but except at the farm itself, where the Lower Greensand crops out between them, it is difficult to separate the gravels of the two terraces.   If the top of the Greensand be traced up the brooks from Burcot, a conspicuous rise in level may be noticed on passing from the second to the third

---

[1] Pocock, T. I., *op. cit.*, p. 83.
[2] Pocock, T I., *op. cit.*, p. 93.

terrace near the 200 ft. contour line, but there is not sufficient evidence to show that there is any outcrop of Greensand between the two. Thus it cannot be proved that the feature just mentioned is any more than a ledge cut by the river in a continuous bed of gravel, although, taken in connection with the evidence at Wolvercot and Radley, it is probable that there are here two beds overlapping, which were formed at successive stages in the development of the river valley.'[1] This opinion, expressed some years ago, is of interest in the light of more recent work. Unfortunately no sections have been seen.

'The patch of gravel S.W. of Chislehampton is noticeable on account of the cone-shaped hill in the middle. On the side near the Thame is a pit showing gravel of the 'second' terrace. The conical hill, which appears also to be gravel, though there is no section, is probably a denuded remnant of the 'third' terrace, cut partly by the Thame and partly by the Baldon Brook.'[2]

On the opposite side of the Thame between Stadhampton and Chalgrove is a plateau of gravel nearly three miles long, corresponding in level to the terrace under discussion. There is a smaller patch at Little Haseley, on the north side of Haseley Brook, in which a section has been seen in the farmyard about a quarter of a mile to the south-west of Haseley Court :—

							Ft.
Soil	..	..	..	..	..	..	$1\frac{1}{2}$
Rubbly ferruginous loam	..	..	..	..	..		1
Fine gravel	..	..	..	..	..	..	1
Sandy clay, passing into gravel at the bottom				..	..		$1\frac{1}{2}$

Fresh flint is abundant, together with black flint pebbles from the Eocene capping of the Chilterns, with much close-set sharp ironsand, similar to that of Shotover. Neither Oolitic material nor remains of the Plateau Drift were noticed here.[3]

Of the large patch to the south Mr. Pocock says :—' No good section was observed, but at an overgrown pit (by the " R " of Rofford) the gravel mainly consists of chalk flints, angular, subangular or rounded ; and since the surface rises 35 feet towards the Chiltern escarpment, it was most probably laid down by a river coming from that direction. There are now two tributaries, one on each side of the plateau—the Great Haseley and the Chalgrove Brooks —which rise in the Chalk hills, but these two combined seem scarcely large enough to have formed a bed of gravel comparable in extent and thickness with that of the Thames itself. It is possible that the gravel marks an old channel of the Thame more direct than the present circuitous course east of the Shotover Hills.'[4]

Mr. Pocock is of opinion that its wide extent and the unworn state of many of the flints are suggestive of melting ice fields, but admits that more must be known of the country between here and Aylesbury before any sound opinion can be given. Of the patch marked at Parson's Farm, north of Waterperry, the writer found no trace, but most of the area is under grass.

[1] Pocock, T. I., op. cit., p. 94.
[2] Ibid.
[3] Sandford, K. S., Quart. Journ. Geol. Soc., vol. lxxx, 1924, p. 129.
[4] Loc. cit., p. 95.

The 'second' terrace is also well preserved in the lower course of the Thame. It rises with a well-marked feature 20–30 ft. above the lowest terrace and an outcrop of Gault clay separates them most of the way. It is trenched in several places by streams flowing from the Kimmeridge Beds of March Baldon, and entering the Thame near Chislehampton and the Thames near Burcot.

The best section seen of recent years is to be found about half a mile south of the edge of the map, on the London and Wallingford road, between the Roman Road and the main road. It is situated in the great patch of gravel between Drayton St. Leonard and March Baldon, which it shows to have been at the confluence of Thames and Thame. Strictly, the gravel at this exposure belongs to the Thames, but it may well be described here. It consists of about 10 ft. of *Thames* gravel—mostly oolite gravel, fine, with sharp quartz sand. Small pebbles of the Plateau Drift occur, with Shotover Ironsand and a fair amount of fresh flint (from the Thame?); also ammonites from the Gault and blocks of a black remanié bed of the Portland Beds, probably brought in by the Thame. It is mostly even bedded, with false-bedded layers of sand. At the base is a coarse pebble bed of material from the Plateau Drift, especially ochreous flint and Bunter quartzite.

'A pit two-thirds of a mile S.W. of Chislehampton showed five feet of small false-bedded gravel consisting mostly of Oolitic Limestone pebbles, among which were found pieces of the Great Oolite white limestone. There was also a large number of lydites, a few quartzites, white quartz pebbles, flints and pieces of ironstone.'[1] Other pits south of Field Farm near the Roman Way showed similar sections. The gravel is weathered to a depth of several feet in places, notably so at a pit rather more than half a mile north of Field Farm, where there is an excess of siliceous pebbles due to the dissolution of the limestone constituents.

'The gravels here described were probably due more to the Upper Thames than to the Thame. The presence of Chalk and other Cretaceous fragments show that the transition from the Oolite gravels of the upper valley to the flint gravel of the Lower Thames had already begun. Some of the feeders of the river rise in the Chalk downs of Berkshire, south of the Vale of the White Horse, and this must have been the source from which the Chalk and Greensand pebbles at Burcot were brought. But the Oolite limestone is still a dominant constituent, and it is not till Dorchester is passed that its place is taken by flint.'[2]

To the above may be added the following notes of H. B. Woodward:—

'An extensive tract of gravel of the same age occurs over the south and east of Waterstock, banked up to a certain extent against the Kimmeridge Clay on the south. The gravel is composed of subangular flints and pebbles of flint, quartz and quartzite. A thickness of 10 feet was opened up (base not seen) to the south of Draycot, and a little to the south-east of the junction with the lane leading to Waterstock.

'In the parishes of Ickford, Worminghall and Waterperry there are occasional thin and irregular gravelly coatings with flints and lydites; but no good gravel occurs, and that used for mending the paths west of the church at Worminghall was brought from Cookham.'

'On the right bank of the Thame below Holton Mill, and again south of the Great Western Railway bridge, there are thin cappings of gravel.

[1] From the notes of J. H. Blake.
[2] Pocock, T. I., *op. cit.*, p. 94.

'South and south-west of Waterperry House the clayey ground of the Corallian merges so gradually into the Alluvial ground that the geological boundary is vague.[1]

In the upper part of the Thame Valley, east of the Shotover range, the gravels are much less conspicuous. They differ from those of the Thames in the absence of Oolitic Limestone pebbles, their place being taken by flints and quartzose pebbles derived from the drift. The Thame does not drain any part of the country of the Lower Oolites, but outliers of Portland Beds lie within its basin. Some of the tributaries may have brought flints directly from the Chilterns, but the principal source of the constituents of the gravel was no doubt the drift which once spread over the whole valley, but is now confined to a few outliers. This drift consists mainly of flints, but there is an admixture of pebbles of quartz and quartzite derived from northern sources.

The composition of the low level gravels is similar, but many of the flints are more water-worn. Near Little Milton there are one or two small patches of gravel belonging to the two lowest terraces. Higher up, near the bend of the river east of Wheatley, is a strip along the left bank one-third of a mile long belonging to the second terrace.

Finally, nearest the river, patches of gravel appear in the Flood Plain, overlapped here and there by the alluvium, which is generally from an eighth to a quarter of a mile wide but extends to half a mile in a number of places east of Wheatley. Of the Flood Plain gravel there is a wide tract at Drayton St. Leonard, extending a mile westwards and 5–6 ft. above the present alluvial flood plain. Mr. Pocock reports one section[2] : —

' The best section of this gravel was seen close to the Thames at Burcot, just beyond the map, where it is made up principally of fragments of brown oolitic limestone, hard Chalk, gritty limestone, quartz, quartzite, flints (rounded and sub-angular), and probably Upper Greensand, nearly all less than an inch in diameter.[3] The full thickness of the deposit was not known, as it extends below the level of the river.'

THE FORMATION OF TERRACES

To-day the material being deposited by the rivers consists almost entirely of fine silt. The ancient river-terraces are made up of gravel of varying degrees of coarseness, with some sand. If, then, the gradients are similar in both the ancient and modern valleys the velocity and probably the volume of the rivers must formerly have been much greater.

Again, the presence of terraces one below the other indicates

---

[1] In 'The Geology of the Country around Oxford' (*Mem. Geol. Surv.*), 1908, p. 95.

[2] *Ibid., p.* 93.

[3] *See also* Blake, J. H., ' Summary of Progress for 1900 ' (*Mem. Geol. Surv.*), 1901, p. 130.

breaks in the periods of deposition, and disturbance of the river basin from source to sea, owing to relative changes of level between land and sea, with a consequent renewal of the power of the rivers to deepen their beds—in a word, rejuvenation.

The most marked of these occurred after the Handborough Terrace had been formed, when the channels were deepened some 50 ft. During the period of instability of the river gradients erosion continued until finally a new base-level was reached and gravel was laid down. Two further periods of deepening took place, followed in each case by an aggradation of the river bed.

Usually, extensive sheets of gravel may be found only to mark the periods of rest succeeding those of degradation, but there is no reason why some patches of gravel should not be deposited and left during the process of erosion—a feature which may well account for some of the difficulties encountered when efforts are made to correlate patches of gravel in different parts of a river system.

The coarseness of the older deposits is connected with the velocity and volume of the rivers and the amount of load they carried ; but it is difficult to find satisfactory explanations for this former greater activity. Two have been suggested :—

(1) Concentration of most of the annual rainfall into one part of the year.
(2) Annual melting of snowfields near the sources of the rivers.[1]

The second may be dismissed for it has been shown that at least two of the terraces are accompanied by a fauna incompatible with the contemporary existence of snowfields in the Cotteswolds.

The first explanation seems the more possible solution, but one would then expect to find intercalated finer deposits on a much greater scale than is the case.

It seems still more probable that, with a rising land area, the rainfall was greater : on both accounts the river must have possessed greater powers of erosion.

As for the terraces, with their marked uniformity and parallelism, relative changes of level of land and sea, affecting the whole river system, may be supposed. There is every reason to believe that at periods of the Ice Age, especially during those following the maximum extension of the ice in the Northern Hemisphere, such changes of level took place ; sometimes owing to direct change in sea-level, sometimes to actual isostatic movements of the land masses. To such movements the terraces of the Upper Thames, in common with those of other rivers and with the raised beaches of the coast, may undoubtedly be assigned in part or in entirety. They mark periods of stability in such movements and their parallelism in the Oxford district indicates that the movements were accomplished without marked tilting of the land, at any rate in this area.

Combined with the above, however, we have the demonstration of an interesting hypothesis by Prof. W. M. Davis in his paper on

---

[1] Pocock, T. I., *op. cit.*, p. 105.

the Drainage of Cuestas[1]—founded on a study of North American river systems.

The following discussion has been drawn from Prof. Davis's paper, with some additions of local application and of recent work, and is intended mostly for students :—

Young coastal plains present an even slope from the base of a hilly background of older land to their simple shore-line. So long as the strata offer essentially uniform resistance to the weather, or so long as the more resistant rocks are below the weaker, no diversion from the ' normal' system of consequent drainage occurs and the upland is cut up into a number of interfluvial strips.

If, however, weaker layers lie below stronger ones the initial transverse drainage may be given up for a longitudinal relief of quite a different kind. The weak under-layers soon undermine their hard cover along the inner part of the coastal plain and waste away close to base-level, forming an inner lowland. The resistant layers now have a rapid descent across their outcropping edges to the inner lowland and a long gentle slope to the coastal lowland. The valleys of the extended consequent rivers are relatively narrow where bordered by the resistant layers of the upland. Blocks of upland with the above significant outline Prof. Davis calls ' Cuestas ' (Spanish, hill or slope), and coastal plains having their upland and lowlands thus arranged in longitudinal belts may be called ' belted coastal plains.'

' The Oolite and Chalk cuestas of the Mesozoic coastal plain of eastern England . . . may be cited as examples having well defined longitudinal relief ' (op. cit., p. 76).

The outline and contour of the in-face of a cuesta depend on the amount of dip, as does the slope of the outer inclined plane—which is indeed a dip-slope. Thus, with a change of dip the in-face may change from a steep escarpment to a gentle slope. ' Yet on all cuestas the residual consequent streams are losing drainage area and the opposite or obsequent streams are gaining, as the in-face wastes and retreats in the direction of dip.' (Loc. cit.).

The precise application of the above to the Cotteswolds is indeed most striking, not only in main outline but in detail, and in that part of the Chiltern escarpment which comes within our area we may have the conception of the Thame playing the part of the pirate stream of the inner lowland (though developmentally this most probably is not its function ; it is that of certain of its tributaries to-day).

There is no need to develop the above argument in detail as the application is sufficiently obvious. The Lias, of course, forms the weak under-layer of Prof. Davis's scheme and the Severn-Avon the river of the inner lowland and so on.

Turning to the rivers in detail Prof. Davis points out (op. cit., p. 98), ' The Cherwell seems to retain a greater share of its original

---

[1] *Proc. Geol. Assoc.*, vol. xvi, 1890, p. 87 *et seq.* See also *Geogr. Journ.*, vol. v, 1895, pp. 127–146, in particular p. 145.

length than any other of the Thames branches '—it still retains some hold on the inner lowland ; the Severn-Avon is approaching it from the west, as also the Ouse from the east. A logical conclusion from the above is that the headwater drainage area of the consequent rivers having been reduced they will survive as misfits in their original valleys.

Such is clearly the case with the Cherwell ; especially is it so immediately to the north of the map at Enslow Bridge, and farther upstream, where there is a most striking contrast between the bold swinging curves of the valley and the minor irregularities of the present stream, wandering aimlessly on the valley floor. The case of the Evenlode is similar, with its head in the broad Vale of Moreton and its beautiful meanders in hard rock near Long Hanborough— meanders which have been partly attacked in later periods of rejuvenation but not destroyed. The Windrush between Witney and Burford repeats these features and rises near the Evenlode. The Coln, though it displays similar phenomena in a particularly interesting manner, lies entirely outside the area of the map and for it, as for other details, reference should be made to the original work.

Many obsequent streams make rapid descent to the Severn-Avon inner-lowland, especially opposite the head of the Coln ; to the northeast the Stour draws much of its water from the Liassic-lowland forming the upper end of the Vale of Moreton, in which also the Evenlode rises. Farther to the north-east the Avon draws its supplies from the foot of the bold escarpment of Edge Hill.

If the above were the only causes of change of volume in the Thames Basin, the branches of the Severn system ought to be as robust as those of the Thames are feeble. Such, however, is not the case, for both the Stour and the Avon are equally misfits. Therefore, general decrease in the volume of the streams must have been superimposed on the above changes, and this almost certainly indicates climatic change.

Miss Tomlinson[1] has shown that in the Avon Basin the gradient of the river, in relation to its length, is greater than that of the Thames and its tributaries above Goring Gap. This indeed might be expected, and the explanation given by Prof. Davis appears to apply in this case. The difference in evolutional history also may account for other points of dissimilarity of the terrace system of the Avon and of the Thames system about Oxford.

---

[1] Tomlinson, Miss, *Quart. Journ. Geol. Soc.*, vol. lxxxi, 1925, pp. 137 *et seq.*

CHAPTER XII

PLEISTOCENE—*continued*

RIVER DEVELOPMENT, CLIMATE AND CHRONOLOGY

IN earlier chapters an account has been given of the different formations which constitute the so-called ' solid geology ' of the country. The latest of the formations now remaining in the region is the Upper Greensand. But beyond these limits, eastward and southward, the Upper Greensand is overlain conformably in the Chiltern Hills and the Berkshire Downs by the Chalk which must once have spread far over the highest summits of the Oxford district. Again, in the Lower Thames valley, sands and clays of Eocene age are found extending up the dip-slopes of the Chalk, and in a few outliers, as at Nettlebed, reach almost to the edge of the escarpments. It is clear that at one time they must have reached farther to the north-west, but it is not known whether the estuary in which they were deposited extended over the site of Oxford, or was bounded by a coast-line of Chalk somewhere to the south-east. In either case, the Oxford region must have been deeply buried beneath the surface in Eocene times, for the highest hill is considerably lower than some of the Eocene outliers on the Chalk Downs.

The initiation of the river system, consequent on emergence of the land from the sea, probably took place in post-Eocene times. Owing to the enormous amount of denudation which has taken place since, it is unlikely that conclusive evidence will be found within the district as to the actual date of the uplift ; but by a study of other regions the limits of time can be narrowed somewhat.

It is known that raised rock-platforms, presumed to be of early Tertiary age, occur on Bodmin Moor[1] and Dartmoor[2] and elsewhere in the Devon-Cornwall peninsula at a height of about 1,000 ft. Another is well-marked in places at about 750 ft. above O.D.,[3] and there are deposits of Tertiary age in South Wales[4] and scattered at great heights over most of the south of England.

Again, there are deposits in the West Country, proved by fossils to be of early Pliocene age, at a height of 430 ft.–500 ft. above O.D.

---

[1] Reid, C., G. Barrow and H. Dewey, ' The Geology of the Country around Padstow and Camelford ' (*Mem. Geol. Surv.*), 1910, p. 78 *et seq.*
[2] Reid, C. and others, ' The Geology of Dartmoor ' (*Mem. Geol. Surv.*), 1912, p. 57 *et seq.* *See also* memoirs on ' Tavistock and Launceston ' and on ' Newton Abbot.'
[3] *Mem. Geol. Surv.* : (1) Padstow and Camelford, *ibid.*
(2) Dartmoor, *ibid.*
Also Tavistock and Launceston and Newton Abbot.
[4] Here there are quartz gravels which are correlated with the St. Erth Beds and Cornish-Devon Pliocene platform. *See* E. E. L. Dixon, ' The Country around Pembroke and Tenby ' (*Mem. Geol. Surv.*), 1921, p. 167 *et seq.*

(18772)   L (as, for instance, the St. Erth Sands of Cornwall,[1] and other deposits and rock-platforms over the peninsula). The Pliocene platform is found at nearly the same height from Land's End to Tintagel,[2] a distance of 60 miles, which indicates that the subsequent change of level was not accompanied by tilting. In the south-east of England marine Pliocene deposits have been found at about the same altitude on the Chalk Downs of Kent, at Lenham.[3]

In Dorset there is the remarkable occurrence of *Elephas meridionalis* Nesti at Dewlish,[4] about 350 ft. above sea-level and 90 ft. above the rivers of the present drainage system. The deposit in which it occurs can be dated with some certainty as Upper Pliocene (freshwater and estuarine).

The country has been profoundly changed since these beds were deposited and from a consideration of these examples and of other evidence of a similar description, it seems probable that the inception of the drainage system of the Oxford district should be placed in late Tertiary times, though there is no direct evidence for placing it in Pliocene times.

The movements which actually determined the courses of the rivers were upheaval in the north-west, which gave the general south-easterly dip of the strata, and undulations of lesser magnitude inclined obliquely to the main line of movement. The Chalk and the overlying Eocene strata on the slopes of the Chilterns have been involved in the movements. Consequent on the uplift a number of streams, some of which are represented to-day by the Windrush, the Evenlode, the Glyme and the Cherwell, were initiated.

In the progress of erosion great thicknesses of soft clay were uncovered and tributary streams cut back rapidly along the clay areas, capturing some of the original consequent streams. Strong ' subsequent ' streams were thus developed, flowing along the strike of the softer strata. Such a river is the Thames above Yarnton where it joins the Cherwell, flowing over Oxford Clay almost from its source. The Ray, the Thame and the Ock are also to be considered as subsequent streams though they are not so clearly defined owing to modifications induced by the structure of the strata, which they have encountered as they have deepened their beds.

It will be noted that the Evenlode and Cherwell do not flow exactly at right angles to the strike of the Oolites, but somewhat obliquely ; Mr. Pocock found that they followed slight downfolds or dislocations of the strata, ' which are apparent if the geological boundaries are traced in reference to the contour lines. At the Sandford gap the Corallian rocks bend upward at low angles on both sides of the river, though the prevalent dip of the region is almost in the direction of flow. Again, higher up the valley, the outlier

[1] See Reid, C., ' The Pliocene Deposits of Britain ' (*Mem. Geol. Surv.*), 1890, p. 59 *et seq.* ; *see also* above and other memoirs on the West Country.
[2] Dewey, H., *Quart. Journ. Geol. Soc.*, vol. lxxii, 1916, pp. 63–76.
[3] Reid, C., *op. cit.*, p. 42 *et seq.*
[4] *Ibid.*, p. 206 *et seq.* See also A. E. Salter, *Proc. Geol. Assoc.*, vol. xv, 1897–98, p. 279.

of Oxford Clay at Tackley indicates a downfold in the Jurassic strata.

'In the case of the Evenlode the Great Oolite strata incline slightly upwards from the river on the Combe side and on the Long Hanborough side, while farther west there is a small fault in the direction of the valley near Stonesfield. The Windrush, again, passes from the Oolite country near Witney on to the Oxford Clay close to a fault. But whether the upper reaches of the valley and those of the Glyme, which lie outside our region, are likewise determined by rock-structures has not yet been ascertained ' . . . .

' The much more powerful dislocations which elevated the Lower Oolites along the present Ray Valley, and the faults between Islip and Wheatley, have had little influence on the course of the rivers, probably because they are of older date and were entirely concealed by Upper Cretaceous strata at the time when the present arteries of drainage originated.

' The early development of the river valley is largely matter of conjecture, though the broad lines upon which it has been worked out can be understood. Before the Gault and Ironsands of the hilltops round Oxford were uncovered by erosion, some 800 feet of Upper Cretaceous strata had been removed.'[1]

At about this time there was probably a plain of Gault clay over the site of Oxford and the escarpment of the Chalk hills stood a few miles to the south. It is probable that the combined waters of the Evenlode and Cherwell breached this range in a narrow gap initiated at a very early stage and of which the gap at Goring may be the survivor.

Before its capture by the Thames the Windrush may have followed an independent course. Mr. Pocock suggests that it may have flowed through the gap in the Berkshire Downs now occupied by the railway line from Didcot to Newbury,[2] though there is no actual evidence of this. Similar consequents may have flowed to the east of the Cherwell, but, if so, they have been captured either by the Ray or by the Thame.

It is impossible to state the exact period at which the above state of affairs was reached, but it was certainly long after the deposition of the Westleton Beds on the Chilterns and preceded the introduction of the Plateau Drift. The latter at its highest point lies upon surviving fragments of such a topography (Boar's Hill and Leafield, the latter to the north-west of the map), but it rests also at lower levels, including the flanks of the Thames valley above and below its confluence with the Cherwell. It is thus indicated that erosion must have been carried much further, at any rate before the deposition or final resorting of the drift, for it is found in the Vale of Moreton to approach the level attained by the river terraces[3];

---

[1] *Op. cit.*, p. 107.
[2] *Ibid.*
[3] *See* Hull, E. ' Geology of the Country round Cheltenham ' (*Mem. Geol. Surv.*), 1857, p. 85 *et seq.* Note : it is not known whether or not Fig. 14 in that memoir (p. 94) is correct in detail.

L 2

so also at The Demesnes and in Bagley Wood. Thus the main lines of drainage and the upper parts of the present valley slopes were already established before the close of the period of the deposition of the Plateau Drift[1].

In the Oxford district the oldest portions of the land surface preserved intact are those which are still capped by Plateau Drift, and of these, according to the Rev. C. Overy, the highest are the oldest. Parts of the surface not so protected have suffered at least some reduction which elsewhere has been borne by the super-incumbent drift.

Although the main lines of drainage of to-day were already established before the deposition of the drift, the topography of the country has changed greatly, owing to erosion, since that time.

After the appearance of the Plateau Drift, development can be studied with more certainty. It seems evident that the drift is the relic of a formation introduced under Glacial conditions ; it may have been resorted but the presence of striated boulders and indications of glaciation in its highest (Boar's Hill) and lowest stages (The Demesnes, Combe) indicate that in places the material cannot have suffered violent erosion in the process.

According to Mr. Overy, the Plateau Drifts and the river gravels, from the highest stage of the former, have been laid down on gradients which are the same as those of the river courses of to-day, though in the process the rivers have shifted their courses, as might be expected.

The whole surface of the ground has been altered, though leaving patches of Plateau Drift capping isolated hills ; the Chilterns still bear some patches on their escarpment (especially to the east of the map), but for the most part all the escarpments have retreated, with the destruction of any drift which lay upon them.

Mr. Pocock describes the general processes by which some of the main features of the topography were formed[2] :—

' Our knowledge of the system of rivers and brooks which carved out the highest summits of our region—Brill, Shotover and Cumnor Hills—is very imperfect, but the survival of these isolated beds of sand is due primarily to their position between the water-courses. There is, however, another cause. Within the limits of our region the Gault clay overlaps in succession all the underlying strata down to the Kimmeridge Clay, so that a large part of the Portland Beds and Ironsands must have been swept away by an earlier denudation preceding the Upper Cretaceous period. The long stretch of relatively low ground between Cumnor and Faringdon is in all probability due to the absence of any resistent strata between the

---

[1] In this connexion it is interesting to note that valleys of the upper tributaries of the Ouse are choked with drift into which the rivers have subsequently cut, forming terraces analogous to those of the Thames Basin. In East Anglia the oldest Glacial drift completely fills the pre-Glacial valleys, the bottoms of which are now much below sea level. P. G. H. Boswell, *Quart. Journ. Geol. Soc.*, vol. lxix, 1913, p. 581 *et seq.* *See also* P. G. H. Boswell and I. S. Double, *Proc. Geol. Assoc.*, vol. xxxiii, 1922, p. 300 *et seq.*

[2] *Op. cit.*, pp. 108, 109.

Kimmeridge and Gault Clays which once covered the Corallian plateau. This is quite in accordance with the fact that in the Vale of the White Horse the two clays are in contact all the way from Culham to Uffington. The wide gap between Shotover and Brill may also in part be ascribed to the same cause.

'The sculpture of the features of lower elevation is closely connected with the growth of the subsequent rivers. There are three belts of soft strata on which these might have been developed : the Oxford, Kimmeridge, and Gault Clays. But in reality the last two are so frequently in contact that they have not given rise to independent river-systems. The escarpment of Corallian rocks which crosses the region from south-west to north-east has been made by the erosion of the Upper Thames and the Ray along the broad belt of Oxford Clay. The Thame and its tributaries cut out the network of valleys among the sandy hills on the eastern border of the county. Yet though the Thame runs approximately in the direction of the strike of the Kimmeridge Clay, it was probably in the first instance a subsequent river on an outcrop of Gault, and the later deepening of the valley since the glacial period has been guided by undulations in the Lower Greensand and Portland strata. Between Thame and Wheatley the direction of the river is nearly east and west along the axis of a downfold, for the strata dip at low angles towards the river-bed on both sides. The sharp bend to the south near Wheatley is occasioned by the uplift of the strata on the west side towards Shotover Hill.'

The highest of the so-called valley gravels—the High or Hand-borough Terrace—is the first actual indicator which can be used for estimating the relative age of the Plateau Drift. It has been shown already that this terrace is later than the lowest of the Plateau Drifts (*see* p. 118). The difference in appearance and composition of the terrace and of the drift is striking and leads an observer to suppose that the interval which elapsed between the completion of the latter and the inception of the high terrace must have been of long duration. Such is probably the case, as will be shown below. When the rivers began to lay down the gravels of the high terrace the present system was fully developed, but without many of the complications which supervened in the later stages.

'The Upper Thames followed a direct course along the Oxford Clay from Fairford to the north of Yarnton, several miles distant from the present channel. The Corallian escarpment on the right bank stood at a greater height and in a position more to the north-west than now, the curve at Appleton not being then in existence. On the left bank the Oxford Clay rose in gentle slopes to the drift-clad hills of North Leigh and Bladon Heath, between which the Evenlode emerged from its upland gorge and formed the delta of gravel at [Long] Hanborough. Farther east the Thames was joined by the Cherwell near the outlier of gravel above Yarnton, and the united rivers flowed over the site of Oxford, crossing the strike of the strata in the same direction as at present, but in a more direct line, as the curves of Nuneham Park and round the hill at Culham had not yet been formed.   Besides these rivers, the Ray was a tributary from the north-east, entering the main valley over the shoulder of Noke Hill, but since it flowed through a clay country and was not fed by any important tributaries from the Oolite uplands, no gravels remain to mark its former channel.   There was a river of considerable magnitude, perhaps the Windrush itself, running through the Wilcote valley into the Evenlode.   But this was probably diverted, and entering the main valley by Witney, laid down its gravels on the margin of the Thames.

'The Vale of the White Horse was traversed by the Ock, but the river bed lay farther to the north than at present, and its old alluvia have for the most part been swept away.

'Lower down the valley of the Thames the main river was joined by the Thame, probably not far south of Stadhampton, though here also the high terrace has almost entirely disappeared.'[1]

In the Handborough Terrace is met a ' warm fauna ' which is that associated with post-Pliocene Chellean Man (in particular *Elephas antiquus* and allied forms and *Rhinoceros leptorhinus*). That such a fauna should have been re-established in this country after the glaciation which certainly preceded it and brought to a close the warm period of the Pliocene, is a remarkable indication of the probable proportions of any time-scale which may be applied to these deposits.

Attention may now be directed to the question of the age of the Plateau Drift.   It has been shown that the drift is intimately connected with, and has the same composition as, true boulder clay in the Midlands, in the upper part of the Cherwell and at the head of the Evenlode.   In the latter, Buckland found flint and red chalk ; flint, supposedly from Norfolk, is a constituent of both boulder clay and drift.   The boulder clay has been associated with the Lower Chalky Boulder Clay and is the relic of the maximum extent of glaciation in this country.   It appears reasonable, therefore, to refer the deposition of the material which forms the Plateau Drift to the same period.   It was during the interval between the arrival of the material under conditions of glaciation and the removal of such conditions from most of the British Isles and the re-establishment of a ' warm fauna ' that the Plateau Drift was deposited.   It is important to note that in the highest and lowest levels of the drift the assemblage of erratic material is the same ; also striated boulders occur in both ; it is thus indicated that at the time of introduction of the material the country between these zones was affected.   The possibility of any of the Plateau Drift in this area being of pre-Glacial age is slight.

The period between the first introduction of erratic material and the deposition of the highest of the river terraces must have been of considerable length, but it is not possible to estimate how much of

---

[1] Pocock, T. I., *op. cit.*, p. 109.

that time the formation of the Plateau Drift occupied, and how much is represented by no deposit at all.

Just as the Plateau Drift and the High Terrace appear to differ widely in age so the latter is to be distinguished from the lower terraces not only on account of level but of topography.

' The enormous denudation which has taken place since the epoch of the high terrace is strikingly illustrated by the position of the outlying remnants.   The water which laid down the gravels would, under present physical conditions, overflow into the basins of the Ouse in the north-east and the Avon in the south-west, besides crossing the Corallian escarpment near Fyfield and drowning many low-lying valleys in the district.   It is clear that at all these points the land must at the time have stood at a much higher level.'[1]

In the case of the Ouse such a possibility has been considered, and it has been shown by Mr. Overy that the higher and older Plateau Drift is apparently graded uniformly down the river valleys to their confluences near Oxford and thence down the main Thames valley and through Goring Gap—the patches of the later 100-foot or high terrace indicating the same direction of grading.   In the clay lowland at the mouth of the Gap the deposits are scanty but the gradients are found above and below this break in the valley sides. It is therefore improbable that at the period of the high terrace or of the Plateau Drift the Thames system drained into the Ouse. High land, now destroyed, must have barred the outflow of the Thames system into the Avon, Ouse, and locally across the escarpment near Fyfield.

After the deposition of the gravels of the Handborough stage degradation of the river beds set in and the valleys were deepened to the extent of some 40 to 60 ft.   In the limestone districts the rivers were compelled, owing to the resistance of the rock, to keep to the channels they had already excavated.   In certain parts of their courses (as at Long Hanborough) the rivers cut through the thin remnants of Oxford Clay almost as soon as degradation set in ; the centre of their channels may have reached the limestone even before this time.   In any case the Cherwell and the Evenlode had their deepening channels fixed in limestone at an early stage of the degradation and have never been able to break from them ; their sinuous course leaves little room for doubt that the Cherwell and the Evenlode above its confluence with the Glyme had previously settled into a meandering course, swinging from side to side in their own gravel-filled valleys.   A state approaching maturity of the river system thus seems to have been reached at the close of the Handborough stage and the new phase marked a rejuvenation of the system.

Prof. W. M. Davis has justly described the magnificent incised meanders of the Evenlode about Long Hanborough as a perfect example of erosion by a meandering river.[2]   The valley swings to

[1] Pocock, T. I., *op. cit.*, p. 109.
[2] *Proc. Geol. Assoc.*, vol. xvi, 1890, p. 87.

and fro with an amplitude of $\frac{1}{2}$ mile between spurs of turf-covered limestone, which project from either side and slope gently down to the flood-plain. The opposing banks, which encountered the full force of the river, rise in steep bluffs thickly covered by woods. The diminutive stream which now wanders over the flood-plain is incompetent to have formed such widely-sweeping curves, and the forms of the valley show, as Prof. Davis has pointed out, that the river which made them flowed with far greater volume.

In a study of these remarkable meanders Dr. A. Morley Davies called attention to another meander, apart from those now incised, which is left at its old level and from which the Evenlode was able to break away, though it could not escape from those farther down stream.[1]

The meander which Dr. Morley Davies describes includes the patches of gravel between Wilcote and North Leigh which are associated with the supposed Windrush-Evenlode confluence ; it would seem to have followed the course of the stream now flowing past Bridewell Farm, looping to the south-east and then flowing north, past Holly Court Farm, to join the Evenlode at Ashford Mill. It has been considered by Mr. Bromehead to be the final meander of the Windrush at the time of its junction with the Evenlode.[2]

In the gorge of the Evenlode the work of erosion went farther than the incision of the original meanders, for each of the projecting spurs has been scarped on the side facing upstream, and the one near the railway bridge at Combe has almost been cut away. The river was steadily breaking down the barriers and straightening its valley when the change of physical conditions deprived it of a part of its waters, and brought the work of destruction abruptly to a close.

During the period of erosion succeeding the formation of the high terrace gravel, the Oxford Clay between the Glyme and the Cherwell, near Bladon, was cut through and the rivers were compelled by the resistant rock to work eastward along the dip of the strata, and thus to lay bare a wide area of Cornbrash.

At the same time the delta of the Windrush, south of Witney, compelled the Thames to undercut the Corallian escarpment on the opposite bank, thus initiating the pronounced curve to the south-east which has been maintained and continually enlarged till the present day.

Of the climate during this great period of erosion no evidence is preserved within the Oxford district, and as yet nothing has been found in the succeeding Wolvercot Terrace gravels which would throw any light on the climate either of the period of erosion or of the deposition of the gravels. Remains of Horse have been found near Charlbury and an abraded Upper Chellean implement near Wolvercot itself ; the slightly abraded flake from Davenant Road

---

[1] 'The Abandonment of Entrenched Meanders,' *Proc. Geol. Assoc.*, vol. xxxiv, 1923, p. 89 *et seq.*

[2] *Geol. Mag.*, 1909, pp. 141, 142. See also Rev. E. C. Spicer, *Quart. Journ. Geol. Soc.*, vol. lxiv, 1908, p. 335 *et seq.*, and A. J. Jukes-Browne, *Geol. Mag.*, 1908, p. 529.

on the Wolvercot Plateau may be of Acheulean age, but too little is known of its discovery by workmen to place much confidence in it.

During the Wolvercot Terrace stage the Evenlode flowed directly into the main valley through the gap by which the railway passes from Long Hanborough to Yarnton, and either the Glyme alone or the Glyme and part of the waters of the Evenlode joined the Cherwell to the north of Bladon Heath. The Cherwell probably joined the Thames at Yarnton, near the Evenlode, and the Ray at Wolvercot. The Thame appears to have flowed to the east of its present course from Chislehampton to Dorchester and made its way along a line to the north of Ascot-Chalgrove, probably receiving tributaries from the Chilterns to the north.

At the close of the stage of the Wolvercot Terrace the process of degradation of the valley floors seems to have been continued, accompanied by the destruction of much of the terrace which had just been formed. The valley floors were lowered some 20–30 ft. and a new base-level was found—that of the Summertown–Radley Terrace.

At this time the Evenlode changed its course towards Yarnton for one at right angles to its direction of flow above its confluence with the Glyme and contrary to the flow of the Thames south of Eynsham. Mr. Pocock attributes this change in the dip of the underlying strata near the railway bridge over the river near Handborough Station :—

'Just south of the railway-bridge, where the alluvium of the Evenlode expands to a breadth of three-quarters of a mile, the Oolites on the right bank roll over slightly and dip towards the south. As soon as the river in the process of eroding its channel struck the Cornbrash rock, it began to cut a notch in the bank in the direction of the dip. Gradually, with the help of the springs thrown out from the neighbouring high terrace gravel, a new channel was cut, and the Evenlode found its way to the Thames between Cassington and Eynsham.'[1]

A marked curve was developed in the main valley opposite the mouth of the Windrush and a great spread of gravel deposited.

The Cherwell still joined the Thames at Yarnton and probably the Ray continued to occupy the valley in which the village of Marston stands. The centre of the course of the Thames appears to have been along a line Cassington-Oxford-Iffley. At Abingdon the Thames had worked its way westward by this time, avoiding the resistant Ironsands, and passing to the Gault plain at a point where it is in contact with the Kimmeridge Clay. Farther down stream the Thame, shifting its course to the south, joined the Thames not far from the present point of confluence.

By the time of this phase of erosion the rivers had spread out the gravels of the Summertown-Radley or 'second' terrace ; most of the adjustments in their courses had been completed, and their

---

[1] *Op. cit.*, p. 113.

gradients were nearly the same as at present.   From the old mouth of the Windrush to the point where the Thames turned southward there is a fall of about 30 ft., but the constriction of the valley by the Corallian escarpment ponded back the flood-waters, and caused them to drop their sediments on an almost level plain as far up as the confluence of the Cherwell with the main river.   Below the Corallian gap there is a drop of 20 ft. to the plain of the second terrace between Radley and Abingdon.[1]

It seems that one period of erosion checked the formation of the actual terrace-gravel and was accompanied by a change of fauna to which attention may now be directed.

At the bottom of the Summertown-Radley Terrace a different fauna is found from that of Handborough—Mammoth, Woolly Rhinoceros, Bison.   The Mammoth in the majority of cases belongs to the true Siberian type but there are a few specimens which may be referred to the older ' Ilford Mammoth '.[2]   Perhaps this serves as a slight indication of time-scale—that the older form of Mammoth, though present, is in insignificant minority, as if it were being replaced by the Siberian form.   Perhaps it might be expected to be found in the Wolvercot Terrace.

The lower gravels of the terrace have been considerably eroded and on them lie others with a fully developed ' warm fauna '— *Elephas antiquus*, *Hippopotamus* and *Corbicula fluminalis* in particular.   This is a remarkable reversal, which nevertheless has been confirmed in many exposures since its discovery.

Upper Chellean and Lower Acheulean (?) implements are found rarely, an example of the latter being very slightly abraded ;   they seem to occur in both upper and lower gravels.   The upper gravels are capped by deposits which will be mentioned shortly.

The Wolvercot Channel must now receive attention.   It lies in a curious position.   Isolated in the low ground between the Thames and the Cherwell it is in contact only with the Wolvercot Terrace, forming, and its deposits filling, a channel eroded in, and therefore certainly later than, that terrace.   The Wolvercot Terrace is cut off by the Summertown-Radley Terrace which lies at its foot, or rather at the foot of a clay step which the Wolvercot Terrace gravel caps. It would seem evident, from this and other exposures, that the Wolvercot Terrace is earlier than that of Summertown-Radley. Is the Wolvercot Channel later or earlier than the latter terrace ?

Taken by itself the series of deposits which fills the channel forms a complete unit and shows a gradual but important change in climate ;   the difficulty is to place such a unit in the general sequence.

At the base of the Wolvercot Channel a gravel rests against the eroded edge of the terrace and contains a ' warm fauna.'   *Elephas antiquus* is certainly present, so are Red Deer and, apparently, *Rhinoceros leptorhinus*.   The teeth of *E. antiquus* are analogous to

---

[1] *Ibid.*
[2] Sandford, K. S., *Quart. Journ. Geol. Soc.*, vol. lxxxi, 1925, pp. 74 *et seq.*

those found in the Summertown-Radley Terrace and distinct from those of Long Hanborough.[1]

The implements include abraded Chellean and Lower Acheulean forms (as in the Summertown–Radley Terrace) with abraded Middle Acheulean and some large unworn implements of uncertain type but possibly Upper Acheulean.   There occur also a few unworn or slightly rubbed implements of definite La Micoque type—*i.e.* the ' warm Mousterian.'

The information supplied by the basement gravel as to climate and industry is thus striking and definite.   There follow sands, with land and freshwater shells of temperate facies.   The sands were once seen to be capped by peat with a cold-temperate flora, including species now absent from the Oxford district and one limited to the north-west Highlands of Scotland, another to Northern Europe.[2]

There is, then, a clear indication of a falling off of ' good ' climate with the filling of the channel—accompanied in this case by decreasing coarseness of deposit.

The sands are capped by 14 ft. of buff and blue clay and silt (mostly redeposited Oxford Clay, with some sand).   The stratum is almost completely barren, and only in the last two or three years has yielded any bones or implements.   Teeth of Horse have been recovered, together with a fragment of deer's antler, of doubtful species ; an antler of Reindeer has recently been brought to light, and there are some grounds for referring it to this silt ; it is the only known specimen from the fluviatile deposits of the district.[3]

The apparent absence of Reindeer[4] and Musk Ox from the bottom of the Summertown-Radley Terrace, although the other three large Siberian mammals occur, is of considerable importance.

In the silts three flakes have been found, but these are typical of no particular industry, although the Mousterian might be suggested from the character and condition of one of them, as from the existence of the La Micoque industry in the underlying gravels.

The clays are crowned and strongly disturbed for a few feet by a non-fluviatile, probably ' frozen soil ' rubble called warp.   This would seem to bring the gradual refrigeration noted in the underlying deposits to a culminating point.

In the Wolvercot Channel then there is preserved the record of a complete change from a warm to a cold climate ; this may be brought to a maximum in the warp.

If this Wolvercot Channel[5] is older than the entire Summertown-

---

[1] *Ibid.*, p. 84.

[2] Bell, A. M., *Quart. Journ. Geol. Soc.*, vol. lx, 1904, p. 120 *et seq.*

[3] Sandford, K. S., *op. cit.*, pp. 63, 64.

[4] Reported vaguely : *see* Sir Joseph Prestwich, *Geol. Mag.*, vol. ix, p. 49 *et seq.*

[5] This question is also discussed in some detail in K. S. Sandford, ' Fossil Elephants of the Upper Thames Basin,' *Quart. Journ. Geol. Soc.*, vol. lxxxi, 1925, pp. 63–66.

Radley terrace then there are no less than three periods of *Elephas antiquus*, and the succession would read :—

Handborough Terrace	*E. antiquus*
Wolvercot ,,	?
,, Channel	*E. antiquus* to cold climate
Summertown-Radley Terrace	
Lower	*E. primigenius*, etc.
Upper	*E. antiquus*
Sunk Channel and Flood Plain	*E. primigenius* ?

On the other hand, if the Wolvercot Channel were considered to be later than the terrace at Summertown the sequence is :—

Handborough Terrace	*E. antiquus*
Wolvercot ,,	?
Summertown-Radley Terrace	
Lower	*E. primigenius*, etc.
Upper	*E. antiquus*
Wolvercot Channel	
Base	*E. antiquus*
Sands	Temperate
Peat	Cold-temperate
Clay	,, ,, ?
Warp	Cold (probably)
Sunk Channel and Flood Plain	[*E. primigenius* ?]

It will be seen that in the second case there is but one rotation of fauna in the deposits later than the HandboroughTerrace, and there is a faunal sequence from the upper gravels of Summertown to the gravels of the Wolvercot Channel, with the loss of Hippopotamus, and then to the sands, with the loss of *Corbicula fluminalis* and so on.[1] Regarded from the evidence of the fauna the second sequence given above seems the more probable.

Further, the evidence provided by implements points in the same direction, though it may be incomplete owing to scarcity of specimens :—

Handborough Terrace	—[Chellean ?)
Wolvercot ,,	Abraded Upper Chellean
	(L. Acheulean ?)
Summertown-Radley Terrace	,, ,,
	,, ,,
Wolvercot Channel	M. Acheulean, little worn
Base	U. Acheulean ?
Unabraded	La Micoque
Clays	Mousterian ?

This again seems more probable than the sequence obtained by placing the Summertown-Radley Terrace after those of the Wolvercot Channel in point of time.

---

[1] On the other hand the form *Fruticicola* (*Capillifera*) *hispida* (Linné) is present in the Channel ; if it can be regarded as a criterion, Messrs. Kennard and Woodward would be inclined to consider that the deposits in which it lies are older than those of the Summertown-Radley Terrace.

[Appendix III, p. 175 ' River Gravels of the Oxford District,' *Quart. Journ. Geol. Soc.*, vol. lxxx, 1924.]

If the sequence suggested by fauna and implements is sound then there is a single aggradation initiated by the formation of the upper gravels (lying on the eroded surface of the lower) of the Summertown-Radley Terrace and carried on until the Wolvercot Channel was full of silt; this represents a rise, above the present summit of the terrace, of some 30 ft.

The question of the age of the warp now arises; if the warp could be shown conclusively to be earlier than the Summertown-Radley Terrace, then it would prove the Wolvercot Terrace and Channel, on both of which it lies, to be earlier also; such, however, does not appear to be the case.

In its full development the warp is seen only on the Wolvercot Plateau, but similar deposits are found elsewhere (as at Chadlington); the Handborough Terrace, as might be expected, is often disturbed at the top. On the Wolvercot Plateau the warp has not been seen at the edge where the Summertown Terrace abuts it.

The top of the Summertown-Radley Terrace is curiously affected :—

(1) In one place (Abingdon Cement Brickworks, Radley Road) a non-fluviatile deposit somewhat similar in appearance to the warp is found; its junction with the underlying gravel is uneven, but there are no signs of contortion or of the presence of frozen conditions, as at Wolvercot. Probably it is mainly formed by the decalcification of the gravel, but such a condition has not been seen elsewhere on the surface of the terrace.

(2) The uppermost few feet of the terrace are often in the greatest disorder, sometimes in regular festoons, probably due in part to solution processes, but

(3) at Summertown (Webb's Pit) a foot of regularly bedded gravel lies evenly on a zone of disordered and 'festooned' material (Fig. 10),

(4) At Eynsham there is an extensive spread of fine gravel lying unconformably on the Upper Summertown-Radley gravels, containing bones in a much fresher state of preservation than those of the terrace-gravel below; it reaches a depth of some four feet. The uppermost few feet of the underlying gravel are greatly disturbed by solution and 'festooning,' especially on the north side of the pit.

Considered in conjunction with the warp of the Wolvercot Plateau the above features are not without significance.

The top of the Flood Plain gravels is not similarly disturbed.

There seems to be evidence, therefore, apart from fauna and implements, to show that :—(1) The Wolvercot Channel is later than the Summertown-Radley Terrace. (2) There was a period of aggradation which connected the two.

(3) In the following period of erosion, leading to the formation of the Sunk Channel and Flood Plain gravels the accumulated material was swept away until the present surface-level of the Summertown-Radley Terrace was attained, when there was a pause.

(4) The 'solution festoons' at Summertown and Eynsham were formed before or during the deposition of the bedded gravel above them.

(5) Probably during the pause the uppermost gravel of Summertown and Eynsham was formed; particularly in the case of the

former it is unlikely that this gravel could have been deposited at any subsequent time.

(6) Erosion was continued and the Sunk Channel excavated.

(7) At some time during the removal of the accumulated gravel and the formation of the Sunk Channel the warp was formed on the surface of the Wolvercot Plateau.

Of the Sunk Channel little is yet known beyond the fact of its existence. It is unsafe to attribute any fauna to it though there are indications that the Siberian Mammoth may occur, as at least one well-preserved tooth has been excavated from some depth,[1] but an assemblage of remains must first be collected.

Of human industries nothing is known, except that by analogy from other districts the Cave Periods might be assigned here, in which case mammoth and reindeer would be expected to occur.

It should be remembered that, with the interpretation suggested above, the silts of the Wolvercot Channel are not very remote in point of time from the Sunk Channel and Flood Plain gravels.

There is evidence to show that the Sunk Channel is probably older than the Flood Plain gravels (see p. 143).

A few changes of river course again took place during this last stage. In the west the delta of the Windrush again compelled the Thames to cut back the Corallian escarpment on its right bank, and the slope of Lower Greensand on the left bank opposite Radley was pushed farther to the southward, but in the intermediate part of its valley between Yarnton and Iffley the river eroded its channel through the middle of the Second Terrace, leaving remnants on either side. It was at this time that the Cherwell deserted its direct channel into the Thames and turned eastward to join the Ray near Islip. The cause of the diversion is similar to those already described. Near Kidlington the Great Oolite formation rises in a low ridge across the valley perhaps along a line connected with the upheaval at Islip. When erosion was renewed after the epoch of the Second Terrace the river avoided the barrier by cutting eastward along the Oxford Clay into the Ray Valley.

As before there is little fall noticeable in the surface of the gravel between Yarnton and Iffley, and there is the same rapid fall below Sandford Gap, some 20 ft. to Abingdon.

Since the deposition of the Flood Plain gravel, little change has taken place; the rivers have deepened their courses some ten feet, cutting into the gravel they had already deposited, with the formation of a nearly equivalent depth of alluvium.

The alluvium which often completely conceals the gravel lies like a blanket over much of the Flood Plain, and stretches up the valleys of subsidiary streams and some old stream courses. The loop of the Thames near Appleton has been pushed farther, and at Shifford the river has formed a new course to the south of the old

---

[1] One, already referred to, in 'Bed of Cherwell'; another, more recently, in the construction of a new railway bridge at Kennington (exact depth not reported).

one. At Kennington, on the other hand, it has cut into its left bank and deserted its old channel.

DEVELOPMENT OF THE RIVER THAME

It has already been stated that only the central limb of the Thame lies within the area of the map. Changes of position in the lower part of the river are dealt with in the general discussion of river development, but attention should now be given to higher parts of its course and to its history.

The position of the Thame is peculiar ; it lies at the foot of the Chalk escarpment of the Chiltern Hills, which is capped by Tertiary deposits ; it flows on Gault, Ampthill and Kimmeridge Clays, with northern feeders rising in the Oxford Clay ; there are Portland outliers to the north at Brill and to the west at Shotover Hill.

A study of the pebbles which constitute its gravels is instructive and shows that not only has the river drawn its material from the formations named, but that at one time a great part of the area must have been covered by Plateau Drift, which the river has eroded and re-sorted, leaving the country almost destitute of this material. Also, it is shown that the confluence with the Thames (bearing Lower Oolitic material) was much farther to the north than it now is. Finally, the proportion and distribution of fresh flint and debris from Tertiary Beds show that the river is not primarily a resultant of the escarpment to its south as might have been supposed. No doubt the Thame has drained the escarpment, as it does to-day, aiding in its retreat, and to a certain extent performing the function of a beheading stream of an ' inner lowland,' transgressing across the uplifted edge of a ' cuesta ' (*see* p. 151). But as Dr. A. Morley Davies has shown,[1] the present curved course of the river is due to a dip-ward shifting of its course, which formerly lay farther to the north and was straighter, on an area of Gault clay now removed, exposing the Ampthill and Kimmeridge clays. At some time the river met harder rock as the erosion proceeded and at these points ' side slipping ' was checked, while at the two ends, where no Portland rocks underlie the Gault clay, the dip-ward shifting continued. So we have a loop beginning and ending in Gault clay and cutting through Lower Greensand and Portland rocks to the Kimmeridge Clay in the middle limb.

While this process was going on the Portland escarpment running from Shotover to Brill and beyond was breached by the Ray on one side and by the Thame on the other, and it has been cut into a number of outliers.

It should be remembered that the original Gault plain was probably extensively covered with drift which acted as an efficient reservoir—to its own destruction, as we have already seen in the more westerly rivers.

---

[1] *Proc. Geol. Assoc.*, vol. xvi, 1899, p. 56 *et seq.*

On the subordination of the drift and the uncovering of the Portland sands and limestones, the main supply of water was gathered from this formation in those places where it was exposed.

It is seen that the present looped course of the Thame may be traced to a pre-Gault eroded surface, with its unconformities ; the absence of the Portland rocks to the west has led to the uncovering of great thicknesses of clays, with consequent effects on the developments of surface drainage.

Springs and Brooks[1]

The brooks which feed the main rivers are chiefly derived from three sources :—

1. The Portland Beds and Shotover Sands of the higher hills.
2. The Corallian formation.
3. The Pleistocene gravels.

Most of these brooks are of small size, and have originated late in the history of the land-surface, yet some of them have cut deep valleys, and have had important influence in imparting to the landscape its present form. The great clay formations have few permanent springs, for most of the water which falls on the surface is carried away, on account of the absence of porous beds through which it can pass underground. The gravels, sands, and limestones, on the other hand, readily absorb rain water, and throw it out in innumerable springs where the impervious clays crop out from beneath them.

Besides the sources mentioned, there are others in the north-west and in the south of equal importance, but only a few brooks derived from them come within the limits of the map. The brooks in the Wilcote valley rise in the limestones of Wychwood Forest. The chief branches of the Great Haseley and the Chalgrove brooks, tributaries of the Thame, flow from the Chalk rocks of the Chiltern Hills. Many of the feeders of the Ock are derived from the same formation in the Berkshire Downs. These belong to distinct hydrographical systems which lie almost entirely outside our area.

The first of the three sources mentioned above is that which gives rise to most of the longer brooks, since they traverse a considerable extent of Corallian and Oxford Clay lands before they reach one of the trunk streams. A number of tributaries of the Thame have their head waters in the sands of the Brill range of hills. Danes or Holton Brook, and the brooks at Oakley and a mile to the west, are the longer. The first rises in a combe on Muswell Hill, and flows in a valley 70 ft. deep along a slight downfold in the Calcareous Grit plateau of Studley as far as Menmarsh Farm, where it is joined on a broad alluvial flat by affluents from the Corallian on both sides. Thence it continues as the Holton Brook along the line of transition between the Coral Rag and the Ampthill Clay, and joins the Thame

---

[1] Note : the account given by Mr. Pocock is reproduced in its entirety, with a few minor additions and alterations, *op. cit.*, pp. 116–119.

between Wheatley and Waterperry. The other two brooks rise in the sands of Brill and flow approximately in the direction of the outcrop of Ampthill Clay. They are probably guided by the strike of hard bands in the clay, which have been eroded into slight escarpments.

The Brill outlier as a whole is drained by a system of brooks which is strikingly radial, illustrating the manner in which similar isolated hills have been attacked on all sides by brooks rising on their flanks. The feature is not well seen on the special geological map since only a part of the outlier is included.

Farther south the Portland Beds and 'Ironsands' are close to the river between Cuddesdon and Great Milton, and the brooks flowing from them are correspondingly short. But the Baldon Brook is longer, for part of its waters head from the sands of Garsington and Toot Baldon on the hillsides facing the Thames, and flow through a gap to the Thame below Chislehampton. The sands of the Shotover range give rise to several large tributaries of the Thames and Cherwell. The Bayswater Brook on the north rises in Forest Hill, and flows through a gorge in the Corallian rocks, from which it gathers many affluents, into the marshland east of Marston, finally escaping by an open valley into the Cherwell, south of the village. The position of the gorge, as in so many other instances, seems to be determined by a slight downfold of the Corallian rocks.

The Northfield or Hollow Brook, rising east of Horsepath, is, perhaps, guided near its source by a downfold of Portland Beds, but lower down, near its confluence with the Isis, it runs almost parallel with the main outcrop of the Coral Rag, and its path has been determined by the strike of the beds. The 'Ironsands' of Boar's Hill and Cumnor are nearer to the Isis than those of Shotover, so that the brooks have a steeper descent to the trunk stream. Accordingly we find that they have cut a series of straight gorges in the Corallian plateau, which for narrowness and steep declivities might be called canons. These are the well-known valleys near North and South Hinksey.

On the west side of Boar's Hill the brooks are tributaries to the Ock, which flows approximately along the boundary of the Corallian and Kimmeridge Clay. There is no limestone plateau to be cut through before they reach the main stream, as on the Oxford side. Hence their valleys are wide and shallow, following the same beds of rock for considerable distances upon the dip-slope. The largest tributary is the Sandford Brook, which gathers its affluents from the northern part of the hill, flows along the boundary of the Coral Rag and Calcareous Grit below Dry Sandford, and reaches the flood-plain of the Ock near Marcham.

The springs derived from the Corallian formation are less important individually than those of the Portland-Ironsand group, but they are more numerous, and a greater population is dependent on them. They are thrown out either by the Oxford Clay at the base, or at points where the plain of saturation reaches the surface,

M

or by impermeable beds within the formation itself.   The springs from the Corallian need not be mentioned individually.   They rise in little combes all along the base of the formation, and descend the slopes of Oxford Clay directly to the Thames, the Cherwell or Ray ; or else are affluents of some larger stream of the Portland-Ironsand group.   They are indicated on the map by the indentations in the boundary of the Oxford Clay and Calcareous Grit, each of which marks a spring.

The Corallian outlier, along the margin of which are situated Elsfield, Beckley and Stanton St. John, illustrates well the rising of these springs.   Calcareous tufa coating fragments of fossils and small branches of trees may be seen in many of them, and again in a stream north of Holton Wood.

The other Corallian streams occur for the most part on the dip-slope west of Boar's Hill, over which in some cases they flow for several miles before they reach the Ock in the Vale of the White Horse.   One of these may be specially mentioned, as it illustrates the geological structure.   Rising near Cumnor, probably in a bed of clay, it flows by Appleton to Fyfield, guided by the outcrop of hard beds of grit.   Here the axis of a downfold is reached, and the spring turns across the strike of the strata till it reaches the Coral Rag, and then once more follows the outcrop to the plain of the Ock at Marcham.   The tributary has been developed partly as a transverse and partly as a longitudinal stream.

The springs derived from the Pleistocene deposits are probably as numerous as those from the Corallian formation.   They flow out from gravels of different ages, for each deposit as soon as it was cut through by the river gave rise to a fresh set of brooks, which have ever since been at work cutting back the gravel from which they originated.   The destruction wrought by the older Pleistocene brooks upon the high terrace and the drift has been so great that these gravels have been reduced to outliers of insignificant size and deeply trenched by combes.   Many of these brooks must have dried up, owing to the complete denudation of the gathering ground, while others have cut into the underlying formations and opened fresh sources of water.   The enormous extent to which this process has been carried has been pointed out in the account of the drift. In the Thame Basin so much of the drift and high terrace gravel has been removed that the natural drainage has been practically remodelled, since the land has, in many parts, been eroded to the base of the Portland Beds, from which a newer set of brooks has taken rise.   Only a few small tributaries now have their sources in the drift plateau by the Thame.[1]

The denudation has not been so great in the region of the Upper Thames.   At one time the whole surface between Witney, North Leigh, and Eynsham was covered by the Northern Drift.   The brooks at first were short tributaries, flowing from the base of the gravels down the clay-banks into the Thames and the Windrush.

---

[1] See also Davies, A. M., Proc. Geol. Assoc., vol. xvi, 1899, p.56.

Gradually they cut backwards and developed secondary tributaries till the Pleistocene deposits were divided into outliers near the local watersheds. Meanwhile the channels were deepened till the Kellaways Sands, near the base of the Oxford Clay, were reached, and new supplies of water came to reinforce the waning springs from the gravel. The brook between Church Hanborough and Freeland has cut back almost to the Evenlode between the high terrace and the Northern Drift, and has laid bare the Cornbrash in part of its course, but its principal feeders still flow from the drift. The Chil and the Limb Brooks, west of Eynsham, are now fed principally from the Kellaways Beds, the gravels being for the most part denuded, though some of the affluents still rise in the drift of Eynsham Park. Near South Leigh there is an interlacing system of marshy hollows formed by affluents which have cut back into the water partings.

The brooks between New Yatt and Witney have gone farther in the work of erosion. Not only has the drift which gave them birth been swept away between New Yatt and North Leigh, but both the Kellaways Beds and the Cornbrash have been cut through, and two fresh sources of water uncovered.

CROSS VALLEYS

In the Oxford district there are certain examples of a type of valley which contains no stream running from end to end but crosses the watersheds from one system of drainage to another.

Valleys of this type are a perplexing problem and they have often been considered to be deserted river channels ; there is, however, another explanation which is more in accord with the facts, *i.e.*, spring-erosion in certain cases of the juxtaposition of clay and limestone. The cross-valleys to which attention will be called are :—

    (I).   South of Ot Moor.
    (II).   The valley through which runs the Oxford-Eynsham road.
    (III).   The valley between Garsington and Toot Baldon.

It was pointed out on p. 145 that the Ot Moor area has four distinct valleys leading out of it. All of them, together with the Moor itself, must be of comparatively recent origin since the valley by Islip appears to have been the route followed by the Ray from high terrace time. The four valleys are as follows :—

(1) To the north of Islip, blocked at the inner end by Flood Plain gravel of the Ray.

(2) At Islip, occupied by the Ray. Both are situated in areas of much faulting.

(3) Near Woodeaton, again in a much faulted area ; the outflow of springs where the Lower Oolite was in contact with the Oxford Clay would cause abnormal erosion at these points and the tributaries of the Cherwell on one side and of the Ray on the other would soon cut back to the water-parting.

(4) A true cross-valley, from the basin of the Ray to that of the Thame. There is here no sign of faulting, ' and yet there is nothing that would indicate that the lacustrine plain was ever drained by a river to the east. But we know that along this line the Corallian Limestone disappears abruptly and is

replaced by clay. Where the permeable rock passed into the impermeable clay the water would be thrown out in springs flowing in opposite directions to Ot Moor and the Thame, and erosion would be especially active. It is the cutting back of such opposing streams into their watersheds which has probably made this remarkable cross-valley along the line of transition between the Coral Rag and the Ampthill Clay.[1]

' The best known instance of a cross-valley in the neighbourhood of Oxford is the one followed by the Eynsham road between the hills of Wytham and Cumnor. This valley at its highest point is only 30 feet above the level of the Thames west of Oxford, and has been supposed to be an old course of the river. But of this there appears to be no evidence, for although the river gravels run up the valley for some distance at either end, they are not continuous through its whole length, and prove no more than that in the later stages of erosion the flood waters carried their debris into bays cut in the hill side. It is more probable that the origin of the valley is connected with the disturbance of the strata which has been shown to occur there. The effect of a fault in bringing Corallian strata in juxta-position with Oxford Clay would be the outflow of copious springs into the Thames in opposite directions along the plane of contact, resulting ultimately in the degradation of their channels below the level of the water-bearing strata.'[2]

A glance at the map shows that a similar process is also going on about a mile to the north, and Wytham Hill is now connected to the main outlier to the south-east only by a narrow neck of Calcareous Grit.[3]

One other instance of a cross-valley may be noticed. This passes from the Thames Valley, between the Portland hills at Garsington and Toot Baldon, into the Thame Valley, and is probably connected with the overlap of the Gault on the eastern side near Chislehampton. Where the two clays are in contact the rate of denudation must necessarily have been greater than where resistant Portland and Ironsand strata were intercalated. For this reason probably the feeders of the Thame were able to cut back into the watershed faster than those of the Thames, and to capture some of their head waters. Hence the Baldon Brook, rising on the west side of the hills, instead of falling into the Thames, passes over an alluvial flat 40 feet above the present rivers, and flows by a circuitous course through hilly ground into the Thame below Chislehampton.

---

[1] Pocock, T. I., *op. cit.*, p. 115.

[2] *Ibid.*

[3] Note : The same thing would happen if, instead of a fault, there is a synclinal fold, for the water would collect and flow out at the lowest level of the permeable beds.

CHAPTER XIII

ECONOMIC GEOLOGY

WATER SUPPLY

A separate memoir on the water supply of Oxfordshire[1] has been published, to which the reader is referred for details concerning wells and sections ; but it may not be inappropriate to point out that the sites of towns and villages in the area have been determined primarily by the occurrence of water-bearing strata. It was mentioned in the first edition that they fall into groups corresponding to the main sources of the springs, namely, those on the Lower Oolites, those on the Corallian outcrop, those on the Portland and Lower Cretaceous rocks, and those on the superficial gravels. The first group includes Oddington, Islip, and Bladon. The second group is represented by the villages extending from Hinton Waldrist to Cumnor, from Sandford to Headington and Beckley, and round the outcrop to Wheatley.

Eastward, on the lands where the Corallian limestone is replaced by the almost waterless Ampthill Clay, a marked decrease takes place in the population. Only two small villages—Studley and Boarstall—are built upon the diminutive representative of the Calcareous Grit north-east of Beckley. The villages of Oakley, Worminghall, and Ickford, though situated on clay-land and drawing their well-water from permeable bands in the clay itself, are in the vicinity of streams flowing from the Portland Beds at Brill. The population in this quarter is concentrated at higher levels, such as Brill, where the Portland and Lower Cretaceous Beds yield an abundant supply of water, that is wanting on the low-lying claylands. Indeed, there is no instance in the district of a village situated on the clay formations except it be close to the boundary of a water-bearing formation, or to a brook flowing from them. In the south-east of the district where the Portland and Lower Cretaceous Beds spread over a wide area, the greater number of villages are dependent on them ; those encircling Shotover Hill, Horsepath, Garsington, Denton, and Cuddesdon ; the suburb of Oxford on Boar's Hill also belong to the same group.

The areas of gravel, however, support by far the largest population, each bed from the lowest river terrace to the plateau drift having been made use of as sites for villages. Brighthampton, Standlake, Northmoor, Kidlington, and the Hinkseys are on the

---

[1] ' The Water Supply of Oxfordshire ' (*Mem. Geol. Surv.*), 1910.

lowest gravel ; Oxford and Abingdon and almost all the villages in the Thames Valley are on the second ; Upper Wolvercot and part of Radley on the third ; Hanborough on the fourth ; Freeland, North Leigh, and New Yatt on the drift. In the Thame Valley the most important places within the map dependent on river-gravels are Drayton, Waterperry, and Waterstock.

It may be noted that the mean annual rainfall at Oxford is $25\frac{1}{2}$ in.

Attempts made to obtain water from the concealed Lower Oolites have not given satisfactory results. In nearly every case the water has proved to be too saline for domestic use. At the well at St. Clement's, Oxford, and in the boring at the City Brewery, Oxford, the water obtained from these rocks proved to be highly saline. The record of the strata passed through at the City Brewery is as follows :—

City Brewery. Messrs. Handley & Co., 1898.
Boring made and communicated by Messrs. Le Grand and Sutcliff.
Description in square brackets by J. H. Blake, from examination of the cores at the time of the boring, with additions by H. B. Woodward and J. Pringle from specimens brought to the museum at Jermyn Street by Messrs. Le Grand and Sutcliff.
Surface of the ground about 209 feet above Ordnance Datum.
Water obtained from depth of about 400 feet overflowed, but proved to be highly saline.

		Thickness Ft. In.		Depth Ft. In.	
[Valley Gravel, etc., 30 ft.]	Top soil [made ground, gravel, etc.] ..	7	6	7	6
	Sand and gravel [derived mostly from Oolites]	5	6	13	0
	Gravel, coarse at 21 ft. [derived mostly from Oolites]	11	6	24	6
[Oxford Clay and Kellaways Beds, 210 ft.]	Yellow clay and stones [gravel and clay]	5	6	30	0
	Blue clay	125	6	155	6
	Clay and shells, *Pteria*	1	6	157	0
	Blue clay, *Pecten*	3	0	160	0
	Blue clay and shells	18	0	178	0
	Blue clay	31	0	209	0
	Blue clay and shells	7	0	216	0
	Shelly rock	1	6	217	6
	Sandy clay, shells and mundic (pyrites), also lignite	5	0	222	6
	Shelly rock	2	0	224	6
	Hard clay and shells	7	0	231	6
	Hard clay, shells and mundic	6	6	238	0
	Sandy clay	1	0	239	0
	Ditto, *Gryphaea dilatata* and iron pyrites	1	0	240	0
[Cornbrash, 17 ft.]	Hard shelly rock [dark bluish-grey limestone at 241 ft.]	17	0	257	0
[Forest Marble, 32⅔ ft.]	Hard clay and shells	12	0	269	0
	Hard shelly rock [thin bands of dark grey oolitic shelly stone, with white grains, Echinoderm spine, (Acrosalenia ?) and sandy clay at 272 ft.] ..	19	0	288	0
	Hard rock and bands of clay [sandy] ..	1	8	289	8

	Thickness Ft. In.	Depth Ft. In.
Hard shelly rock [grey and whitish oolitic stone at 300 ft.]	29 0	318 8
Bands of rock and clay with shells [sandy limestone at 327 and 332 ft., micaceous, whitish and greenish-grey]	39 4	358 0
Rock	6 0	364 0
Bands of rock and clay	1 6	365 6
Rock	1 7	367 1
Bands of rock and clay	6 1	373 2
Hard rock [light grey oolitic limestone, freestone at 375 ft.]	4 6	377 8

[Great Oolite Series 116½ ft.]

Bands of rock and clay [grey and black carbonaceous clay, silt or black mud, and a few thin beds of marl and rock, with shells, iron pyrites, "beef," black wood and other vegetable matter.]..

[Sandy marl, greenish, *Ostrea sowerbyi*, *Rhynchonella subtetrahedra*, Echinoderm spine at 378 ft. ..

Thin bed of grey clay (fuller's earth) at 379 ft. ..

Sandy marl, greenish, *Ostrea sowerbyi*, *Perna* sp., *Hinnites*, *Mytilus* sp., *Placunopsis socialis* ? M. and L. at 380 ft.

Thin bed of dark grey oolitic shelly rock and greenish and grey sandy marl, *Ostrea sowerbyi* at 382 ft. .. ..

Blackish grey clay, slightly sandy, with shells, iron pyrites, and thin irregular bands of " beef " at 386 ft. ..

Black silty clay with shells and iron pyrites, *Cyrena* ? at 390 ft. .. ..

Small bivalve shells, pyritous, (valves united) in black clay, with many pellets or little spherical grey stones, the size of large shot, *Cyrena* ? at 395 ft. 28 6   406 2

Black shelly clay and marl; very thin seams of brown and whitish sand, and black laminated carbonaceous shale with lignite at 396 ft. .. ..

Black sandy shale with concretions and wood (? piece of branch) and other vegetable matter, and iron pyrites at 398 ft. .. .. ..

Small irregular-shaped fragments and nodules of light mottled pinkish and grey hard limestone in black clay, with seams of brown sand, at 402 ft. and 404 ft. .. .. ..

Black papery carbonaceous shale, very friable, seemingly composed of straplike leaves, longitudinally striated and iron pyrites at 404½ ft. .. ..

Hard blackish-grey oolitic stone, 4 in. thick, at 405 ft. .. .. ..

Black shaly clay and marl at 405½ ft. ..

		Thickness Ft. In.	Depth Ft. In.
[Chipping Norton Limestone and ? Inferior Oolite.]	Hard rock, hard blackish-grey coarse oolitic shelly limestone, presenting a vesicular appearance, and containing lignite, at 406 ft. 2 in. ; passing down into light and dark grey ragged and coarse oolitic limestone rock, with yellow buff and brown oolitic grains, and shelly throughout to 419 ft. ..	12 10	419 0
	Hard dark grey shelly compact limestone, almost entirely devoid of oolitic structure. *Terebratula* sp., *Pecten demissus, Mytilus* sp... ..	3 6	422 6
[Lower Lias 17 ft.]	Blue clay. [Bluish-grey and light grey micaceous clays and marl, with shells in places. A good specimen of the Ammonite *Androgynoceras maculatum* (Y. and B.) was obtained in light grey clay at 431 ft. White opaque and transparent spar, and iron pyrites occur in its chambers] ..	17 0	439 6

BUILDING-STONE

Various local stones from the Great Oolite, Forest Marble, Calcareous Grit, Corallian Limestone, and Portland Beds have been and are still employed for building purposes, but there is no freestone of first-rate quality in the area. Indeed, Oxford itself supplies a bad advertisement for the local stone. That which has proved most durable was obtained from the Great Oolite outside the limits of our area.

As remarked by Hull : ' The freestone at Tainton Quarries has furnished the stone for some of the oldest buildings in Oxford, viz., those of the 12th, 13th and 14th centuries, and is still in good preservation ; the mouldings being sharper and less weathered than of some buildings of the 17th and 18th centuries, which are cut out of blocks from Headington Hill quarries, near Oxford.'[1] Thus Taynton stone has been used in the ancient parts of the Cathedral (Christ Church), in Merton College and Chapel, also in Blenheim Palace. The Clipsham Stone (Inferior Oolite) from Clipsham, in Rutlandshire, was used in 1889 in the new buildings of Brazenose College.

Freestone of good quality is now largely quarried, beneath a considerable thickness of superincumbent strata, at Milton, near Taynton.

The Stonesfield Slate has been used in roofing many of the old buildings, but it is not quarried within the limits of the map.[2]

Beds of Oolite and shelly oolitic limestone belonging to the Great Oolite Series are quarried for building purposes at Bladon and Long Hanborough.

Among the Corallian rocks the Headington Stone (" Shotover

[1] *See* Hull, ' Geology of the country around Cheltenham ' (*Mem. Geol. Surv.*), 1857, p. 58.
[2] ' The Jurassic Rocks of Britain ' (*Mem. Geol. Surv.*), vol. iv, 1894, p. 484.

Limestone ") has been employed as a freestone, though it is for the most part exceedingly poor, many of the buildings in Oxford where it was used having come to a deplorable state of decay. The upper beds of impure comminuted shell-limestone were those so much used ; but all the beds are variable and shelly, false-bedded shelly limestone passes laterally into rubbly coral-rock ; and there are layers of shelly sand and hard lenticular bands of grey oolitic limestone. In the village of Headington Quarry most of the better stone has been removed, but here and there old quarries have been re-opened. A layer of the " best stone " (of its kind) occurs near the base of the limestones, about five feet above the top of the sands of the Calcareous Grit.

According to Plot, stone from the Wheatley Quarries was used for some of the older buildings in Oxford ;[1] it is a variable stone, but on the whole more durable than that of Headington. Tombstones were formerly made from the freestone of the Lyehill Quarries, Wheatley. In other localities, as at Marcham, Beckley, etc., building-blocks are obtained.

Phillips mentioned that " At Great Hazeley the Portland Stone has been quarried from ancient time, and it there furnishes a limited supply of better quality than usual for building, being of good colour and firm and equal texture, except for the shells, which, however, mostly lie in bands. A thick grey or greenish sand is at the bottom ; over this the stony series, the lower part workable freestone, the top hard splintery limestone, two feet thick, much jointed, fit for road and rough walling, called ' Curl.' "[2] This ' Curl stone ' was formerly used for chimney-pieces. It is a grey and somewhat gritty limestone with fossils.

Much of the better building-stone has been worked out in the neighbourhood of Great Haseley. (*See* p. 82.)

The cemented gravel of Church Hanborough and Stanton Harcourt has been locally used for building purposes.

LIME

Lime for building and agricultural purposes is made from the limestone belonging to the Great Oolite, Corallian, and Portland Beds.

The white limestones in the upper part of the Great Oolite are burnt for lime, and as the layers vary in quality it is usual to mix them ; these beds are capable of yielding a strong lime.

An excellent white lime has been made at Whitehill Wood, near Ashford Mill.

The Corallian Beds are employed in various localities—the lime from the coral rocks being in some places of a stronger nature than that made from the more oolitic freestone.

The limestones of the Portland Beds have also been burnt for lime at Brill, near Wheatley, Great Milton, and Great Haseley.

[1] Plot, Nat. Hist. Oxfordshire, 1677, p. 76.
[2] Geology of Oxford, etc., p. 417.

Road-metal

The Coral Rag Limestone is used for foundations of roads, and occasionally for surface metal on by-roads; but it is not good for heavy traffic. The Calcareous Grit is similarly used.

Locally the Cornbrash and Forest Marble limestones are employed; also the doggers or " sand-ballers," in the Kimmeridge Sands near Headington, and some of the harder Portland rocks elsewhere.

Sand

At Shotover Hill, in the Kimmeridge Beds the coarse white gritty sands (with ' sand-ballers ') are used for mortar, and the finer sands for moulding bricks, while a lower bed yields a soft mealy sand that is used for moulding in iron-furnaces as ' foundry loam.'

The fine silica sand in the Shotover Beds has been utilized in the preparation of scouring-soap.

Brick Materials

Brick and tile earths are worked in the Oxford Clay near Oxford, and in the Kimmeridge Clay at Shotover Hill, Wheatley and Cumnor. Many of the smaller pits that were at one time worked have been closed owing to their inability to compete with the larger brickyards. The fluviatile loam of the third terrace at Upper Wolvercot forms a good brickearth. This kind has not been observed elsewhere in the district, but there may be some on the third terrace north of Begbroke.

At Brill, the higher beds of the Kimmeridge Clay furnish a ' mild earth ' well adapted for brick-making, while below the clay is stiffer and suitable for making tiles and drain-pipes.

Brickearth has also been worked in the Shotover Sands at Great Milton, and in the Gault near Warpsgrove.

Fuller's Earth

The occurrence of fuller's earth in the Shotover Sands has long been noted, but the quantity is insufficient to be of commercial value.

Ochre

R. Plot, in 1677, gave an account of the ochre that was dug on the east side of Shotover Hill,[1] and " yellow ochre of good quality " was noted by John Phillips as but three inches thick. His section[2] may be compared with that given on p. 90. The ochre is no longer worked.

---

[1] Natural History of Oxfordshire, pp. 56, 57.
[2] Geology of Oxford and the Valley of the Thames, 1871, p. 414.

APPENDIX I

LIST OF PRINCIPAL WORKS ON THE GEOLOGY OF THE DISTRICT[1]

1677. PLOT, Dr. R.—The Natural History of Oxfordshire. Fol. Oxford.

1699. LHUYD, E.—Lithophylacii Britannici Ichnographia. 8vo. London. 2nd Edition. Oxford, 1760.

1809. YOUNG, A.—View of the Agriculture of Oxfordshire. 8vo. London.

1815. KIDD, Dr. J.—A Geological Essay. [Description of Oxford gravel, in Chap. 17.] 8vo. Oxford.

1819. SMITH, WILLIAM.—Geological Map of Berkshire.

1820. ———— ————Geological Map of Buckinghamshire.

———— ————Geological Map of Oxfordshire.

1821. BUCKLAND, Rev. Prof. W.—Description of the Quartz Rock of the Lickey Hill . . . with considerations on the evidences of a Recent Deluge afforded by the gravel beds of Warwickshire and Oxfordshire, and the valley of the Thames from Oxford downwards to London. *Trans. Geol. Soc.*, vol. v., p. 506.

1823. ———— ————Reliquiæ Diluvianæ; or Observations on the organic remains contained in Caves, Fissures, and Diluvial Gravel, and on other geological phenomena, attesting the action of an universal Deluge. 4to. London. 2nd Edition, 1824.

1829. CONYBEARE, Rev. W. D.—On the Hydrographical Basin of the Thames, with a view more especially to investigate the causes which have operated in the formation of the valleys of that river, and its tributary streams. *Proc. Geol. Soc.*, vol. i., 145–149.

1834. MITCHELL, Dr. JAMES.—On the strata of Quainton and Brill in Buckinghamshire. *Proc. Geol. Soc.*, vol. ii., pp. 6, 7.

1835. DAUBENY, Dr. C. G. B.—[Analysis of the Mineral Spring lately discovered near Oxford.] *Proc. Geol. Soc.*, vol. ii., p. 204.

1836. FITTON, Dr. W. H.—Observations on some of the Strata between the Chalk and the Oxford Oolite, in the South-East of England. *Trans. Geol. Soc.*, ser. 2, vol. iv., pp. 103–388.

1839. DAUBENY, Dr. C. G. B.—On a Saline Spring near Oxford. *Trans. Geol. Soc.*, ser. 2, vol. v., p. 263.

1848. STACPOOLE, ANDREW D.—Environs of Oxford, enlarged from the Ordnance Map; the Geological Survey and Sections by Andrew D. Stacpoole, M.A., Fellow of New College.

1851. ORLEBAR, A.B.—On the Geology of the neighbourhood of Oxford, within the limits of Mr. Stacpoole's map. *Proc. Ashmolean Soc.*, vol. ii., p. 253.

1858. PHILLIPS, Prof. J.—On the Estuary Sands in the upper part of Shotover Hill. *Quart. Journ. Geol. Soc.*, vol. xiv., pp. 236–241.

1859. HULL, Prof. E.—The Geology of the Country around Woodstock, Oxfordshire. *Mem. Geol. Survey.* 8vo. London.
Sheet 13.—Oxford, Abingdon. *Geol. Survey.* London.
Sheet 45, S.W.—Woodstock, Witney, Eynsham. *Geol. Survey.* London.

1860. HULL, Prof. E.—On the South-easterly Attenuation of the Lower Secondary Formations of England; and the probable Depth of the Coal-measures under Oxfordshire and Northamptonshire. *Quart. Journ. Geol. Soc.*, vol. xvi., pp. 63–81.

[1] See also W. Whitaker, List of Works on the Geology and Palæontology of Oxfordshire, of Berkshire, and of Buckinghamshire.—*Rep. Brit. Assoc.*, 1882.

1860. PHILLIPS, Prof. J.—Notice of some Sections of the Strata near Oxford. No. 1. The Great Oolite in the Valley of the Cherwell. No. 2. Sections South of Oxford. *Quart. Journ. Geol. Soc.*, vol. xvi., pp. 115–119, 307–311.

1861. CLUTTERBUCK, Rev. J. C.—On the Course of the Thames from Lechlade to Windsor, as ruled by the Geological Formations over which it passes. *Rep. Brit. Assoc.* for 1860, Sections, p. 75.

HULL, E., and W. WHITAKER.—The Geology of Parts of Oxfordshire and Berkshire. *Mem. Geol. Survey*. 8vo. London.

WHITEAVES, Dr. J. F.—On the Invertebrate Fauna of the Lower Oolites of Oxfordshire. *Rep. Brit. Assoc.* for 1860, Sections, pp. 104–108.

—————On the Oolitic Echinodermata of the Neighbourhood of Oxford. *Geologist*, vol. iv., pp. 174, 175.

—————On the Palæontology of the Coralline Oolites of the Neighbourhood of Oxford. *Ann. Nat. Hist.*, ser. 3, vol. viii., pp. 142–147.

1863. CLUTTERBUCK, Rev. J. C.—The Perennial and Flood Waters of the Upper Thames. *Proc. Inst. Civ. Eng.*, vol. xxii., p. 336.

Sheet 45, S.E.—Islip, Brill. *Geol. Survey*. London.

1864. GREEN, A. H.—The Geology of the country around Banbury, Woodstock, Bicester, and Buckingham. *Mem. Geol. Survey*. 8vo. London.

1867. BRODIE, Rev. P. B.—On the Presence of the Purbeck Beds at Brill, in Buckinghamshire; and on the Superior Estuarine Sands there, and at certain places in Oxfordshire, etc. *Quart. Journ. Geol. Soc.*, vol. xxiii., p. 197.

HULL, Prof. E.—Horizontal Sections, Sheet 71. By Cuddesdon and Shotover Hill, Oxford, Stanton St. John, Islip, etc. *Geol. Survey*.

MORRIS, Prof. J.—On the Ferruginous Sands of Buckinghamshire, with Remarks on the Distribution of the equivalent Strata. *Geol. Mag.*, vol. iv., pp. 456–462.

1869. THORNE, James.—Excursion to Oxford. Reports of Excursions, Geologists' Association, 1869. [*Separately printed.*]

1870. HULL, Prof. E.—Horizontal Sections, Sheet 81. East of Abingdon, Boar's Hill, Cumnor Hurst, Wytham Hill, to Pinsley Wood.

—————and Prof J. W. JUDD. Sheet 82. From Handborough, near Combe, etc. *Geol. Survey*.

PERCEVAL, S. G.—On the Occurrence of Schorl in Drift near Oxford. *Geol. Mag.*, p. 96.

1871. PHILLIPS, Prof. J.—Geology of Oxford and the Valley of the Thames. 8vo. Oxford.

1876. PRESTWICH [Sir] J.—On the Geological Conditions affecting the Water Supply to Houses and Towns, with special reference to the modes of supplying Oxford. 8vo. Oxford and London.

—————On the Mineral Water discovered in sinking the Artesian Well at St. Clement's, Oxford. *Proc. Ashmolean Soc.*

—————Thickness of the Oxford Clay. *Geol. Mag.*, pp. 237–239.

1877. BLAKE, Rev. J. F., and W. H. HUDLESTON.—On the Corallian Rocks of England. *Quart. Journ. Geol. Soc.*, vol. xxxiii., pp. 304–312.

1878. JONES, Prof. T. Rupert.—Notes on some Fossil Bivalved Entomostraca. [Describes six species from Shotover.] *Geol. Mag.*, pp. 103–110, 277.

1879. PRESTWICH, J.—On the Discovery of a Species of Iguanodon in the Kimeridge Clay near Oxford; and a Notice of a very Fossiliferous Band of the Shotover Sands. *Geol. Mag.*, pp. 193–195.

1880. BLAKE, Rev. J. F.—On the Portland Rocks of England. *Quart. Journ. Geol. Soc.*, vol. xxxvi., pp. 189–235.

COBBOLD, E. S.—Notes on the Strata exposed in laying out the Oxford Sewage-farm at Sandford-on-Thames. *Quart. Journ. Geol. Soc.*, vol. xxxvi., pp. 314–320.

1880. HULKE, J. W.—*Iguanodon Prestwichii*, a new species from the Kimeridge Clay. . . . *Quart. Journ. Geol. Soc.*, vol. xxxvi., pp. 433–456.
PRESTWICH [Sir] J.—Note on the Occurrence of a new species of *Iguanodon* in a brick-pit of the Kimeridge Clay at Cumnor Hurst, three miles W.S.W. of Oxford. *Quart. Journ. Geol. Soc.*, vol. xxxvi., pp. 430–432.
1881. PRESTWICH, Sir J.—An Index Guide to the Geological Collections in the University Museum, Oxford. 8vo. Oxford.
1882. ——————On the Occurrence of the *Cyrena fluminalis* at Summertown, near Oxford. *Geol. Mag.*, pp. 49–51.
1884. ——————A Letter on the Oxford Water Supply. 8vo. Oxford.
1885. ——————Oxford Water Supply, Letters and Report. 8vo. Oxford.
1888. BATHER, Dr. F. A.—Note on the Geology of Cumnor Hurst. *Journ. Oxf. Univ. Jun. Sci. Club*, vol. i., pp. 30–32.
1893. BLAKE, Prof. J. F.—Excursion to Brill. *Proc. Geol. Assoc.*, vol. xiii., pp. 71–74.
WOODWARD, H. B.—Jurassic Rocks of Britain, vol. iv. Lower Oolitic Rocks of England (Yorkshire excepted). 8vo. London.
1894. DAWKINS, Prof. W. B.—The Probable Range of the Coal-Measures under the Newer Rocks of Oxfordshire and the Adjoining Counties. *Rep. Brit. Assoc.* for 1894, pp. 646–648.
GREEN, Prof. A. H.—Some Points of Special Interest in the Geology of the Neighbourhood of Oxford. *Rep. Brit. Assoc.* for 1904, pp. 644, 645.
WOODWARD, H. B.—Jurassic Rocks of Britain, vol. v. Middle and Upper Oolitic Rocks of England (Yorkshire excepted). [With Bibliography relating to Jurassic formations.] 8vo. London.
1897. WHITE, H. J. Osborne.—On the origin of the High-Level Gravel with Triassic débris adjoining the valley of the Upper Thames. *Proc. Geol. Assoc.*, vol. xv., pp. 157–174.
WOODWARD, H. B.—The Chalky Boulder-clay and the Glacial Phenomena of the Western-Midland Counties of England. *Geol. Mag.*, pp. 485–497.
1898. SALTER, A. E.—Pebbly and other Gravels in Southern England. *Proc. Geol. Assoc.*, vol. xv., p. 264.
SOLLAS, Prof. W. J.—The Influence of Oxford on the History of Geology. *Science Progress*, vol. vii. (N.S., vol. ii.), pp. 23–52 ; reprinted in " The Age of the Earth and other Geological Studies," 1905.
1899. DAVIES, A. Morley.—Contributions to the Geology of the Thame Valley. *Proc. Geol. Assoc.*, vol. xvi., pp. 15–58.
DAVIS, Prof. W. M.—The Drainage of Cuestas. [Notes on Cherwell, Evenlode, and other valleys.] *Proc. Geol. Assoc.*, vol. xvi., pp. 75–93.
1902. BLAKE, Rev. J. F.—Excursion to Headington, Shotover, and Wheatley. *Proc. Geol. Assoc.*, vol. xvii., pp. 383–385.
BLAKE, J. H., with contributions by W. WHITAKER.—The Water Supply of Berkshire from Underground Sources. *Mem. Geol. Survey*. 8vo. London.
LAMPLUGH, G. W.—Fossils of the Oxford Iron-Sands. *Geol. Mag.*, pp. 574, 575.
1904. BELL, A. Montgomerie.—Implementiferous Sections at Wolvercote (Oxfordshire). *Quart. Journ. Geol. Soc.*, vol. lx., pp. 120–132.
FISHER, W. W.—On the Salinity of Waters from the Oolites. *Analyst*, Feb., 1904.
HEALEY, Maud.—Notes on Upper Jurassic Ammonites, with special reference to Specimens in the University Museum, Oxford. *Quart. Journ. Geol. Soc.*, vol. lx., pp. 54–64.
SOLLAS, Prof. W. J., and Miss M. HEALEY.—Excursion to Cumnor. *Proc. Geol. Assoc.*, vol. xix., p. 57.

1905. LAMPLUGH, G. W., and T. I. POCOCK.—Notes on the Oxford Area. *Summary of Progress of Geol. Survey* for 1904, pp. 17–22.

SALTER, Dr. A. E.—On the Superficial Deposits of Central and parts of Southern England. *Proc. Geol. Assoc.*, vol. xix., pp. 1–56.

1906. HARMER, F. W.—Lake Oxford and the Goring Gap. *Geol. Mag.*, 1906, p. 470 ; *Rep. Brit. Assoc.* for 1906 (1907), pp. 572, 573.

WALFORD, E. A.—On some new Oolitic Strata in North Oxfordshire. 4to. Buckingham.

1907. DAVIES, A. Morley.—The Kimeridge Clay and Corallian Rocks of the Neighbourhood of Brill (Buckinghamshire). *Quart. Journ. Geol. Soc.*, vol. lxiii., pp. 29–47.

—————————Excursion to Dorton, Brill, and Arngrove. *Proc. Geo*. *Assoc.*, vol. xx., 183–186.

1907. HARMER, F. W.—On the Origin of certain Cañon-like Valleys associated with Lake-like Areas of Depression. *Quart. Journ. Geol. Soc.*, vol. lxiii., pp. 470–513.

NEWTON, E. T.—Note on specimens of " Rhaxella Chert " or " Arngrove Stone " from Dartford Heath. *Proc. Geol. Assoc.*, vol. xx., pp. 127, 128.

1909. DOUGLAS, J. A.—The Oxford and Banbury District. *Geology in the Field*, p. 192.

1910. TIDDEMAN, R. H.—The Water Supply of Oxfordshire (*Mem. Geol. Surv.*), 1910.

1913. ODLING, M.—The Bathonian Rocks of the Oxford District. *Quart. Journ. Geol. Soc.*, vol. lxix., p. 484.

1924. SANDFORD, K. S.—The River-Gravels of the Oxford District. *Quart. Journ. Geol. Soc.*, vol. lxxx., p. 113.

APPENDIX II

List of Geological Survey Photographs: Special Oxford Sheet and Adjacent Areas

Copies of these photographs may be seen in the Library, Geological Survey and Museum, Jermyn Street, S.W.1. Prints and lantern slides may be obtained on application to the Director.

Registered Number of Negatives. A	Subject.	Locality.
3170 ..	Quarry in Great Oolite, Forest Marble and the Cornbrash.	Kirtlington Cement Pit, about 1½ m. N. of Bletchington Station.
3171 ..	,, ,, ,,	,, ,, ,,
3172 ..	,, ,, ,,	,, ,, ,,
3173 ..	,, ,, ,,	,, ,, ,,
3174 ..	Vertical joints in the Great Oolite limestones.	,, ,, ,,
3175 ..	False-bedded limestones of the Forest Marble.	Greenhill Quarries, about ¼ m. S.E. of Bletchington Station.
3176 ..	,, ,, ,,	,, ,, ,,
3177 ..	,, ,, ,,	,, ,, ,,
3178 ..	Section showing upper part of Forest Marble and the lower half of the Cornbrash.	Smith's Quarry, Islip.
3179 ..	Quarry in Great Oolite Series, Forest Marble and the Cornbrash.	Quarry, ¼ m. E. of Handborough Station.
3180 ..	False-bedded limestones of the Forest Marble.	,, ,, ,,
3181 ..	Section in Handborough Gravels or Handborough Terrace.	Gravel-pit, N. of Swan Inn, Long Hanborough.
3182 ..	,, ,, ,,	,, ,, ,,
3183 ..	,, ,, ,,	,, ,, ,,
3184 ..	Section in Cornbrash	Hanborough Quarry, Long Hanborough.
3185 ..	Section in Cornbrash, showing lower and upper Clydoniceras Beds.	,, ,, ,,
3186 ..	Eroded surface of the lower Clydoniceras Bed.	,, ,, ,,
3187 ..	,, ,, ,,	,, ,, ,,
3188 ..	Pipes in Gravels forming the Handborough Terrace.	Blenheim Estate Pit, Long Hanborough.
3189 ..	,, ,, ,,	,, ,, ,,
3190 ..	Section of Oxford Clay.. ..	Wolvercot Brickyard, 2 m. N. of Oxford.
3191 ..	Lower Greensand on Kimmeridge Clay.	Chawley Brickyard, near Cumnor Hurst.
3192 ..	,, ,, ,,	,, ,, ,,

Registered Number of Negatives. A	Subject.	Locality.
3193 ..	Concretionary masses, known as "Giants Marbles" in the sands of the Pectinatus Zone of the Kimmeridge Clay.	Shotover Hill Brickyard, Headington.
3194 ..	,, ,, ,,	,, ,, ,,
3195 ..	,, ,, ,,	,, ,, ,,
3196 ..	,, ,, ,,	,, ,, ,,
3197 ..	Upper Corallian Beds	Vicarage Pit, Headington.
3198 ..	,, ,,	,, ,,
3199 ..	,, ,,	Magdalen Pit, Headington.
3200 ..	,, ,,	Lye Hill Quarries, near Wheatley.
3201 ..	Section in Shotover Sands (Wealden).	Sand-pit at Windmill, S. of Wheatley Brickyard, Wheatley.
3202 ..	,, ,, ,,	,, ,, ,,
3203 ..	,, ,, ,,	,, ,, ,,
3204 ..	Section of Lower Calcareous Grit with layers of partially decalcified beds of grit-stone.	Littlemore Railway-cutting. Quarry.
3205 } 3205a }	Section in Lower and Upper Corallian Beds .. .. }	,, ,, ,,
3206 ..	,, ,, ,,	,, ,, ,,
3207 ..	,, ,, ,,	,, ,, ,,
3208 ..	Section in Upper Corallian Beds	Lamb & Flag Pit, 2 m. W. of Kingston Bagpuize.
3209 ..	,, ,, ,,	,, ,, ,,
3210 ..	Sands of the Lower Calcareous Grit.	,, ,, ,,
3211 ..	Tree-like concretions in Lower Calcareous Grit.	Sand-pit, Tubney Wood.
3212 ..	Lower Calcareous Grit	,, ,,
3213 ..	,, ,,	,, ,,
3214 ..	,, ,, current bedded.	,, ,,
3215 ..	Disturbed layers of Lower Calcareous Grit.	Sheepstead Farm Pit.
3216 ..	Lower Calcareous Grit ..	,, ,,
3217 ..	,, ,,	,, ,,
3218 ..	Section in Lower Gault and Kimmeridge Clay.	Culham Brickyard, Culham.
3219 ..	,, ,, ,,	,, ,, ,,
3220 3221 3222 3223 3224 3225 }	Sections in Oxford Clay ..	Calvert Brickyard, Calvert.

INDEX

Woodhouse Farm, 45.

Woodperry, 58.

Woodside Farm, 45.

Woodstock, 19; railway-cutting, 16.

Woodward, H. B., 12, 22, 23, 41, 43, 44, 50, 51, 59, 83, 86.

Wooton, 48.

Worminghall, 38, 41, 60, 61, 148.

Wychwood Forest, 168.

Wytham, boring at, 3, 5.

Wytham Great Wood, 51.

Wytham Hill, 25, 29, 30, 37, 50, 114, 129, 135, 144.

Yarnton, 33, 121, 122, 124, 128, 129, 145, 154.

Yelford, 119.

Yorkshire, 21, 65.

Young, A., 6.

———

Zones, of the Inferior Oolite, 10; Great Oolite, 13; Forest Marble, 13; Cornbrash, 16; Kellaways Beds, 30; Oxford Clay, 32, 33; Corallian, 40; Kimmeridge Clay, 66, 67; Portland Beds, 77; Gault, 101, 103.

MAPS AND MEMOIRS RELATING TO THE GEOLOGY OF THE SOUTH-EAST OF ENGLAND AND OXFORDSHIRE.

Issued by the Geological Survey of Great Britain.
(Museum of Practical Geology, London, S.W. 1.)

MAPS.

PRICE.
Coloured. Uncoloured.
s. d.   s. d.

Geological Map of the British Islands.
Scale, 25 miles to the inch, second edition, colour-
printed, 1912. Reprinted, 1924 –   –   –   2 0   1 0
Uncoloured copies showing the Sheets on the
Quarter-inch and One-inch Scales, with par-   PRICE.
ticulars of Memoirs, Maps, Sections, &c., printed   s. d.
on back –   –   –   –   –   –   –   1 0

Quarter-inch Geological Map of England and Wales.
(A quarter of an inch to one mile, colour-printed.)

PRICE.
Solid.   Drift.
s. d.   s. d.

Sheet 15.—Birmingham, Northampton, Gloucester,
  Oxford, Worcester –   –   –   3 0   —
Sheet 16.—Cambridge, Colchester, Ipswich –   –   3 0   3 0
Sheet 19.—Bath, Guildford, Abingdon, South-
  ampton –   –   –   –   –   3 0   —
Sheet 20 with 24.—London, Dover and Brighton –   3 0   3 0

One-inch Geological Map of England and Wales.
(One inch to one mile.)

PRICE.
Drift Edition.
s. d.

Special London Map in four sheets (colour-printed, 1903) :—
  Sheet 1 (North-west).—Hyde Park to Rick-
    mansworth –   –   –   –   –   2 0
  Sheet 2 (North-east).—Westminster to Kel-
    vedon Hatch –   –   –   –   2 0
  Sheet 3 (South-west).—Westminster to Wey-
    bridge –   –   –   –   –   2 0
  Sheet 4 (South-east).—Southwark to Kings-
    down –   –   –   –   –   2 0
Special Map of the Oxford District (colour-printed,
  1908) –   –   –   –   –   –   –   –   2 0
Special Map of the Isle of Wight (colour-printed,
  1903) –   –   –   –   –   –   –   –   3 0

New Series One-inch Sheets (Colour-printed).
  *Sheet 207.—Ipswich –   –   –   –   –   –   —
  Sheet 238.—Aylesbury. (1923) –   –   –   –   2 0
  Sheet 239.—Hertford. (1924) –   –   –   –   2 0
  Sheet 254.—Henley. (1905) –   –   –   –   2 0
  Sheet 255.—Beaconsfield. (1922) –   –   –   2 0
  Sheet 256.—North London. (1925) –   –   –   2 0
  Sheet 257.—Romford. (1925) –   –   –   –   2 0
  Sheet 266.—Marlborough. (1925) –   –   –   2 0
  Sheet 267.—Hungerford and Newbury. (1905) –   2 0
  Sheet 268.—Reading. (1904) –   –   –   –   2 0

* In preparation.

	PRICE. Drift Edition. s. d.
Sheet 269.—Windsor and Chertsey. (1920) – –	2 0
Sheet 270.—South London. (1921) – – –	2 0
Sheet 271.—Dartford. (1924) – – – –	2 0
Sheet 282.—Devizes. (1905) – – – –	2 0
Sheet 283.—Andover. (1905) – – – –	2 0
Sheet 284.—Basingstoke. (1905) – – –	2 0
*Sheet 285.—Aldershot – – – – –	—
Sheet 298.—Salisbury. (1903) – – – –	2 0
Sheet 299.—Winchester. (1905) – – – –	2 0
Sheet 300.—Alresford. (1905) – – – –	2 0
Sheet 313.—Shaftesbury. (1923) – – –	2 0
Sheet 314.—Ringwood. (1902) – – – –	2 0
Sheet 315.—Southampton. (1904) – – –	2 0
Sheet 316.—Fareham and Havant. (1905) – –	2 0
Sheet 317.—Chichester. (1902) – – – –	2 0
Sheet 318.—Brighton. (1924) – – – –	2 0
*Sheet 319.—Lewes – – – – – –	—
Sheet 328.—Dorchester. (1904) – – – –	2 0
Sheet 329.—Bournemouth, Wimborne Minster. (1904) – – – – –	2 0
Sheet 330.—S.E. parts of New Forest and N.W. part of I. of Wight. (1903) – –	2 0
Sheet 331.—Portsmouth and N.E. part of I. of Wight. (1903) – – – –	2 0
Sheet 332.—Bognor, Selsey, Littlehampton. (1905) – – – – –	2 0
Sheet 333.—Worthing. (1924) – – – –	2 0
Sheet 334.—Newhaven, Eastbourne. (1905)– –	2 0
Sheet 341.—West Fleet. (1905) – – –	2 0
Sheet 342.—Weymouth. (1904) – – –	2 0
Sheet 343.—Swanage. (1904) – – – –	2 0

Old Series One-inch Sheets (Hand-coloured).	PRICE. Drift Edition. s. d.	Solid Edition. s. d.
1 N.E.—Billericay, Maldon. (1871) – – –	7 6	3 9
1 S.E.—Gravesend, Southend. (1871) – –	5 3	3 9
2.—Sheerness, Burnham, Bradwell. (1883) – –	4 3	3 6
3.—Sheppey, Margate, Dover. (1889) – – –	18 0	—
4.—Folkestone, Rye. (1863) – – – –	—	4 3
5.—Newhaven, Ashdown Forest, Winchelsea. (1893) – – – – – – – –	18 0	18 0
6.—Bromley, East Grinstead, Rochester. (1889) –	18 0	—
†13.—Oxford, Reading, Henley. (1859) – – –	—	14 0
34.—Stroud, Cirencester, Fairford, Swindon. (1859)	—	17 0
44.—Evesham, Tewkesbury, Cheltenham, Burford. (1856) – – – – – – –	—	18 0
45 N.W.—Banbury, Deddington, Chipping Norton. (1871) – – – – – – – –	—	8 3
45 N.E.—Buckingham, Brackley. (1873) – –	5 3	5 3
45 S.W.—Woodstock, Witney. (1859) – – –	—	6 9
45 S.E.—Bicester, Brill. (1867) – – – –	—	6 9

* In preparation.
† Replaced largely by New Series Maps.

	PRICE.	
	Drift Edition.	Solid Edition.
	s. d.	s. d.
46 N.W.—Newport Pagnell. (1864) – – –	—	5 3
46 N.E.—Hitchin. (1891) – – – – –	9 0	5 3
46 S.W.—Leighton Buzzard. (1865) – – –	—	5 3
46 S.E.—Hatfield, Luton. (1898)– – – –	9 9	—
47.—Hertford, Braintree, Royston. (1884) –	18 0	8 0
48 N.W.—Ipswich. (1882) – – – – –	9 9	—
48 N.E.—Harwich. (1882) – – – – –	6 9	—
48 S.W.—Colchester. (1883) – – – –	8 3	—
48 S.E.—Coast-line S. of Harwich. (1876) –	2 3	—
53 S.E.—Towcester, Daventry, Weedon. (1870) –	—	8 3

Six-inch Sheets (Hand-Coloured).

(Six inches to one mile.)

Manuscript copies of the six-inch maps contained in the New Series of one-inch sheets enumerated on pages ix and x (with the exception of parts of Sheets 207, 313, 318 and 319) are deposited in the Survey Office for public reference. Copies of these maps can be supplied at the cost of drawing and colouring. Applications should be made to the Director, Geological Survey, Jermyn Street, London, S.W.1.

MEMOIRS.

THE CRETACEOUS ROCKS OF BRITAIN, by A. J. Jukes-Browne, with contributions, by W. Hill : Vol. I., THE GAULT AND UPPER GREENSAND OF ENGLAND, price 9s. ; Vol. II., THE LOWER AND MIDDLE CHALK OF ENGLAND, price 10s. ; Vol. III., THE UPPER CHALK OF ENGLAND, price 10s.

THE JURASSIC ROCKS OF BRITAIN : Vol. I., Yorkshire, price 8s. 6d., and Vol. II., YORKSHIRE, TABLES OF FOSSILS, price 12s. by C. Fox-Strangways ; Vol. III., THE LIAS OF ENGLAND AND WALES, price 7s. 6d. ; Vol. IV., THE LOWER OOLITIC ROCKS OF ENGLAND, price 10s. ; Vol. V., THE MIDDLE AND UPPER OOLITIC ROCKS OF ENGLAND, price 7s. 6d., by H. B. Woodward.

THE PLIOCENE DEPOSITS OF BRITAIN, by C. Reid, 5s. 6d. ; THE VERTEBRATA OF THE PLIOCENE DEPOSITS OF BRITAIN, by E. T. Newton, 4s.

GEOLOGY OF THE LONDON DISTRICT, by H. B. Woodward (second edition, revised, by C. E. N. Bromehead and C. P. Chatwin). (1922.) 1s. 6d.

ON THE MESOZOIC ROCKS IN SOME OF THE COAL EXPLORATIONS IN KENT, by G. W. Lamplugh and F. L. Kitchin. (1911.) 3s. 6d.

THE CONCEALED MESOZOIC ROCKS IN KENT. By G. W. Lamplugh, F. L. Kitchin and J. Pringle. (1923.) 7s. 6d.

THE GEOLOGY OF THE ISLE OF PURBECK AND WEYMOUTH. By Aubrey Strahan. (1898). 10s. 6d.

GUIDE TO THE GEOLOGICAL MODEL OF THE ISLE OF PURBECK. By A. Strahan. (1906). 6d.

A SHORT ACCOUNT OF THE GEOLOGY OF THE ISLE OF WIGHT, by H. J. Osborne White. (1921.) 7s.

GEOLOGY OF THE THAMES VALLEY NEAR GORING, as illustrated by the Model in the Museum of Practical Geology. By Sir Aubrey Strahan. (1924.) 6d.

Memoirs Descriptive of the New Series One-inch Geological Sheets.

Sheet 207.—The Geology of the Country around Ipswich. *In preparation.*
Sheet 238.—The Geology of the Country around Aylesbury and Hemel Hempstead. By R. L. Sherlock, with contributions by J. Pringle, C. P. Chatwin and R. W. Pocock. (1922.) 2s.

Sheets 330, 331.—(Mainland). Geology of the Country near Lymington and Portsmouth. By H. J. Osborne White. (1915.) 1s. 6d.
Sheet 332.—The Geology of the Country around Bognor. By C. Reid. (1897.) 6d.
Sheet 334.—The Geology of the Country around Eastbourne. By C. Reid. (1898.) 6d.

Memoirs Descriptive of the Old Series One-inch Geological Sheets.
Sheet 34.—Parts of Wiltshire and Gloucestershire. 8d.
Sheet 44.—Cheltenham. 2s. 6d.
Sheet 45.—Banbury, Woodstock, Bicester and Buckingham. 2s.
Sheet 45 (S.W.)—Woodstock. 1s.
Sheet 48 (N.E. and N.W.)—Ipswich, Harwich, &c. 2s.
Sheet 48 (S.W.)—Colchester. 1s.
Sheet 48 (S.E.)—Eastern end of Essex. 9d.

Memoirs on the Underground Water Supply of the following Counties have been published or are in preparation:—
Bedfordshire and Northamptonshire, 1909. 4s. 6d.
Berkshire, 1902. 3s.
Buckinghamshire and Hertfordshire, 1921. 16s.
Cambridgeshire, Huntingdonshire and Rutland, 1922. 7s.
Derbyshire. *In preparation.*
Dorset. *In the Press.*
Essex, 1916. 15s.
Gloucestershire. *In preparation.*
Hampshire (including Isle of Wight), 1910. 5s.
Kent, 1908. 8s. 6d.
Lincolnshire, 1904. 4s. 6d.
Norfolk, 1921. 10s.
Nottinghamshire, 1914. 5s.
Oxfordshire, 1910. 2s. 3d.
Somerset. *In preparation.*
Suffolk, 1906. 3s. 6d.
Surrey, 1912. 7s.
Sussex, 1899. *(Out of print).* (Supplement, 1911.) 2s. 6d.
    ,, (New Edition). *In preparation.*
Warwickshire. *In preparation.*
Wiltshire, 1925. 4s. 6d.
Worcestershire. *In preparation.*
Yorkshire, East Riding, 1906. 3s.

RECORDS OF LONDON WELLS, 1913. 4s. 6d.

THICKNESSES OF STRATA IN THE COUNTIES OF ENGLAND AND WALES, EXCLUSIVE OF ROCKS OLDER THAN THE PERMIAN. 4s. 6d.

See also List of Memoirs, Maps, Sections, &c., issued by the Geological Survey of Great Britain. (1925.) 1s.

GEOLOGICAL SURVEY MAPS may be obtained from the Ordnance Survey Office, Southampton, or from their local agents, B. R. Morland, Banbury; Norman, Sawyer & Co., Ltd., Cheltenham; Parker and Son, Oxford; W. Smith and Son, Reading; Miss F. Woodhams, Swindon.

GEOLOGICAL SURVEY MEMOIRS may be obtained from the Ordnance Survey, and their local agents, or through any bookseller from the Ordnance Survey. Copies can also be obtained from H.M. Stationery Office, Adastral House, Kingsway, London, W.C. 2, and 28, Abingdon Street, London, S.W. 1 (and Edinburgh, Manchester, Cardiff and Belfast).

Printed under the authority of HIS MAJESTY'S STATIONERY OFFICE.
By Wyman & Sons, Limited, Fetter Lane, London, E.C. 4.